Recommended Country Hotels OF BRITAIN 1997

INCLUDING COUNTRY HOUSE HOLIDAYS

FHG PUBLICATIONS, Paisley

The Cornish Arms

16th century coaching inn

Pendogett, Port Isaac,
North Cornwall PL30 3HH

Tel: 01208 880263
Fax: 01208 880335

Situated in the small rural village of Pendogett, just one mile from the coast. Anyone who makes The Cornish Arms a base for exploring the area will not be disappointed by the attractive accommodation or the warmth of welcome extended. Whilst retaining the character of a traditional coaching inn, The Cornish Arms offers all modern amenities in every bedroom; colour and satellite TV, telephone, trouser press, tea and coffee making facilities, etc.

The highly recommended restaurant specialises in locally caught seafood and an extensive range of other dishes. Complement your meal with wine from the extensive cellars of The Cornish Arms. Pendogett Special Bitter is famous for its strength – the locals won't touch it – it's so strong. With Bass straight from the barrel, together with other real ales, you will see why both CAMRA and the Good Pub Guide recommend The Cornish Arms.

ETB ♛♛♛ Commended RAC ★★ Les Routiers Good Food Guide

Rose in Vale

Country House Hotel

Mithian, St. Agnes,
Cornwall TR5 0QD

Tel: 01872 552202
Fax: 01872 552700

♛♛♛♛
Highly Commended

AA ★★★ RAC

Occupying a secluded position in its own small valley amidst beautiful Cornish countryside and near the coast, this Georgian country house hotel has grounds extending to 11 acres including beautiful gardens, woodland and pasture as well as a heated swimming pool and waterfowl ponds. Inside the house, guests will find ensuite bedrooms equipped with hairdryer, radio, telephone, tea-maker and television; ground floor rooms are available, as well as luxurious four-poster suites. Opie's Room is the elegant setting for the enjoyment of one's choice from the table d'hôte and à la carte menus, fresh local produce including newly-landed fish and seafood featuring prominently in each day's selection. The hotel's central location makes it an ideal base for exploring this most fascinating country.

The Old Rectory Country House Hotel

St. Keyne, Near Looe, Cornwall PL14 4RL Tel: 01579 342617 ♛♛♛ COMMENDED

Peacefully secluded in its own three acres of gardens but ideally situated for touring Cornwall and South West Devon. Enjoy the welcoming ambience of a family-run country house, excellent Cordon Bleu Dinners and hearty breakfasts, comfortable en suite bedrooms all with colour TV and hospitality trays. Cosy lounge and honesty bar with open fires on cooler evenings. No smoking in dining room. Pets welcome. AA**. One Rosette. Telephone for brochure.

Bed and Breakfast from £27.00-£35.00 per person per night; short breaks (minimum 2 nights) from £38.00 per person per night dinner, bed and breakfast.

NANNY BROW COUNTRY HOUSE HOTEL & RESTAURANT

Clappersgate, Ambleside, Cumbria LA22 9NF
Tel: 015394 32036 Fax: 015394 32450

Elegant Country House with spectacular views of the River Brathay has direct access on to the fell. The award-winning restaurant features superb cuisine and fine wines. Relax in the elegant lounge or hall and there are log fires on chilly evenings with fresh flowers attended to daily. All suites and rooms are individually furnished in traditional style with caring consideration given to guests by attentive staff. Personally managed by resident owners Michael and Carol Fletcher.

AA Red Rosette RAC Merit Awards 1995
ETB ♛♛♛♛ Highly Commended Johansens Best Loved Hotels
European Connection Egon Ronay Ashley Courtenay

Link House

Bassenthwaite Lake, Cockermouth, Cumbria CA13 9YD
Telephone: (017687) 76291 Michael & Marilyn Tuppen

A family run traditional Victorian country house at the quieter end of the Lake District and surrounded by lovely scenery, yet providing easy access to all the popular areas. An ideal base for walkers and motorists alike. All 8 bedrooms (one on the ground floor) are ensuite with colour TV, tea/coffee making equipment, central heating, etc. There is a delightful conservatory plus a comfortable lounge with log fire to make the winter evenings even more cosy. Many antique and period pieces of furniture throughout, but more relaxing than formal. The modestly priced wine list complements imaginative four-course dinners served on Wedgwood china. Bed and Breakfast from £20-£25. Dinner £13. Special Terms weekly, and winter. Leisure Club Membership.

ETB ♛♛♛ Commended AA QQQQ Selected

Brantwood Country Hotel

STAINTON · PENRITH · CUMBRIA · CA11 0EP
Telephone: (01768) 862748 · Fax: (01768) 890164

Pleasant rural country Hotel in 3 acres of secluded gardens. Relaxed and friendly atmosphere. Personally run for the last ten years by Susan and John Harvey with their sons Stephen and Mark. Comfortable ensuite rooms with colour television, tea/coffee making facilities, central heating and direct-dial telephone. Enjoy a formal dinner in the Restaurant or choose from an extensive à la carte menu in the Bar.

£27 bed & breakfast per person sharing double room. 3 day break £75 per person bed & breakfast.

Bridge House Hotel

♛♛♛ Commended RAC Highly Acclaimed

Bridge House is situated in the centre of Grasmere enjoying a quiet secluded position just off the main road. There are two acres of mature gardens beside the River Rothay, with fine views of the surrounding fells. The twelve tastefully furnished bedrooms have private facilities, television, tea trays, telephone and hairdryer. Splendid food completes your holiday, a full English breakfast to start the day and an excellent five course evening meal, with coffee served by the fire, to round it off. You are ensured a warm, friendly welcome, your comfort and enjoyment being our prime concern. Open throughout the year. Details on request from:

Mrs Rushton, Bridge House, Stock Lane, Grasmere, Cumbria LA22 9SN. Tel: 015394 35425; Fax: 015394 35523

THE EDGEMOOR HOTEL

Haytor Road, Bovey Tracey TQ13 9LE
Telephone 01626 832466 Fax 01626 834760

♛♛♛♛ **HIGHLY COMMENDED**

AA RAC ★★★ Les Routiers Johansens

'Loaded with charm' the Edgemoor 'epitomizes a gracious English Retreat' (*Dallas Morning News*). This relaxing Country House Hotel is literally adjacent to Dartmoor National Park, yet is only three miles from the main A38 Exeter/Plymouth dual carriageway. Personally run by resident proprietors. The Edgemoor has twelve delightful bedrooms, including some Four-Posters, lovely gardens, good food (AA Rosette) and helpful caring staff. Wonderful countryside abounds, with numerous places to visit including many National Trust properties. Bargain Breaks available for stays of two days or more. Elegance without pretension.

Poltimore Guest House

Ramsley, South Zeal, Okehampton EX20 2PD
Telephone: 01837 840209

Delightful thatched house set on the fringe of Dartmoor in 3 acres of grounds with breathtaking views. A lovely place to relax with a warm and friendly atmosphere. Oak beamed lounge with inglenook, cosy bar and panelled dining-room. Very comfortable bedrooms with colour television and drinks tray. Good English home cooking with a choice of menu at every meal. Extensive wine list and well stocked bar. With direct access to Dartmoor this is a walkers' paradise and many West Country attractions are only a short drive away. Also ideal for fishing/horse riding/golf. Children and pets welcome. Charming self-catering accommodation also available. Open all year including Christmas. ♛♛♛ **Approved. AA QQQ.**

GET AWAY FROM IT ALL

There will always be times when you wish there was somewhere you could go to get away from it all, relax in beautiful surroundings, and sample delicious food.

THE CHERRYBROOK HOTEL

IS THE IDEAL CHOICE

Set in the heart of Dartmoor National Park, it is an excellent base for walking, touring or simply enjoying the breathtaking scenery.

To find out more Phone or Fax Margaret & Andy on **01822 880260**

CHERRYBROOK HOTEL
Two Bridges, Yelverton, Devon PL20 6SP

AA QQQQ Selected

♛♛♛ **Commended**

THE WOODLANDS LODGE HOTEL

Bartley Road, Woodlands, New Forest, Hampshire SO40 2GN

AA ★★★ **Reservations: (01703) 292257** ETB ♛♛♛♛ Highly Commended

A LUXURY GEORGIAN COUNTRY HOUSE HOTEL

The Woodlands Lodge Hotel is a luxury hotel set in 4 acres of grounds opening onto the beautiful New Forest. Although the hotel is totally refurbished with a stunning interior it still offers the peace and tranquillity often only found in buildings of age and establishment. All 18 bedrooms and suites enjoy full ensuite facilities of jacuzzi bath, separate thermastic shower with some bathrooms also having bidets. The sumptuous kingsize pocket sprung beds are possibly the most comfortable beds guests have slept on (this opinion is constantly being expressed by guests).

All other amenities are present including 21" fast text television, writing desks, armchairs, hairdryer, trouser press, Teasmaid and telephone. At Woodlands Lodge the hotel service is extremely friendly and informal thus enabling guests to totally relax and feel at home. Our dinner menu is modestly priced at a maximum of £16.95 (inc. à la carte) for three courses and coffee. It offers succulent giant king prawns, garlic mushrooms and many more mouth-watering starters with main courses ranging from fresh local rainbow trout, New Forest venison, poulet sauté Marengo (chicken flamed in brandy and cooked with marsala wine and tomatoes) or plain traditional Scotch sirloin steaks, etc. Modestly priced wine list from £6.95.

Something for absolutely everyone!

Luxury doubles from £99;
De luxe doubles from £119;
Single occupancy from £69.
All prices are inclusive of
Full English Breakfast and VAT.

String of Horses

Mead End, Sway, Lymington, Hampshire SO41 6EH
Telephone / Fax: 01590 682631

Unique secluded, exclusive hotel set in four acres in the heart of the New Forest, with a friendly relaxed atmosphere. Eight luxurious double bedrooms, each with its own fantasy bathroom with spa bath and shower. Every facility is offered including colour television, direct-dial telephone, radio and tea-making facilities. Four-poster rooms are also available, making this an ideal honeymoon setting. Dine in our intimate 'Carriages' restaurant. For relaxation there is a heated outdoor swimming pool. This is superb riding country, and the hotel is close to excellent yachting resorts and several good golf courses.

ETB ♛♛♛♛ Highly Commended AA Rosette**

Bramble Hill Hotel

Bramshaw, Near Lyndhurst, Hampshire SO43 7JG
Telephone: 01703 813165

Peacefully located in tranquil surroundings, this country house hotel is only three miles from Junction 1 of the M27 and is set in ancient woodland with 30 acres of glades, lawns and shrubbery to enjoy. Ideal for country walks and horse riding. A short drive from many places of interest including Salisbury, Stonehenge, Winchester and Beaulieu. All bedrooms have en suite bathrooms and some have antique four-poster beds. Cosy public bar and restaurant. A warm friendly welcome and good home cooking assured.

Three day special breaks, weekly terms, daily rates – please phone for details.

Waterhead Hotel
CONISTON

P&T Classic Hotels

3 magnificent period-built Hotels ideally situated in prime UK locations open throughout the year offering superb value to discerning guests.

Waterhead Hotel, Coniston, Cumbria LA21 8AJ
Tel: 015394 41244 Fax: 015394 41193

Dumbleton Hall, near Evesham, Worcestershire WR11 6TS
Tel: 01386 881240 Fax: 01386 882142

Friars Carse Country House Hotel, Auldgirth, Dumfries
Tel: 01387 740388 Fax: 01387 740550

Dumbleton Hall
WORCESTERSHIRE

Eagle Lodge Hotel

A country house hotel of outstanding beauty situated in large gardens in the centre of Woodhall Spa. Twenty-three superbly fitted en suite bedrooms. The Kestrel Suite Restaurant, overlooking the gardens, offers table d'hôte and à la carte menus while the Osprey Bar and Brasserie offers a wide choice of real ales and bar meals from the blackboard menu which changes daily. Approximately 20 miles from Lincoln, Sleaford, Boston and Louth, the hotel is ideally situated as a holiday centre for touring Lincolnshire.

Terms on application.

The Broadway, Woodhall Spa LN10 6ST. Tel: 01526 353231; Fax: 01526 352797

AA ★★ 73%

The Briarfields Hotel

ETB ♛♛♛ Commended

Main Street, Titchwell, King's Lynn, Norfolk PE31 8BB

Tel: 01485 210742 Fax: 01485 210933

This delightful country hotel is located in an area rich in wildlife, overlooking the sea and Titchwell RSBP reserve. Many places of interest can be visited and there are sandy beaches close by and golf at Brancaster and Hunstanton. The 17 individually furnished bedrooms are all en suite and have tea/coffee facilities, telephone and colour TV. Two have four-poster beds. Also two family suites, one with own lounge/dining area. Restaurant serves delicious food prepared from fresh ingredients.

Riverdale Hall Hotel & Restaurant

BELLINGHAM, NORTHUMBERLAND ♛♛♛♛ COMMENDED

Victorian country house hotel with RAC Merit awarded restaurant. All bedrooms have bath and shower, television, telephone and tea/coffee making facilities. Riverdale Hall is the nearest hotel to the beautiful Kielder Water and Forest. The Borders, the Pennine Way, and National Park with Hadrian's Wall close by. This hotel is popular with the sporting enthusiast and has its own indoor swimming pool, sauna, cricket field, and salmon and trout river, with Bellingham golf course opposite.

TERMS ON REQUEST. TEL: 01434 220254.

Fine Georgian Country House built by Lord Boyne in1789. Outstanding country setting yet just four miles from historic Ludlow, amid real explorers country. Superb views. Lovely informal atmosphere. Two sitting rooms. Wonderful gardens with water features. Four Posters. Open Fires. Licenced bar, exceptional food and of course - good old fashioned hospitality.

Tel: 01584 823209 / 333 Fax: 01584 823387

All bedrooms are individually styled with en-suite facilities, beverage making, radio alarms & colour televisions

Fishing available • Licensed

B&B fr. £23.00

The Bath Tasburgh Hotel

Warminster Road, Bath, Somerset BA2 6SH
Tel: 01225 425096 Fax: 01225 463842

This family-owned Victorian country house, built for a photographer to the Royal family, is set in two acres of lovely gardens and grounds, with magnificent views across the Avon valley.

Extensively refurbished, the house retains many original features, and offers tastefully furnished rooms with all the modern comforts of a good hotel – en suite bath/shower, direct-dial telephone, radio, colour television and tea/coffee facilities in all rooms. Residential licence. Four-poster and ground floor rooms available. The sitting rooms are delightful and include a conservatory for guests. Children welcome. One of the important features is the personal care and attention given by David and Susan Keeling, creating a country house atmosphere so near and convenient to Bath city centre.

• ETB Highly Commended • AA Selected • RAC Highly Acclaimed
• Les Routiers • Johansens Country Houses

Cleavers Lyng

16th Century Country Hotel

Church Road, Herstmonceux,
East Sussex BN27 1QJ
Tel: (01323) 833131
Fax: (01323) 833617

For excellent home cooking in traditional English style, comfort and informality, this small family-run hotel in the heart of rural East Sussex is well recommended. Peacefully set in beautiful landscaped gardens extending to 1·5 acres featuring an ornamental rockpool with waterfall. Adjacent to Herstmonceux Castle's West Gate, the house dates from 1577 as its oak beams and inglenook fire-place bear witness. This is an ideal retreat for a quiet sojourn away from urban clamour. The castles at Pevensey, Scotney, Bodiam and Hever are all within easy reach as are Battle Abbey, Kipling's House, Batemans, Michelham Priory and the seaside resorts of Eastbourne, Bexhill and Hastings. The bedrooms are fully ensuite, and all have central heating and tea/coffee making facilities, some with separate sitting area with colour TV. On the ground floor there is an oak-beamed restaurant with a fully licensed bar, cosy residents' lounge with television and an outer hall with tele-phone and cloakrooms. Cleavers Lyng does not have any single rooms, however at certain times of the year, we offer a reduced single occupancy rate for double/twin bedroom. At Cleavers Lyng we observe a strictly non-smok-ing policy in our restaurant and TV lounge. Smoking is permitted in the lounge.

Pets welcome. Peace, tranquillity and a warm welcome await you. Special Attraction: Badger Watch.
Room rate from £22.50 pp sharing Double/Twin rooms.

Picture shows the rear of Fairseat House.

Fairseat House

Newick, Near Lewes, East Sussex BN8 4PJ
Tel: 01825 722263

Edwardian period house which enjoys a rural aspect yet is easily accessible to main routes, coast, Gatwick Airport. Convenient for Glyndebourne Opera, Sussex Gardens and Bluebell Railway. Open fires, buttoned Chesterfields, a four-poster bed, ancestral portraits and family artifacts are part of the charm. Roy and Carol Pontifex offer a very high standard of care and attention. Covered heated swimming pool. Ample parking. This is a non-smoking house.

AA Premier Selected QQQQQ
Tourist Board 'Listed' Highly Commended

Rye Lodge

Hilder's Cliff, Rye, East Sussex TN31 7LD

Estuary views yet adjacent High Street, monastery and historical 14th century landgate. Elegant de luxe rooms named after French wine regions, tastefully furnished. Delicious food, candlelit dinners, fine wines. Room service and private car park. The stylish place to stay in this ancient Cinque Ports town.

Short Break package: 2 nights inc. 3 course dinner and coffee, room and full English breakfast from £87.50.

Telephone: 01797 223838 Fax: 223585

Jeake's House

Mermaid Street,
Rye, East Sussex TN31 7ET
Tel: 01797 222828 Fax: 01797 222623

♛♛ Highly Commended
AA Premier Selected
RAC Highly Acclaimed
Good Hotel Guide Cesar Award 1992

Dating from 1689, Jeake's House stands on one of the most beautiful cobbled streets in Rye's medieval town centre. Each stylishly restored bedroom with brass, mahogany or four-poster bed combines traditional elegance and luxury with every modern comfort. A roaring fire greets you on cold mornings in the elegant galleried chapel, which is now the dining room. Choosing either a traditional or vegetarian breakfast, the soft chamber music, airy setting and unhurried atmosphere will provide the perfect start to any day. There is a comfortable sitting room and bar with books and pictures lining the walls. 10 en suite rooms. Honeymoon suite.

ACCESS VISA MASTERCARD ***accepted***

Off the beaten track ...
yet only 4½ miles from the City ...
alongside the River Ouse ... right at
the heart of Yorkshire.

The Manor
Country House

Acaster Malbis
York YO2 1UL
Tel: York (01904) 706723
Fax: York (01904) 706723

AWARDED ETB
Highly Commended

Part of the Gar

Atmospheric Manor in rural tranquillity with own private lake set in 5½ acres of beautiful mature grounds. Preservation orders on all trees with abundant bird life. Fish in the Lake, cycle or walk, bring your own boat for river cruising. Close to Racecourse and only 10 minutes' car journey from the city or take the leisurely river bus (Easter to October). Conveniently situated to take advantage of the Dales, Moors, Wolds and splendid coastline.

Find us via A64 exiting for Copmanthorpe–York, Thirsk–Harrogate or Bishopthorpe (Sim Balk Lane).

Chapel in the W

Centrally heated. 10 en suite bedrooms with full facilities. Cosy lounge and lounge bar; licensed, open fire. Conservatory dining room with Aga-cooked food. Four-poster. Stair lift. Bed and Breakfast from £22.50 to £30.00 per person per night.

For details,
SAE or telephone
Susan Viscovich.

Appleton Hall

Country House Hotel & Restaurant

Situated in the North Yorkshire Moors National Park this elegant Victorian House is set in over 2 acres of award winning gardens. The Hotel is personally run by the owners Norma and Graham Davies and is an ideal base for walking or touring. Offering elegance, comfort and tranquillity at sensible prices, Appleton is a hotel which having visited, you will certainly wish to return to.

Appleton-le-Moors, North Yorkshire YO6 6TF
Telephone: Pickering (01751) 417227
Fax: (01751) 417540

• RED HALL •

Great Broughton, Stokesley, North Yorkshire TS9 7ET

Tel/Fax 01642 712300

Red Hall offers the calm and elegance of the small country house, providing personal service in a caring friendly atmosphere. Our lovely Grade 2 Listed Country House has spacious, centrally heated, ensuite bedrooms; guests' private dining/reading room with garden access. Lovely walks, tennis, horse-riding and stabling, ample parking; village half mile. A visit to Red Hall gives easy access to the North Yorks' Moors' dramatic and beautiful scenery, also superb in autumn and winter. Fishing villages, market towns, moorland hamlets and many places of interest can be visited; let the proprietors with their extensive local knowledge help you plan your visits.

Frenchman's Cove Country Hotel

AWAY FROM IT ALL!

Our delightful family-run country hotel is set amongst National Trust downland, not far from the Needles and safe sandy beaches. Ideal for ramblers, birdwatchers, cyclists and those that enjoy the countryside. We have almost an acre of grounds with outdoor play equipment. Cots and high chairs are available. Most rooms are en suite, all with colour TV and tea/coffee making facilities. Guests can relax in the cosy bar or in the attractive lounge. Also available is the Coach House, a delightfully appointed apartment for two adults and two children. Please contact Sue and Chris Boatfield for details. AA **QQ**. *ACCESS, VISA, AMEX accepted.*

Alum Bay Old Road, Totland PO39 0HZ Tel. 01983 752227 Fax. 01983 755125

The Kildare Hotel & Country Club

Straffan, Co. Kildare, Ireland

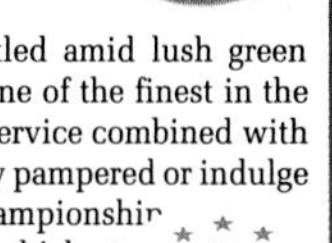

Tel: 353 1 627 3333 Fax: 353 1 627 3312 Reservations
Tel: 353 1 627 3111 Fax: 353 1 627 3990 Golf Reservations

'Luxurious comfort, superb facilities'

★★★★★ The 330-acre grounds of the Kildare Hotel & Country Club are nestled amid lush green woodlands, just 17 miles from Dublin, Ireland's capital city. Already acclaimed as one of the finest in the world, this magnificent 5 star Hotel offers you the highest standards of comfort and service combined with the elegance and unique charm of an Irish country home. You can relax and be lavishly pampered or indulge in any of the quality leisure activities available, including our prestigious par 72 championship golf course designed by Arnold Palmer. 45 bedrooms, all individually appointed to the highest standard. Be it for business or pleasure, The Kildare Hotel & Country Club is the most rewarding place to stay. *Venue for the Smurfit European Open 1997.*

SMURFIT European Open

AA ★★★★ DELUXE ♛♛♛♛♛ RAC ★★★★

SMALL LUXURY HOTELS OF THE WORLD

1995 Regional Hotel of the Year

Recently awarded the supreme accolade of 4 Red Stars

Balbirnie is a delightful Grade 'A' listed mansion house, the centrepiece of a 400 acre estate, which includes an 18 hole golf course. Located in the heart of Fife, only half an hour between both Edinburgh and St. Andrews, the hotel comprises memorable and delightful public rooms, 30 individually designed bedrooms and suites, private dining rooms, together with a range of traditional or hi-tech special event, banqueting and conference areas. Balbirnie is many things to many people and several things to individuals – feature breaks, corporate gatherings, tailor-made special events, just call for details.

Alan C. Russell, Managing Director and Co-Proprietor.

BALBIRNIE PARK, MARKINCH, GLENROTHES, FIFE KY7 6NE
TELEPHONE: 01592 610066 FAX: 01592 610529

THE GREEN HOTEL

KINROSS, SCOTLAND KY13 7AS Tel: (01577) 863467 Fax: (01577) 863180

Independently owned holiday hotel, only 5 minutes from the M90. Well-appointed bedrooms and family suites. Restaurant, bar meals. Spacious indoor pool and leisure complex, own two 18-hole golf courses, two all weather tennis courts, and world famous trout fishing. Ideal touring base, with Edinburgh, Glasgow, Perth, Stirling, St. Andrews, Pitlochry and Highland Perthshire within the hour. ♛♛♛♛♛ Highly Commended.

MANSFIELD HOUSE HOTEL

AA ★★★ RAC ♛♛♛♛ Highly Commended

The Mansfield House Hotel is an elegant Victorian Country House under the personal management of the Lauritsen family. It is situated in the heart of the Highland golfing area, only 10 minutes from The Royal Dornoch Golf Club, and within easy reach of at least a dozen others. The Hotel can arrange discounted green fees at Tain Golf Club. With de luxe rooms, good conference facilities, and first class dining facilities, the hotel makes an excellent venue for business or social golf. We also take special care of non-golfing guests. Please call or fax for brochure and tariff.

Scotsburn Road, Tain, Ross-shire IV19 1PR. Tel: 01862 892052; Fax: 01862 892260.

THE TASTE OF SCOTLAND

BORTHWNOG HALL COUNTRY HOUSE HOTEL & RESTAURANT

Bontddu, Dolgellau, Gwynedd LL40 2TT Tel: 01341 430271 Fax: 01341 430682

Once described as '*a little gem*', Borthwnog Hall (a listed building) is a great favourite of those seeking comfort, relaxation and excellent hospitality all set in a magnificent location overlooking the beautiful Mawddach estuary in southern Snowdonia. Uniquely, in your bedroom you will find a personalised guide to the area covering a variety of walks and attractions with personal comments on each by either your hosts or by previous guests. Couple this with the excellent menu and wine list and it is not difficult to see why Borthwnog is so popular. Weekly, short break, and seasonal special rates are available.

AA Premier Selected QQQQQ RAC Highly Acclaimed WTB ♛♛♛♛ Highly Commended

CASTELL CIDWM HOTEL

Betws Garmon, Caernarvon, Gwynedd LL54 7YT
Telephone: 01286 650243

In one of the most beautiful settings in Wales on the west side of Snowdon, this delightfully tranquil lakeside hotel offers magnificent views of mountain, forest and water. Warm friendly hospitality is offered. Eight bedrooms (all en suite), a cosy bar, a lakeside café and an à la carte restaurant with a subtly different cuisine. Children welcome. Car park. Two and three day breaks available.

AVAILABLE FROM THE HOTEL OR NEARBY

★ Private Trout Fishing ★ Boating ★ Water Sports
★ Walking ★ Climbing ★ Pony Trekking

WTB ♛♛♛ Highly Commended

Maes-y-Gwernen Hotel

School Road, Abercraf, Swansea Valley, South Wales SA9 1XD
Tel: 01639 730218 Fax: 01639 730765

A well furnished hotel in private grounds on southern edge of Brecon Beacons National Park. All rooms ensuite; luxury garden chalets available. Health Spa, Sauna, Solarium, Bar, Lounges and gardens exclusive to residents. Winner of several National Quality Awards.

AA, RAC, Les Routiers & Wales Tourist Board.

♛♛♛♛ Highly Commended. B&B from £24.00. Major credit cards accepted.

Recommended COUNTRY HOTELS OF BRITAIN 1997

Publishers' Foreword

"... WELL-PRESENTED FACTS that immediately form a mental picture, that are easy to read and easy to understand ..." were the stated aims of Peter Stanley Williams, the original publisher of *RECOMMENDED COUNTRY HOTELS*, in his first edition of 1973. Succeeding issues have continued this theme and in our 1997 edition you will find what we believe are factual descriptions of a selection of hundreds of Britain's best Country and Country House Hotels. For a well-earned holiday or a surprise Short Break, there's nothing like the individual attention and the dignified hospitality of a well-run small hotel with a resident proprietor and close-knit staff. Equally, the market-conscious larger chain competes with the latest facilities and smooth-running comfort. Both are represented in the pages that follow.

In addition to information about location, accommodation, cuisine and cellar, with most entries we also give an indication of price range and of course whatever ratings or awards individual hotels may have achieved. Our hotels are 'recommended' for their reputation, facilities and in many cases, through long association rather than by inspection. As publishers we cannot accept responsibility for any errors or misrepresentations in the descriptions that follow and we are always interested to hear from our readers about their own experiences. Problems are best settled on the spot with the hotel itself but we will record any complaint we receive and follow it up. We regret, however, that we cannot act as intermediaries or arbiters.

In the many years since the first edition of *RECOMMENDED COUNTRY HOTELS* was published, complaints have been few, and rarely serious. You will find straightforward and mainly factual descriptions of a selection of many old favourites and newer entries. As far as we can establish, all details are correct as we go to press, but we suggest that you confirm prices and any other terms when you enquire about bookings.

In the interests of 'well-presented facts' we have introduced two new sections which give separate, quick-reference listings for those hotels offering special Conference Facilities and those with special Leisure Facilities. These listings complement the main descriptive entry under the appropriate county heading.

We hope that this will add to the value and the ease of use of *RECOMMENDED COUNTRY HOTELS OF BRITAIN* and we do appreciate your naming our guide when you make enquiries and bookings. Give yourself a treat! Make the most of the rich choice of country hotels all around Britain.

Peter Stanley Williams
Editorial Consultant

Peter Clark
Publishing Director

Recommended
Country Hotels
OF BRITAIN

CONTENTS

Other FHG Publications

Recommended Wayside & Country Inns of Britain
Recommended Short Break Holidays in Britain
Pets Welcome!
Bed and Breakfast in Britain
The Golf Guide: Where to Play/Where to Stay
Farm Holiday Guide England/Wales, Ireland & Channel Islands
Farm Holiday Guide Scotland
Self-Catering Holidays in Britain
Britain's Best Holidays
Guide to Caravan and Camping Holidays
Children Welcome! Family Holiday and Atttractions Guide
Bed and Breakfast Stops
Scottish Welcome

We thank Rose-in-Vale Country House Hotel, St.Agnes, Cornwall
for the use of their picture on our Outside Front Cover.

Cover design: Cyan Creative Consultants, Glasgow.

Please note: owing to recent boundary changes
the following counties no longer exist:

England
Avon — see under Gloucester and Somerset
Cleveland — see under Durham
Humberside — see under Yorkshire(East) and Lincolnshire

Scotland
Banffshire — see under Moray and Aberdeenshire
Kincardineshire — see under Aberdeenshire
Kinross-shire — see under Perth and Kinross

In **Wales** the changes have been more extensive
and we have arranged the section as follows:
North Wales — formerly Clwyd and Gwynedd
Dyfed
Powys
South Wales — formerly Glamorgan and Gwent

1997 Edition
ISBN 1 85055 218 5

Cartography by GEO Projects, Reading.
Maps are based on Ordnance Survey Maps with the permission of
the Controller of Her Majesty's Stationery Office. Crown Copyright reserved.

Typeset by FHG Publications Ltd, Paisley.
Printed and bound in Great Britain by Bemrose Ltd, Derby.

Distribution. **Book Trade**: WLM, Downing Road, West Meadows Ind. Estate, Derby DE21 6HA
(Tel: 01332 343332 Fax: 01332 340464).
News Trade: USM Distribution Ltd, 86 Newman Street, London W1P 3LD
(Tel: 0171-396 8000. Fax: 0171-396 8002. E-mail:usm.co.uk)

Published by FHG Publications Ltd.
Abbey Mill Business Centre, Seedhill, Paisley PA1 1TJ (0141-887 0428; Fax: 0141-889 7204).

US ISBN 1-55650-766-6
Distributed in the United States by
Hunter Publishing Inc.,300 Raritan Center, Parkway, CN94, Edison, N.J., 08818, USA.

Buckinghamshire

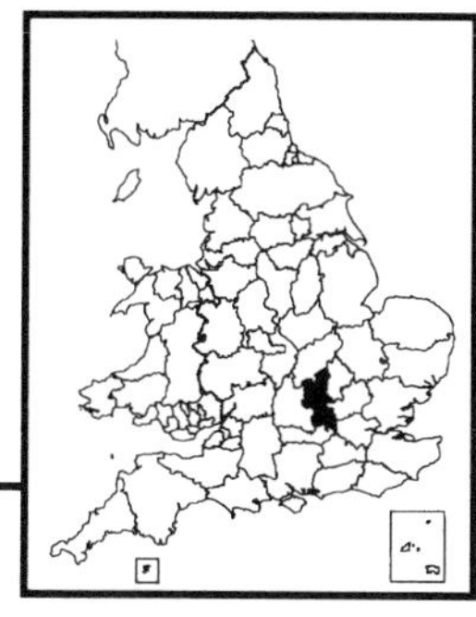

THE GROVEFIELD HOTEL,
Taplow Common Road, Burnham,
Buckinghamshire SL1 8LP

Tel: 01628 603131
Fax: 01628 668078

Fully licensed; 40 bedrooms, all with private bathrooms; Children and pets welcome; Conference facilities; Windsor 6 miles; £££.

Built at the turn of the century for a member of the Fuller brewing family, this handsome, well proportioned establishment stands secluded in over seven acres of lawns and woodland — indeed it is hard to believe that it lies only minutes from Heathrow Airport and the motorway network. A variety of en suite bedrooms, all stylishly appointed, offer accommodation to suit all requirements; romantic four-poster rooms and spacious suites provide a very special touch of luxury for a celebration weekend. Elegant decor, fine cuisine and a carefully selected wine list combine to make the Paddocks Restaurant a very popular venue for discerning diners. And to complete the picture, first rate conference and banqueting facilities can cater for all types of functions. ♛♛♛♛.

The **£** symbol when appearing at the end of the italic section of an entry shows the anticipated price, during 1997, for single full Bed and Breakfast.

Under £40	**£**	**Over £55 but under £70**	**£££**
Over £40 but under £55	**££**	**Over £70**	**££££**

This is meant as an indication only and does not show prices for Special Breaks, Weekends, etc. Guests are therefore advised to verify all prices on enquiring or booking.

Cambridgeshire

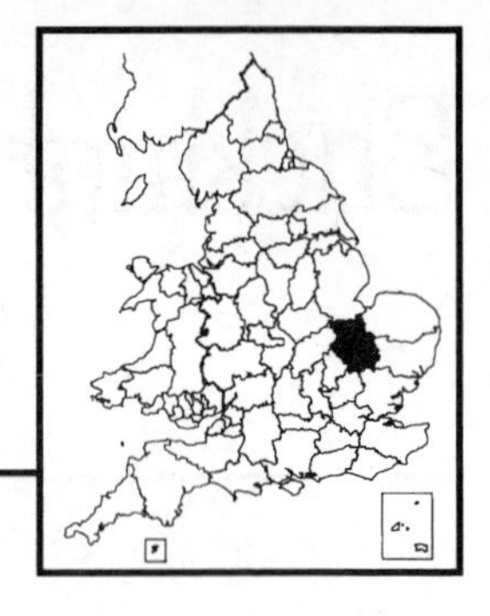

THE NYTON,
7 Barton Road, Ely,
Cambridgeshire CB7 4HZ

Tel: 01353 662459
Fax: 01353 666619

Fully licensed; 14 bedrooms, all with private bathrooms; Children welcome; Conference facilities; Cambridge 14 miles; £.

Just 10 minutes' walk from Ely's beautiful cathedral, this most comfortable and well-appointed hotel stands in two acres of attractive grounds and adjoins the 18-hole golf course on which reduced green fees apply to guests. Bedrooms are charmingly furnished and decorated, with en suite facilities, central heating, colour television, radio and beverage makers; some family rooms are available. A pleasant panelled dining room is the setting for the presentation of excellent English and Continental dishes from both à la carte and table d'hôte menus. Morning coffee and afternoon tea may be enjoyed in the spacious lounge area with its interesting period fireplace and the spruce cocktail bar is a good place for meeting new friends. *EATB* ♛♛♛ *Commended, AA/RAC* *

MELBOURN BURY,
Melbourn,Royston,
Cambridgeshire SG8 6DE

Tel: 01763 261151
Fax: 01763 262375

Residential licence; 3 bedrooms, all with private bathrooms; Historic interest; Children over 8 years welcome; Conference facilities; Royston 3 miles; ££.

A lovely house which has been in the same family for over 175 years, Melbourn Bury is typically Victorian in character although parts of the house date back to the 17th century. Rooms are graciously proportioned and open fires and flowers add to the air of warm tranquillity. This mood is accentuated by the extensive and well-planned gardens which include a small lake. The accommodation is limited so book early if possible. The luxurious bedrooms are spacious and all have a private bathroom and colour television. Not far south of Cambridge and near Royston main line station, this is an ideal venue for a quiet, refreshing break from routine.

PUBLISHER'S NOTE

While every effort is made to ensure accuracy, we regret that FHG Publications cannot accept responsibility for errors, omissions or misrepresentations in our entries or any consequences thereof. Prices in particular should be checked because we go to press early. We will follow up complaints but cannot act as arbiters or agents for either party.

Cheshire

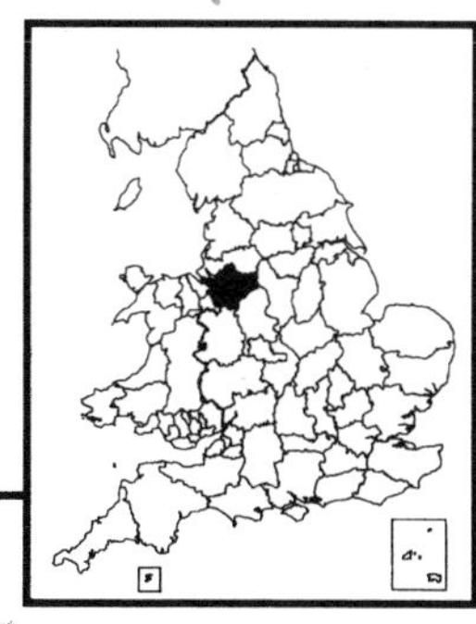

ALDERLEY EDGE HOTEL,
Macclesfield Road, Alderley Edge, Cheshire SK9 7BJ

Tel: 01625 583033
Fax: 01625 586343

Fully licensed; 32 bedrooms, all with private bathrooms; Children welcome; Conference facilities; Wilmslow 2 miles; ££££.

The comparatively recent refurbishment of this well-known hotel has been inspirational; from the cellars to the attic, everything is in the de-luxe class. Its range of services is breathtaking, hence a rapidly-growing clientele and a reputation for being one of the finest hotels in Europe. Executive and de luxe rooms are impeccably appointed and have a very high standard of decor; some have whirlpool baths and a personal bar whilst all have full en suite facilities, colour television, direct-dial telephone, radio alarm, toiletries and tea and coffee-makers. Special cottage rooms of great character have four-posters and their own entrance. The gourmet cuisine is simply superb with a supporting wine list that is truly remarkable for its size and scope, featuring 100 champagnes and 600 wines. With an air of tranquil elegance, the hotel is a most popular venue for functions being so conveniently near the urban centres of the north-west. Mention should also be made of La Boulangerie, the hotel's own bakery providing an outstanding variety of breads, cakes, pastries and puddings daily. 👑👑👑👑 *Highly Commended, AA*** and Two Rosettes.*

BROXTON HALL COUNTRY HOUSE HOTEL,
Whitchurch Road, Broxton, Chester, Cheshire CH3 9JS

Tel: 01829 782321
Fax: 01829 782330

Fully licensed; 11 bedrooms,all with private bathrooms; Historic interest; Children and pets welcome; Conference facilities; Whitchurch 8 miles; £££.

This picturesque half-timbered mansion dates from 1671 and was restored and altered in Victorian times. In 1967 the Hall was skilfully converted into the first-class hotel it is today, blending Elizabethan charm and Victorian opulence with modern appointments. Tasteful antique furnishings blend harmoniously with period features such as the Jacobean fireplace and the carved oak staircase, while bedrooms are comfortably equipped with en suite bathrooms, colour television, tea and coffee making facilities, telephone, and full central heating. The candlelit dining room offers a superb selection of classic French and traditional English dishes in an atmosphere of quiet elegance. Set in five acres of lawned gardens this is an ideal base for visiting Chester, Snowdonia and the delightful coastline. *AA Rosette for Food.*

WILLINGTON HALL HOTEL,
Willington, Tarporley, Cheshire CW6 ONB

Tel: 01829 752321
Fax: 01829 752596

Fully licensed; 10 bedrooms, all with private bathrooms; Historic interest; Children and pets welcome; Leisure and conference facilities; Nantwich 9 miles; ££.

An uncontrived, even old-fashioned country house hotel in extensive parkland, Willington Hall, built in 1829, sticks to the time-honoured values of hospitality and comfort, at the same time providing the facilities demanded by the modern-day guest. In an unhurried and laid-back atmosphere visitors, many of them businessmen from Chester, Liverpool or Manchester, may pop in for a drink and substantial bar meal or dine formally and well in an attractive dining room. Bedrooms have bathrooms en suite, colour television, radio, telephone and tea and coffee tray. There are pleasant woodland walks in the vicinity and there is a hard tennis court in the grounds. ♛♛♛♛ *AA/RAC* ***.

ROOKERY HALL,
Worleston, Near Nantwich, Cheshire CW5 6DQ

Tel: 01270 610016
Fax: 01270 611211

Fully licensed; 45 bedrooms, all with private bathrooms; Historic interest; Children welcome, pets by arrangement; Leisure and conference facilities; Crewe 3 miles; ££££.

With many rich features of architectural interest, this Grade II Listed Building stands resplendent in some 200 acres of landscaped gardens and woods alongside which runs the River Weaver. Although Georgian in origin, this fine country house was subsequently transformed into a baronial chateau in the late 19th century. Today, under Select Country Hotels ownership, it has the reputation for being one of the best regarded hotels in the country for cuisine, comfort and service. The spacious bedrooms are opulently furnished and beautifully decorated. Internationally acclaimed, the cuisine is modern European in style and augmented by an impressive wine list. ♛♛♛♛♛ *De Luxe, AA Three Red Stars and Three Rosettes, RAC Blue Ribbon, ETB Hotel of the Year 1994, Egon Ronay, Good Food Guide.*

Cornwall

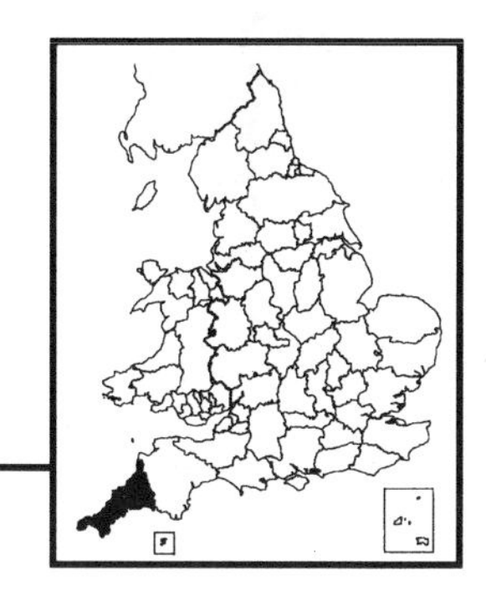

TREDETHY COUNTRY HOTEL,
Helland Bridge, Bodmin,
Cornwall PL30 4QS

Tel: 01208 841262
Fax: 01208 841707

Residential and restaurant licence; 11 bedrooms, all with private bathrooms; Historic interest; Children welcome; Leisure and conference facilities; Bodmin 3 miles; £.

Equidistant from Cornwall's north and south coasts, this delightful retreat basks in 9 acres of glorious grounds, a haven of peace and contentment. Through the lush valley in which Tredethy stands, the River Camel meanders its way to Padstow and the sea. In these idyllic surroundings, there are opportunities for riding, walking, sailing, golf and both river and sea fishing; in the grounds there is a fine sheltered heated swimming pool. The accommodation is spacious and of a high standard, guest rooms all having en suite facilities, colour television and telephone. In the grounds there are also several self catering cottages. All arrangements are under the personal supervision of proprietors, Beryl and Richard Graham. ♛♛♛.

WILLAPARK MANOR HOTEL,
Bossiney, Near Tintagel,
Cornwall PL34 0BA

Tel: 01840 770782

Restaurant and residential licence; 14 bedrooms, all with private bathrooms; Children and pets welcome; Camelford 4 miles; £.

ONE OF THE MOST BEAUTIFULLY SITUATED HOTELS IN ENGLAND. Beautiful character house, perched on the cliffs amidst 14 acres of landscaped gardens and secluded woodland overlooking the Bay. Direct access to coast path and beach with wonderful walks in every direction. Fourteen bedrooms, all en suite, with colour television and tea makers. Excellent cuisine, well stocked cocktail bar and a unique friendly and informal atmosphere. *ETB ♛♛♛ Commended.*

TRELAWNE HOTEL,
Mawnan Smith, Falmouth,
Cornwall TR11 5HS

Tel: 01326 250226*
Fax: 01326 250909

Licensed; 16 bedrooms, 14 with private bathrooms; Children and pets welcome; Leisure facilities; Truro 13 miles, Falmouth 5; ££.

Nestling on the coastline between the Helford and Fal rivers in a beautiful and tranquil corner of Cornwall, this fine country house hotel enjoys a magnificent outlook across Falmouth Bay to the Roseland Peninsula. Maenporth beach is a short distance away and there are numerous idyllic coves nearby. The tastefully furnished and centrally heated bedrooms have en suite facilities, as well as colour television, radio, telephone and tea and coffee makers. There is a charming cocktail bar where new friends are easily made, and is an indoor pool and games room. The cuisine comes high on the list of attractions at this well-run hotel, dishes being prepared by award-winning chefs and backed by an extensive wine list. ♛♛♛♛, AA***.

MEUDON HOTEL,
Mawnan Smith, Falmouth,
Cornwall TR11 5HT

Tel: 01326 250541*
Fax: 01326 250543

Restaurant and residential licence; 29 bedrooms, all with private bathrooms; Historic interest; Children and pets welcome; Conference facilities; Falmouth 4 miles; ££££.

The most picturesque part of the Cornish coast between the Fal and Helford rivers is the enviable setting of this luxury hotel where the cuisine is something of a legend, with locally caught seafood especially worthy of mention. The beautifully landscaped gardens of eight acres lead down to the sea, and here one may relax in utter peace with rare flowering plants and shrubs providing a blaze of colour. Appointments throughout the hotel are of the highest standard and among the facilities available is a laundry service and a hairdressing salon.A wide range of leisure amenities are available in the area, including golf, sea and river fishing, bowls, riding, and watersports; delightful unspoilt villages and peaceful coves wait to be explored. *AA***, RAC *** and Merit Awards.*

PLEASE MENTION THIS GUIDE WHEN YOU WRITE

OR PHONE TO ENQUIRE ABOUT ACCOMMODATION.

IF YOU ARE WRITING, A STAMPED,

ADDRESSED ENVELOPE IS ALWAYS APPRECIATED.

STEEP HOUSE,
Portmellon Cove, Mevagissey,
Cornwall PL26 2PH

Tel: 01726 843732

Residential licence; 7 bedrooms, 2 with private bathrooms; Children over 10 years welcome; Leisure facilities; Newquay 20 miles, St Austell 6

Steep House stands in an acre of ground by the sea, in a natural cove with a safe sandy beach twenty yards from the large garden. Comfortable, centrally heated double bedrooms with washbasins and sea or beach views, colour television and tea/coffee makers; some are en suite. Generous English breakfast served. Covered summertime swimming pool. Guests welcome all year. Modest prices, special weekly and winter break rates. Residential drinks licence. Private parking. Fire Certificate. Colour brochure. *ETB* 👑👑.

KILBOL COUNTRY HOUSE HOTEL,
Polmassick, Mevagissey,
Cornwall PL26 6HA

Tel: 01726 842481

Residential and restaurant licence; 6 bedrooms, 5 with private bathrooms; Historic interest; Pets welcome; Leisure facilities; St Austell 5 miles; £.

Inland from Mevagissey Bay, leafy lanes wind through a green and gentle land, after about three miles reaching a scatter of cottages that is Polmassick. Stop, for it is here, swathed in rustic tranquillity, that one finds the perfect retreat from the rat-race. Kilbol is a charming little country house that dates from the 16th century: the demands of a modern era have ordained that it now carries out the functions of a distinguished cottage-style hotel, although many of its original features remain. It stands in a beautiful valley in 7½ acres, and within the grounds there is an outdoor swimming pool and a croquet lawn.The cuisine is simply superlative and the accommodation comfort personified. “Perfect Cornish peace”. 👑👑👑*Commended.*

---

* The appearance of an asterisk after the telephone number indicates that the hotel in question is closed for a period during the winter months. Exact dates should be ascertained from the hotel itself.

PENRYN HOUSE,
The Coombes, Polperro,
Cornwall PL13 2RG

Tel: 01503 272157*
Fax: 01503 273055

Residential and restaurant licence; 10 bedrooms, all with private bathrooms; Children and pets welcome; Looe 4 miles; £.

Set in its own grounds, Penryn House is a country house-style property in the heart of Cornwall's most photographed and painted fishing village. It offers delightfully appointed en suite bedrooms with colour television, telephones, courtesy trays, and central heating, and a comfortable lounge with log fires on cooler evenings. Enjoy the warmth and ambience of our candlelit restaurant where our speciality chef offers a wide selection of freshly prepared dishes, with local produce in season and fresh local fish. Nearby attractions include many National Trust properties, peaceful gardens, and a lovely variety of walks for serious and casual walkers. Ample parking within the grounds. Murder Mystery Weekends March and October. 👑👑👑, *RAC, Les Routiers.*

THE CORNISH ARMS,
Pendoggett, Port Isaac,
Cornwall PL30 3HH

Tel: 01208 880263
Fax: 01208 880335

Fully licensed; 7 bedrooms, 5 with private bathrooms; Historic interest; Children welcome; Wadebridge 8 miles, Polzeath 6, Port Isaac 1; £.

A delightful 16th century Coaching Inn in the small rural village of Pendoggett, just one mile from the coast. Anyone who makes The Cornish Arms a base for exploring the area will not be disappointed by the attractive accommodation or the warmth of welcome extended. Whilst retaining the character of a traditional coaching inn, The Cornish Arms offers all modern amenities in every bedroom; colour and satellite TV, telephone, trouser press, tea and coffee making facilities, etc. The highly recommended restaurant specialises in locally caught seafood and an extensive range of other dishes. Complement your meal with wine from the extensive cellars of The Cornish Arms. Pendoggett Special Bitter is famous for its strength — the locals won't touch it, it's so strong. With Bass straight from the barrel, together with other real ales, you will see why both CAMRA and The Good Pub Guide recommend The Cornish Arms. *ETB* 👑👑👑 *Commended, RAC **, Les Routiers, Good Food Guide.* **See also Colour Advertisement on page 2.**

PENVENTON HOTEL,
West End, Redruth,
Cornwall TR15 1TE

Tel: 01209 214141
Fax: 01209 219164

Licensed; 49 bedrooms, all with private bathrooms; Historic interest; Children and pets welcome; Leisure and conference facilities; Truro 8 miles; £.

A beautiful 18th century mansion house set in acres of parkland, well situated for touring Cornwall. A health and leisure spa offers an indoor swimming pool, sauna, spa bath, new gym, beautician and masseur. The famous Dining Galleries Restaurant serves a large choice of locally caught fish, meat and home produced vegetables, with extensive à la carte menus featuring Italian, French and English dishes. All bedrooms are en suite, with colour television and tea and coffee making facilities. A Cornish welcome awaits you. Would you like a FREE room? Phone for details. *AA*** and Red Rosette, RAC****.

ROSE-IN-VALE COUNTRY HOUSE HOTEL,
Mithian, St Agnes,
Cornwall TR5 0QD

Tel: 01872 552202
Fax: 01872 552700

Residential and restaurant licence; 17 bedrooms, all with private bathrooms; Children and pets welcome; Leisure facilities; St Agnes 2 miles; ££.

Occupying a secluded position in its own small valley amidst beautiful Cornish countryside and near the coast, this Georgian country house hotel has grounds extending to 11 acres including beautiful gardens, woodland and pasture as well as a heated swimming pool and waterfowl ponds. Inside, guests will find en suite bedrooms equipped with hairdryers, radio, telephone, tea-makers and television; ground floor rooms are available as well as luxurious four-poster suites. Opie's Room is the elegant setting for the enjoyment of one's choice from the table d'hôte and à la carte menus, fresh local produce including newly landed fish and seafood featuring prominently in each day's selection. The hotel's central location makes it an ideal base for exploring this most fascinating county. ♛♛♛♛ *Highly Commended, AA/RAC****. **See also Colour Advertisement on page 2.**

THE COUNTRYMAN AT TRINK,
Old Coach Road, St.Ives,
Cornwall TR26 3JQ

Tel: 01736 797571

Restaurant and residential licence; 6 bedrooms, all with private bathrooms; Children over 9 years welcome; Penzance 7 miles; £.

Set in two acres of landscaped gardens complete with trout stream, pond and paddock, this little gem of a place is equidistant from the beautiful beaches of St.Ives and Carbis Bay; an idyllic holiday venue. The accommodation comprises delightfully appointed bedrooms, all of which have en suite shower and toilet, colour television, radio and tea-makers with the added bonus of fabulous views. This is an area ideal for walkers with excellent facilities for golf and horse riding nearby. Dining by candlelight in the restaurant will surely confirm this as one of the most delectable smaller hotels we have featured. Its cosy comforts are ideal for off-season breaks with roaring log fires conquering winter chill.This is a non-smoking hotel. ♛♛♛ *Commended.*

NOTE

All the information in this book is given in good faith in the belief that it is correct. However, the publishers cannot guarantee the facts given in these pages, neither are they responsible for changes in policy, ownership or terms that may take place after the date of going to press. Readers should always satisfy themselves that the facilities they require are available and that the terms, if quoted, still apply.

THE OLD RECTORY COUNTRY HOUSE HOTEL,
St Keyne, Liskeard,
Cornwall PL14 4RL

Tel: 01579 342617*

Fully licensed; 8 bedrooms, 7 with private bathrooms; Historic interest; Children and pets welcome; Conference facilities; Liskeard 2 miles; £.

The Old Rectory is peacefully secluded in three acres of gardens, but is ideally situated for touring Cornwall and South West Devon. Enjoy the welcoming ambience of a family-run country house, the excellent tasty dinners and breakfasts, the comfortable en suite bedrooms, all with colour television and hospitality trays. For relaxation, there is a cosy lounge and honesty bar; open fires are lit on cooler evenings. No smoking is allowed in the dining room. Please telephone for brochure. ♛♛♛ *Commended, AA** and Rosette.* **See also Colour Advertisement on page 3.**

TREBREA LODGE,
Trenale, Near Tintagel,
Cornwall PL34 0HR

Tel: 01840 770410*
Fax: 01840 770092

Residential and restaurant licence; 7 bedrooms, all with private bathrooms; Historic interest; Pets welcome; Camelford 4 miles; ££.

From the delightful rooms of this historic house one may gaze across open fields to the sea beyond. The attractions of the Cornish coast lie within easy reach and there is plenty to do and see nearby. Inside, the atmosphere is one of comfort and tranquillity — one can relax in front of a crackling log fire or stroll through the wooded gardens. In the oak-panelled dining room, which has an AA Rosette for fine food, the emphasis is very firmly on freshness and variety, with specialities such as locally caught wild salmon and sea trout. And after a delicious meal, a peaceful night's rest is assured in the traditionally furnished bedrooms, each with private bathroom. *AA** and Rosette, Johansens Country House of the Year 1994, Egon Ronay, Good Hotel Guide.*

Please mention
Recommended COUNTRY HOTELS
when seeking refreshment or
accommodation at a Hotel
mentioned in these pages.

BOSSINEY HOUSE HOTEL,
Tintagel,
Cornwall PL34 0AX

Tel: 01840 770240
Fax: 01840 770501

Residential and restaurant licence; 19 bedrooms, 17 en suite, 2 with private facilities; Children and dogs welcome; Leisure facilities; Bodmin 20 miles, Bude 19, Camelford 6; ££.

At one time Bossiney had its own mayor and corporation, and in the 16th century Sir Francis Drake was one of its two MPs. Today a cluster of houses nestle close to a sandy cove with interesting rock formations, ideal for bathing, surfing or just unwinding. With wonderful cliff walks on either side this is the glorious situation of the beautifully furnished Bossiney House Hotel, standing in grounds of two and a half acres. Guests may relax in the gardens, the indoor heated swimming pool, the sauna or solarium; take in the sweeping sea views; or try their skills on the putting green. Inside, one is immediately impressed by the spacious cleanliness of the public and private rooms,and by the imaginative and pleasing colour schemes. This is a really happy place in which to stay, and the proprietors and staff work hard to achieve this end. Pleasant lounges, one with a bar, are convivial meeting places in which to enjoy refreshment; the well-appointed bedrooms have television, hairdryers and tea/coffee facilities. In the catering department, fine English cooking is a feature of the menus which offer excellent choice and variety. Quaint Tintagel is near at hand, and the surrounding King Arthur's country provides a superb choice of beauty spots, historic locations and sporting activities. ♛♛♛ *Approved, AA and RAC **, Ashley Courtenay Highly Recommended.* **See also Inside Front Cover.**

POLSUE MANOR,
Ruanhighlanes, Near Truro,
Cornwall TR2 5LU

Tel and Fax: 01872 501270*

Residential and restaurant licence; 12 bedrooms, all with private bathrooms; Historic interest; Children and pets welcome; St Mawes 6 miles; £.

Cornwall must surely rank as one of the most delightful of English counties, and Polsue Manor's idyllic situation approximately half way along the south coast allows visitors to enjoy its many and varied attractions to the full. Sandy bathing coves, the picturesque Coastal Path, many lovely gardens and National Trust properties are all within easy reach; combine all this with a mild climate and friendly hospitality to make an ideal holiday spot. Set in 4 acres of garden and woodland, this 19th century mansion, secluded and tranquil, offers comfort and personal attention in an atmosphere of spacious elegance, with hosts Lee and Lorna Robinson taking special care of every guest. All bedrooms have private bathrooms, colour television, hospitality trays and direct-dial telephones. In the elegant dining room peaceful garden views are the perfect background to the enjoyment of the excellent table d'hôte menu with choice, together with an international wine list to enhance the pleasure. *RAC**, Ashley Courtenay.*

PENDOWER HOTEL,
Gerrans Bay, Ruanhighlanes, Near Truro,
Cornwall TR2 5LW

Tel: 01872 501257*

Residential and restaurant licence; 14 bedrooms, all with private bathrooms; Children over 12 years and pets welcome; Truro 12 miles; ££.

Probably the nearest most of us will get to a tropical paradise, this superbly-run hotel nestles in solitary Cornish splendour in 3 acres of grounds which slope gently down to a beach of golden sand and rocks (ideal for clambering over, we are informed by our most junior colleague!). Sunshine (invariably), fresh, clean air and long vistas over a blue, blue sea cast a wondrous spell over guests on arrival; although the amenities provided by this fine hotel contribute markedly to this happy frame of mind with the superb cuisine one of the most impressive factors. Bright and spacious public and private rooms are impeccably decorated and family suites are available for those with older children. A hotel with a smile on its face.

ALVERTON MANOR,
Tregolls Road, Truro,
Cornwall TR1 1XQ

Tel: 01872 76633
Fax: 01872 222989

Licensed; 34 bedrooms, all with private bathrooms; Historic interest; Children and pets welcome; Conference facilities; St Austell 14 miles; £££.

An impressive Grade II Listed building with fine mullioned windows and Cornish slate roof, Alverton Manor has immense character. It has close ecclesiastical connections, quite apart from its hillside position in the cathedral city of Truro, for it was acquired by the Bishop of Truro in 1880 and was later occupied by the Sisters of the Epiphany. Today, this splendid place retains its air of gentility in its role as a country house hotel of distinction. Elegant, beautifully furnished and with an enviable reputation for its superb cuisine, the Manor has all the requisites for an unforgettable West Country holiday, as well as being a popular venue for conferences. ♛♛♛♛ *Highly Commended, AA *** and Two Rosettes for Food, RAC ***.*

Key to Tourist Board Ratings

The Crown Scheme
(England, Scotland & Wales)

Covering hotels, motels, private hotels, guesthouses, inns, bed & breakfast, farmhouses. Every Crown classified place to stay is inspected annually. *The classification*: Listed then 1-5 Crown indicates the range of facilities and services. Higher quality standards are indicated by the terms APPROVED, COMMENDED, HIGHLY COMMENDED and DELUXE.

The Key Scheme
(also operates in Scotland using a Crown System)

Covering self-catering in cottages, bungalows, flats, houseboats, houses, chalets, etc. Every Key classified holiday home is inspected annually. *The classification*: 1-5 Key indicates the range of facilities and equipment. Higher quality standards are indicated by the terms APPROVED, COMMENDED, HIGHLY COMMENDED and DELUXE.

The Q Scheme
(England, Scotland & Wales)

Covering holiday, caravan, chalet and camping parks. Every Q rated park is inspected annually for its quality standards. The more ✔ in the Q – up to 5 – the higher the standard of what is provided.

Cumbria

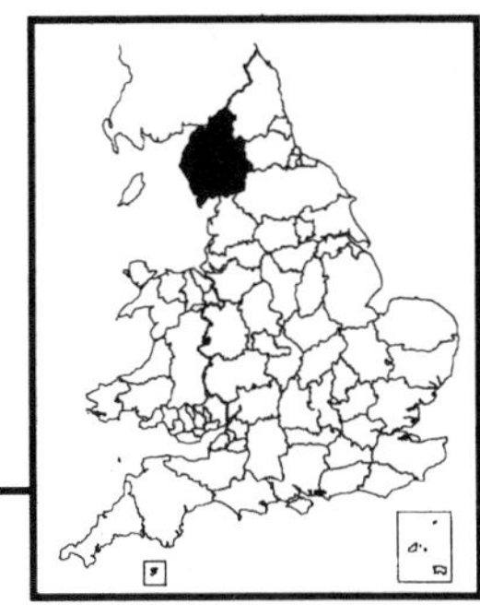

LOVELADY SHIELD COUNTRY HOUSE HOTEL,
Nenthead Road, Near Alston, Tel: 01434 381203*
Cumbria CA9 3LF Fax: 01434 381515

Residential and restaurant licence; 12 bedrooms, all with private bathrooms; Children welcome, pets in bedrooms only; Leisure facilities; Penrith 16 miles; ££.

A lovely early-Victorian country house, Lovelady Shield offers seclusion and the ultimate in comfort, a veritable oasis amidst the rolling fells of the Pennines. Centrally situated for exploring all of the North of England, the house stands in 2 acres of grounds which incorporate a hard tennis court and croquet lawn. Golf, fishing, shooting and riding are available locally. The hotel is centrally heated and log fires burn in the library and drawing room most of the year. Bedrooms have a bathroom or shower en suite, colour television, electric blankets, direct-dial telephone and radio; also well-appreciated is a washing, drying and ironing service. Dining here is a memorable experience, from the hearty English breakfast to the varied and attractively presented four-course dinners. ♛♛♛♛ *Highly Commended, AA Two Red Stars and Two Rosettes, RAC** and HCR Merit Awards, Johansens, Egon Ronay.*

NANNY BROW COUNTRY HOUSE HOTEL,
Clappersgate, Ambleside, Tel: 015394 32036
Cumbria LA22 9NF Fax: 015394 32450

Residential licence; 18 bedrooms, all with private bathrooms; Children welcome, dogs by arrangement; Leisure and conference facilities; Ambleside 1½ miles; £££.

Elegant country house with spectacular views of the River Brathay has direct access onto the Fell. The award winning restaurant features superb cuisine and fine wines. Relax in the elegant lounge or hall and there are log fires on chilly evenings with fresh flowers attended to daily. All suites and rooms are individually furnished in traditional style with caring consideration given to guests by attentive staff. Personally managed by resident owners Michael and Carol Fletcher. ♛♛♛♛ *Highly Commended, AA Red Rosette, RAC Merit Awards, Egon Ronay, Johansens, Ashley Courtenay.* **See also Colour Advertisement on page 3.**

HIGHFIELD HOUSE COUNTRY HOTEL,
Hawkshead Hill, Ambleside,
Cumbria LA22 0PN

Tel: 015394 36344
Fax: 015394 36793

Restaurant and residential licence; 11 bedrooms, all with private bathrooms; Children welcome, pets by arrangement; Windermere 9 miles; £.

Built in traditional Lakeland stone in late Victorian times, Highfield House has been impressively converted into a country hotel of some standing – and stand it does, amidst a lovely garden bedecked with colourful shrubs and with far-reaching views across the undulating countryside from its large windows. Brightly decorated and furnished with style and taste, the house offers peace and quiet, superb food and charming accommodation, each room having en suite facilities, remote-control colour television, easy chairs, hairdryer, clock/radio, electric blanket and tea and coffee tray; fine amenities to add to its individual character. This is good walking terrain and in the spacious lounge a selection of maps, guides and books will facilitate planning one's excursions, returning with happy anticipation at the end of the day, assured of a tempting choice of dishes from an inspired menu that changes every day. Vegetarians and those on special diets are well catered for, as are children. Brisk exercise is certainly recommended here, for the magnificent food, including traditional breakfasts and puddings, will pay no heed to waistlines. A small but well-stocked bar serves excellent local bitter and there is an interesting selection of reasonably priced wines. The hotel is just three-quarters of a mile from Hawkshead village on the road to Tarn Hows (1½ miles) and Coniston (3½ miles). whilst a bus service operates to Ambleside (5 miles) and Windermere (9 miles). ♛♛♛ *Highly Commended, RAC** and Merit Award, AA**, Ashley Courtenay.*

ROTHAY MANOR HOTEL,
Rothay Bridge, Ambleside
Cumbria LA22 0EH

Tel: 015394 33605
Fax: 015394 33607

Residential and restaurant licence; 18 bedrooms, all with private bathrooms; Historic interest; Children welcome; Conference facilities; Windermere 4 miles; ££££.

Rothay Manor, an elegant Regency house run by the Nixon family for over 25 years, stands in its own grounds a quarter of a mile from the head of Lake Windermere. The drawing rooms and candlelit dining room still retain the relaxed atmosphere of a private house. Care, consideration and comfort are evident throughout. The menu is varied and meals are prepared and served with flair and imagination to the highest of standards, complemented by a comprehensive wine list. Residents have free use of a nearby Leisure Centre, with swimming pool, steam room and jacuzzi, and free fishing permits are also available. ♛♛♛♛ *Highly Commended, AA*** and Rosette.*

GLEN ROTHAY HOTEL,
Rydal, Ambleside,
Cumbria LA22 9LR

Tel: 015394 32524
Fax: 015394 31079

Fully licensed; 11 bedrooms, all with private bathrooms; Historic interest; Children and pets welcome; Windermere 4 miles; £.

Close to the shores of peaceful Rydal Water, this is an outstanding example of a traditional country hotel. Standing in its own grounds, the lovely house was built in the early 17th century and its beamed ceilings, oak-panelled lounge and open log fires remain to captivate modern-day guests. Tastefully decorated bedrooms are blessed with such contemporary facilities as bath or shower en suite, w.c., colour television, telephone, tea and coffee makers and central heating. The cuisine here represents English cooking at its very best, with a good choice of delicious five-course table d'hôte dinners. Coffee and liqueurs are served in the relaxing comfort of the Oak Lounge whilst the attractive Badger Bar dispenses local real ale and a selection of malt whiskies. ♛♛♛, *AA and RAC **.*

The **£** symbol when appearing at the end of the italic section of an entry shows the anticipated price, during 1997, for single full Bed and Breakfast.

Under £40	**£**	**Over £55 but under £70**	**£££**
Over £40 but under £55	**££**	**Over £70**	**££££**

This is meant as an indication only and does not show prices for Special Breaks, Weekends, etc. Guests are therefore advised to verify all prices on enquiring or booking.

APPLEBY MANOR COUNTRY HOUSE HOTEL,
Roman Road, Appleby-in-Westmorland,
Cumbria CA16 6JB Tel: 017683 51571

Fully licensed; 30 bedrooms, all with private bathrooms; Historic interest; Children and pets welcome; Leisure facilities; Penrith 13 miles, Brough 8; £££.

Set in wooded grounds overlooking Appleby's fine castle, with panoramic views of the Pennines and Eden Valley, Appleby Manor is a hotel in which you will feel immediately at home. Where nicer to return to after a great day out in the Lakes or Yorkshire Dales than this relaxing and friendly country house with its log fires, beautiful public rooms and high quality, fully equipped bedrooms. Take a refreshing dip in the heated indoor pool in the leisure club before enjoying a superb meal in the award-winning restaurant, and then retiring to one of the comfy chairs in the lounge with a malt whisky selected from a choice of over 70. ♛♛♛♛ *Highly Commended, AA and RAC ***.*

SCAFELL HOTEL,
Rosthwaite, Borrowdale, Near Keswick, Tel: 017687 77208*
Cumbria CA12 5XB Fax: 017687 77280

Fully licensed; 24 bedrooms, all with private bathrooms; Historic interest; Children and dogs welcome; Derwent Water 3 miles; ££.

Former coaching inn set in the heart of impressive Borrowdale. 24 en suite bedrooms, with lounges warmed by log fires in winter, and a restaurant renowned for fine food and wines. Run by a staff providing warm and friendly service.

TARN END HOUSE HOTEL,
Talkin Tarn, Brampton, Carlisle, Cumbria CA8 1LS

Tel: 016977 2340
Fax: 016977 2089

Licensed; All bedrooms with private bathrooms; Children and pets welcome; Conference facilities; Brampton 3 miles; ££.

Tarn End House Hotel is situated in its own grounds running down to the shores of the Tarn, and is only 500 yards from Brampton Golf Club. The bar, restaurant and residents' lounge all overlook the Lake, as do most of the bedrooms, all of which have colour television and tea/coffee facilities. Other relaxations include fishing, birdwatching, sailing and walking. Hadrian's Wall, Lanercost Abbey and the Roman Army Museum are all close at hand, as is the renowned Settle to Carlisle railway line. Resident proprietors, David and Vivienne Ball, invite you to relax and wind down at this traditional hotel in its own delightful secluded setting. All food in the restaurant and bar is home-made and freshly cooked to order. Telephone for colour brochure and tariff. ♛♛♛, *Egon Ronay, AA/RAC**, Johansens.*

AYNSOME MANOR HOTEL,
Cartmel, Near Grange-over-Sands, Cumbria LA11 6HH

Tel: 015395 36653*
Fax: 015395 36016

Restaurant and residential licence; 12 bedrooms, all with private bathrooms; Historic interest; Children and pets welcome; Newby Bridge 4 miles; ££.

Beckoning the discriminating country lover, particularly those who appreciate superb home cooking, Aynsome Manor has a happy and informal air and enjoys a tranquil setting in a sheltered valley just four miles from Lake Windermere. Rooms are delightfully furnished and bedroom amenities include private bathroom, colour television, radio alarm, tea/coffee making facilities and direct-dial telephone. Central heating and cheerful log fires ensure added comfort for those taking Spring or Autumn holidays. The Varley Family personally supervise the well-being of guests and, assisted by a friendly and efficient staff, present a highly regarded cuisine. Dining is by candlelight in elegant surroundings, and the sumptuous sweet trolley will tempt the most obdurate palate. ♛♛♛ *Highly Commended, AA** and Red Rosette.*

PLEASE MENTION THIS GUIDE WHEN YOU WRITE OR PHONE TO ENQUIRE ABOUT ACCOMMODATION. IF YOU ARE WRITING, A STAMPED, ADDRESSED ENVELOPE IS ALWAYS APPRECIATED.

LINK HOUSE,
Bassenthwaite Lake, Cockermouth, Cumbria CA13 9YD

Tel: 017687 76291*
Fax: 017687 76670

Residential and restaurant licence; 8 bedrooms, all with private bathrooms; Historic interest; Children over 7 years welcome; Keswick 6 miles; £.

A family-run traditional Victorian country house at the quieter end of the Lake District and surrounded by lovely scenery, yet providing easy access to all the popular areas. An ideal base for walkers and motorists alike. All eight bedrooms are en suite with colour television, tea/coffee making equipment, central heating, etc. We have single, double, twin and family rooms (one on the ground floor). There is a delightful conservatory to enjoy the evening sun or a pre-dinner drink, plus a comfortable lounge with log fires to make winter evenings even more cosy. Many antique and period pieces of furniture throughout, but more relaxing than formal. The wine list, at modest prices, is selected to complement imaginative four-course freshly prepared dinners (plus coffee), served on Wedgwood china. Credit cards accepted. ♛♛♛ *Commended, AA QQQQ Selected.* **See also Colour Advertisement on page 3.**

BRIDGE HOUSE HOTEL,
Stock Lane, Grasmere, Cumbria LA22 9SN

Tel: 015394 35425*
Fax: 015394 35523

Residential and restaurant licence; 12 bedrooms, all with private bathrooms; Children welcome; Ambleside 3 miles; £.

Bridge House is situated in the centre of Grasmere, enjoying a quiet, secluded position just off the main road. There are two acres of mature gardens beside the River Rothay, with fine views of the surrounding fells. The 12 tastefully furnished bedrooms have private facilities, television, tea tray, telephone and hairdryer. Splendid food completes your holiday — a full English breakfast to start the day and an excellent five-course evening meal with coffee served by the fire, to round it off. You are assured of a warm, friendly welcome, your comfort and enjoyment being our prime concern. Open throughout the year. ♛♛♛ *Commended, RAC Acclaimed.* **See also Colour Advertisement on page 4.**

SWINSIDE LODGE HOTEL,
Newlands, Keswick, Cumbria CA12 5UE

Tel: 017687 72948*

Unlicensed; 9 bedrooms, all with private bathrooms; Children over 12 years welcome; Penrith 16 miles; ££.

Stroll along the placid shores of Derwentwater, taking in the breathtaking scenery of one of the most idyllic spots in Lakeland, and direct your feet towards this lovely Victorian house. It is lucky you booked in earlier, for Swinside Lodge is fast gaining a reputation for its well-appointed accommodation, and, in particular, for its award-winning cuisine. A hearty Cumbrian breakfast sets the standard and after a day's sightseeing, one has the assurance of a delicious five-course dinner prepared by Cordon Bleu chefs and served in the candlelit dining room. The hotel operates a no smoking policy and is unlicensed, but guests are welcome to bring in their own favourite wines and there is no corkage charge. ♛♛♛ *De Luxe, AA Red Star and Two Rosettes for Food.*

DALE HEAD HALL,
Lake Thirlmere, Keswick,
Cumbria CA12 4TN

Tel: 0800 454166
Fax: 017687 71070

Residential and restaurant licence; 9 bedrooms, all with private bathrooms; Historic interest; Children welcome; Keswick 4 miles, Grasmere 4; £.

Sheltered by a lush cushion of trees and the only building on Lake Thirlemere, to many the prettiest of the Lakes, this lovely Elizabethan Hall stands at the foot of lofty Helvellyn (3113ft) offering elegance, ease and a fine cuisine. The hotel's restaurant has been awarded the AA Red Rosette, the RAC Restaurant Award and is featured in both the Michelin Guide and the Good Food Guide. Guest rooms (including a four-poster suite) represent the ultimate in cosseted comfort, being blessed with private bath/shower, radio, direct-dial telephone, books and tea and coffee-makers. Free fly fishing is available to guests, who may also play croquet in the grounds. Specially themed breaks are organised throughout the year. ♛♛♛♛ *Highly Commended, AA** and Red Rosette, RAC** and Merit Awards.*

HIPPING HALL,
Cowan Bridge, Kirkby Lonsdale,
Cumbria LA6 2JJ

Tel: 015242 71187*
Fax: 015242 72452

Residential licence; 7 bedrooms, all with private bathrooms; Historic interest; Children over 12 years and pets welcome; Kirkby Lonsdale 2½ miles; £££.

A tranquil retreat ideally placed between the Lake District and Yorkshire Dales, this small and informal country hotel holds the promise of good company, comfort and magnificent home cooking in the hands of culinary expert and joint proprietor, Jocelyn Ruffle. Guests dine together at one table in the Great Hall under its minstrels' gallery in country house party style. Traditional full English breakfasts, however, are served at separate tables — we are not always at our social best in the mornings! Parties for 10-14 guests are organised out of season. Ian Bryant, the other half of the equation, plays a major part in the smooth running of the hotel, the care of wines his speciality. In beautiful open country to the west of lofty Ingleborough (2375ft.) and but 15 minutes from the M6, this happy place is set in verdant walled gardens that extend to 4 acres. The bedrooms, all with en suite facilities, are furnished with attractive antiques and have colour television and direct-dial telephone as standard appointments. There are also two pretty cottage suites across the courtyard which may be used on a Dinner, Bed and Breakfast basis or as self-catering accommodation from October to April. There are numerous places of scenic interest in the locality with the waterfalls and caves at Ingleton and with Windermere and Wensleydale only half-an-hour's drive away. Walkers, too, find this a most rewarding area. *AA Premier Selected.*

BRANTWOOD COUNTRY HOTEL,
Stainton, Penrith,
Cumbria CA11 0EP

Tel: 01768 862748
Fax: 01768 890164

Fully licensed; 11 bedrooms, all with private bathrooms; Historic interest; Children welcome; Conference facilities; Penrith 2½ miles; £.

Standing in secluded gardens in the picturesque village of Stainton, this attractive country residence retains its olde worlde charm with oak beams and open log fires. It is situated two and a half miles west of Penrith, three miles from Lake Ullswater, and just two minutes from the M6 and A66. All bedrooms have private shower room and WC, colour television, direct-dial telephone, tea/coffee making facilities and full central heating. Guests can enjoy a formal dinner in the restaurant or choose from an extensive bar menu. This relaxed and friendly hotel has been personally run for the last ten years by Susan and John Harvey and sons Stephen and Mark. *Commended, AA and RAC* **. **See also Colour Advertisement on page 3.**

GLENBURN HOTEL,
New Road, Windermere,
Cumbria LA23 2EE

Tel: 015394 42649
Fax: 015394 88998

Residential licence; 16 bedrooms, all with private bathrooms; Children over 5 years welcome; Kendal 7 miles; £.

Glenburn Hotel is one of the best known family-owned hotels in Windermere. Originally a guest house, it has been extended and upgraded. There are 16 en suite bedrooms to suit all occasions: double, twin, and family rooms; Four-poster and Coronet rooms, some with spa baths. All rooms have television, radio, direct-dial telephone and tea/coffee facilities, and there is a delightful dining room, bar and lounge. Full English breakfast and a five-course dinner are served; the à la carte menu is changed daily and there is an extensive wine list. Free leisure facilities are available at Parklands Country Club, and at the exclusive Spinnaker Club at Windermere Marina for a nominal charge. Glenburn is conveniently situated a short distance from the Lake and close to all amenities. Large private car park. Special Breaks are available throughout the year. *Highly Commended, AA and RAC* **.

Please mention
Recommended COUNTRY HOTELS
when seeking refreshment or
accommodation at a Hotel
mentioned in these pages.

Derbyshire

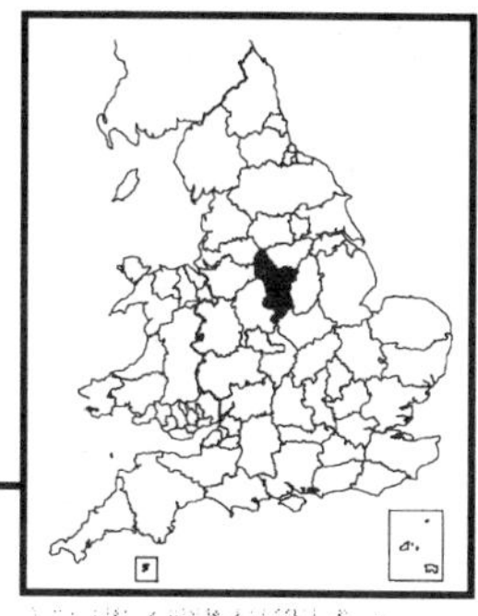

RIVERSIDE COUNTRY HOUSE HOTEL,
Ashford-in-the-Water, Bakewell,
Derbyshire DE45 1QF

Tel: 01629 814275
Fax: 01629 812873

Fully licensed; 15 bedrooms, all with private bathrooms; Historic interest; Small pets welcome; Conference facilities; Bakewell 2 miles; ££££.

This splendid hotel, so well tended by Sue and Roger Taylor and aided by a willing and friendly staff, has an idyllic setting on the River Wye with the beauties of the Peak District National Park on all sides. Delectably appointed with elegant furnishings, oak panelling and the added cheer of crackling log fires in cool weather, the house, Georgian in origin, stands in mature gardens in an unspoilt village between Bakewell and Buxton, a wonderful spot for those seeking respite from the hurly-burly of urban life. The charming bedrooms, with four-posters or half-tester beds, all have en suite facilities, colour television, radio, direct-dial telephone and tea and coffee-makers. The first-rate cuisine is both varied and original. ♛♛♛♛ *Highly Commended, AA*** and Two Rosettes.*

CAVENDISH HOTEL,
Baslow,
Derbyshire DE45 1SP

Tel: 01246 582311
Fax: 01246 582312

Fully licensed; 24 bedrooms, all with private bathrooms; Historic interest; Children welcome; Conference facilities; Bakewell 3 miles; ££££.

With a history as an inn which goes back over 200 years, the Cavendish Hotel is luxuriously and warmly appointed throughout and it is obvious that the Proprietor, Eric Marsh, has put his 30-plus years experience as a hotelier to the most effective use. Guest rooms are beautifully equipped with twin or double beds, colour television, telephone, refrigerated bar, and bathroom with shower and a host of thoughtful extras. The attraction of the public rooms is enhanced by a unique collection of over 300 pictures. Breakfast may be taken at any time in the morning, and lunch formally or casually in the restaurant or garden room, whilst dinner is a delight that almost defies description.

FISCHER'S BASLOW HALL,

Calver Road, Baslow,
Derbyshire DE45 1RR

Tel: 01246 583259
Fax: 01246 583818

Full table licence; 6 bedrooms, all with private bathrooms; Historic interest; No children after 7pm; Conference facilities; Bakewell 3 miles; ££££.

Elegant and of modest size, this skilfully restored house gives the impression of being Elizabethan in origin; it was, in fact, built as recently as 1907 as a private residence. Max and Susan Fischer saw its potential and in 1989 set about creating a reputation for first-class cuisine. Success has greeted their efforts, for recognition of their culinary prowess emanates from numerous informed sources. The very best in modern European food is presented in the restaurant or, alternatively, in the Cafe Max. A splendid base for exploration of the Peak District, the Hall has delightfully appointed guest rooms, all of which have en suite facilities, colour television, radio, direct-dial telephone and hair dryers. ♛♛♛♛ *Highly Commended, AA Three Red Stars, Egon Ronay UK Restaurant of the Year 1995.*

DANNAH FARM COUNTRY GUEST HOUSE,

Bowmans Lane, Shottle, Belper,
Derbyshire DE56 2DR

Tel: 01773 550273
Fax: 01773 550590

Restaurant and residential licence; 8 bedrooms, all with private bathrooms; Historic interest; Children welcome; Belper 3 miles; £.

Proud winners of several awards for its outstanding farmhouse cooking, this lovely Georgian working farm has been skilfully restored and adapted to provide superb modern accommodation. It is beautifully furnished in style with antiques and old pine very much in evidence. All rooms have private facilities, colour television and hot drinks trays. All members of the family will be enchanted, especially the children who will thrill to meet the farm animals at close quarters. The glorious slopes of the Peak District stretch away from the very doorstep, inviting exploration. On return from a day's excursions, near or far, challenging appetites will be more than satisfied in the fully licensed Mixing Place Restaurant. ♛♛♛ *Highly Commended, AA Premier Selected, RAC Highly Acclaimed, Johansens.*

PUBLISHER'S NOTE

While every effort is made to ensure accuracy, we regret that FHG Publications cannot accept responsibility for errors, omissions or misrepresentations in our entries or any consequences thereof. Prices in particular should be checked because we go to press early. We will follow up complaints but cannot act as arbiters or agents for either party.

Devon

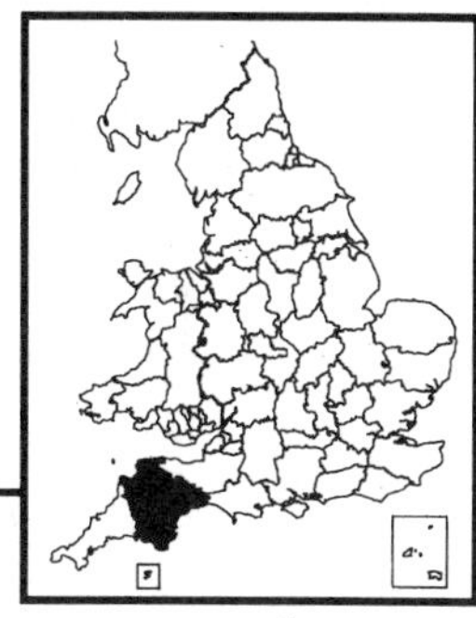

THE EDGEMOOR, Haytor Road, Bovey Tracey, Devon TQ13 9LE

Tel: 01626 832466
Fax: 01626 834760

Residential and restaurant licence; 12 bedrooms, all with private bathrooms; Historic interest; Children and pets welcome; Conference facilities; Exeter 12 miles, Newton Abbot 8; ££.

Set in two acres of delightful gardens, minutes from the A38 Exeter to Plymouth road and on the edge of Dartmoor, The Edgemoor is ideally located for enjoying the beauty of the surrounding countryside. The delightfully decorated bedrooms are all en suite, with direct-dial telephone, television, tea-making facilities, hairdryer, trouser press and other thoughtful details. The hotel bar and lounge offer comfortable surroundings, and the candlelit restaurant has a wide selection of French and English dishes, accompanied by a carefully chosen wine list. There are many interesting and beautiful riverside and moorland walks nearby; fishing, shooting and golf are available locally. 👑👑👑👑 *Highly Commended, AA*** and Rosette, RAC ***, Johansens, Les Routiers.* **See also Colour Advertisement on page 4.**

EASTON COURT HOTEL, Easton Cross, Chagford, Devon TQ13 8JL

Tel and Fax: 01647 433469*

Restaurant and residential licence; 8 bedrooms, all with private bathrooms; Historic interest; Children over 12 years and pets welcome; Moretonhampstead 4 miles; ££.

This lovely, thatched Tudor house has a warm and welcoming ambience and great care has been taken to preserve its original structure although modern conveniences have been skilfully introduced. A place of great character, the house is ideally placed for savouring the pleasures of Dartmoor as well as the varied seaside attractions of both north and south Devon coasts. The accommodation is attractively arranged with each room having en suite facilities, colour television and tea and coffee-makers. The honeymoon suite has a king-sized four-poster bed. The romantic mood may be extended to the splendid restaurant where one may dine by candlelight, a sumptuous five-course meal being prepared each evening by the resident chef. 👑👑👑 *Commended, AA Rosette.*

TYTHERLEIGH COT HOTEL,
Chardstock, Axminster,
Devon EX13 7BN

Tel: 01460 221170
Fax: 01460 221291

Restaurant licence; 19 bedrooms, all with private facilities; Historic interest; Children over 12 years welcome; Leisure and conference facilities; Axminster 4 miles, Chard 3; ££.

A classic, picture-book building in idyllic countryside, this thatched 14th century gem is full of charm and character. The old barn and outbuildings have been renovated to provide luxury units with en suite facilities. Each is individually furnished to the highest standard with colour television, video, telephone and beverage-makers; prestige suites have four-poster beds and/or double jacuzzis and mini-bars. One of the most popular rendezvous in the south-west, the Conservatory Restaurant is renowned for its superb modern and traditional French cuisine and attractive views over the garden, pond and waterfall. ♛♛♛♛ *Commended, AA *** and Rosette for Restaurant, RAC ***.*

ROYAL BEACON HOTEL,
The Beacon, Exmouth,
Devon EX8 2AF

Tel: 01395 264886
Fax: 01395 268890

Fully licensed; 25 bedrooms, all with private bathrooms; Historic interest; Children and pets welcome; Exeter 9 miles; ££.

The Royal Beacon is magnificently situated directly overlooking the beautiful coastline of Torbay. Originally a Georgian posting house, it is conveniently located a short walk from the beach and town centre. All bedrooms, including two private apartments, are tastefully decorated and furnished to a high standard and a lift provides easy access to all floors. For special occasions enjoy the luxury of a four-poster bedroom; champagne, flowers and chocolates can be arranged for your arrival. The restaurant offers light or more substantial fare at lunchtimes and throughout the evenings; morning coffees and cream teas are also served. Room service and 24hr laundry service are available. ♛♛♛♛, *AA/RAC ***.*

FOSFELLE COUNTRY HOUSE HOTEL,
Hartland, Bideford,
Devon EX39 6EF

Tel: 01237 441273

Fully licensed; 7 bedrooms, 4 with private bathrooms; Historic interest; Children and pets welcome; Clovelly 4 miles; £.

This 17th century manor house is set in six acres of grounds in peaceful surroundings with large ornamental gardens and lawns. Fosfelle offers a friendly atmosphere with excellent food, a licensed bar, and a television lounge with log fires on chilly evenings; central heating throughout. There is a games room for children. The comfortable bedrooms, some en suite, all have washbasins and tea making facilities; family rooms and cots are available. Within easy reach of local beaches and ideal for touring Devon and Cornwall. Trout and coarse fishing, clay shooting available at the hotel; riding and golf nearby. Open all year. Reductions for children. *AA Listed.*

BEL ALP HOUSE COUNTRY HOTEL,

Haytor, Near Bovey Tracey,
Devon TQ13 9XX

Tel: 01364 661217
Fax: 01364 661292

Residential and restaurant licence; 9 bedrooms, all with private bathrooms; Children and pets welcome; Plymouth 33 miles, Exeter 14; ££££.

The views from Bel Alp House's spectacular setting on the edge of Dartmoor are simply breathtaking. The other great attractions are superb set dinners, beautiful furnishings, large comfortable bedrooms and the English Country House atmosphere. Dartmoor, Southern England's last great wilderness, has its own magical beauty and is a wonderful area to explore. Bel Alp House is ideally situated for discovering the heritage, beautiful countryside and coastline of Devon and into Cornwall. Excellent local golf, walking and riding. ♛♛♛ *Highly Commended, AA*** and Rosette.*

THE BELFRY COUNTRY HOTEL,

Yarcombe, Near Honiton,
Devon EX14 9BD

Tel: 01404 861234
Fax: 01404 861579

Residential and restaurant licence; 6 bedrooms, all with private bathrooms; Children over 12 years and pets welcome; Honiton 7 miles, Chard 5; £.

This skilfully converted Victorian village school offers the comforts and luxuries of a country house hotel. Each en suite room is comprehensively equipped and has beautiful views over the Yarty valley. It is ideally placed for exploring the West Country, visiting the many National Trust properties, sporting activities, places of scenic beauty and coastal resorts in the locality. Free entry for hotel guests to 12 classic gardens nearby, and the local heated swimming pool. Jackie and Tony Rees, the resident proprietors, offer a warm welcome to their guests. Jackie's home cooking has been awarded an AA Rosette for high quality; the table d'hôte menu changes daily and there is a superb à la carte menu. The cosy restaurant with its corner bar and log fire, comfortable lounge and pretty, terraced garden make this a peaceful, relaxing and friendly hotel of high quality. ♛♛♛♛ *Commended, AA ** 75%.*

WESTWELL HALL HOTEL,
Torrs Park, Ilfracombe,
Devon EX34 8AZ

Tel and Fax: 01271 862792

Residential and restaurant licence; 10 bedrooms, all with private bathrooms; Historic interest; Children and pets welcome; Barnstaple 9 miles; £.

This elegant licensed hotel was formerly a Victorian gentleman's residence. Set in its own grounds in an elevated and secluded position, it enjoys fine views of sea and countryside. Close to National Trust coastal walks. Spacious bedrooms are all en suite, with colour television and tea/coffee making facilities. There is ample car parking space in the grounds. For further details call Colin and Rosemary Lomas — BROCHURE HOTLINE 0500 607006. ♛♛♛, *AA Recommended, RAC Acclaimed.*

ILSINGTON COUNTRY HOTEL,
Ilsington, Near Bovey Tracey,
Devon TQ13 9RR

Tel: 01364 661452
Fax: 01364 661307

Fully licensed; 25 bedrooms, all with private bathrooms; Historic interest; Children and pets welcome; Leisure and conference facilities; Ashburton 4 miles; ££.

Extensive private grounds surround this superb hotel which has maintained the highest standards of accommodation, cuisine and service since we first made its acquaintance. Footpaths lead directly to the rugged and romantic acres of the Dartmoor National Park where freedom and folklore cast their spell. Also casting a spell are the splendid leisure facilities recently introduced here. The en suite guest rooms are of de luxe standard; many have antique beds and all are equipped with remote-control colour television, direct-dial telephone and a variety of thoughtful extras. Dartmoor and the Devon air breed hearty appetites which we confirm are readily assuaged by the magnificent, chef-supervised cuisine. ♛♛♛♛, *AA/RAC* ***

EASTWREY BARTON HOTEL,
Moretonhampstead Road, Lustleigh,
Devon TQ13 9SN

Tel: 01647 277338

Residential licence; 6 bedrooms, all with private bathrooms; Historic interest; Children over 12 years and pets welcome; Moretonhampstead 4 miles; £.

Developed from a 17th century farmhouse, this charming little place enjoys one of the most picturesque situations within the Dartmoor National Park, with splendid views along the Wrey Valley and across to Lustleigh Cleave. Lustleigh itself is a delightful village and there are numerous other beauty spots within easy reach. The emphasis here is on traditional English cooking of a very high order. The accommodation is thoughtfully appointed and comfortable; each of the spacious bedrooms is individually designed and has full en suite facilities, colour television and tea and coffee makers. This is a friendly and laid-back retreat with a cosy bar and a good selection of reasonably priced wines to complement the fine cuisine. ♛♛♛ *Commended, AA QQQQ Selected.*

BUCKLAND-TOUT-SAINTS,
Goveton, Kingsbridge,
Devon TQ7 2DS

Tel: 01548 853055
Fax: 01548 856261

Restaurant and residential licence; 13 bedrooms, all with private bathrooms; Historic interest; Children and pets welcome; Conference facilities; Kingsbridge 2 miles; ££.

A gracious Queen Anne manor house of immense charm, Buckland-Tout-Saints has adapted magnificently to its role as a country hotel of character and now provides the highest standards of comfort, cuisine and amenities for its discerning guests. In tranquil surroundings and standing resplendent in seven acres of beautiful gardens, this superb hotel is within easy reach of the coast, Dartmoor and many places of sporting and historic interest. Each suite and bedroom is in the de luxe class with a private bathroom, colour television, telephone and a host of practical extras as standard. The cuisine is impressive and imaginative, meals being served in the 17th century panelled Queen Anne Restaurant. *AA ***, Two Rosettes and Merit Award, RAC *** and Merit Awards, Good Food Guide, Good Hotel Guide..*

LYDFORD HOUSE HOTEL,
Lydford, Okehampton,
Devon EX20 4AU

Tel: 01822 820347
Fax: 01822 820442

Licensed; 13 bedrooms, all with private bathrooms; Leisure and conference facilities; Children over 5 welcome; Exeter 33 miles, Plymouth 25; £.

On the fringe of Dartmoor, this splendid early Victorian house is one of the finest country hotels in the area. Centrally heated throughout, the delightful guest rooms all have colour television, direct-dial telephones, radio, tea/coffee making facilities, and private bathrooms and WCs. Food here is a high priority, starting with a full English breakfast and concluding with a superb dinner, with a wide choice at each course. There is a comfortable lounge, with a log fire in winter, and a cosy cocktail bar with lounge and summer room adjoining. Fishing and golfing enthusiasts are well catered for nearby. Free use of local tennis courts and leisure pool facilities for residents. The hotel has its own stables in the grounds, serving riders of all ages and abilities. Inclusive riding holidays or riding by the hour is offered for the entire family at reasonable rates. *ETB ♛♛♛♛ Highly Commended, AA ** 73%, RAC **, Minotel.*

WHITE HART HOTEL,
The Square, Moretonhampstead,
Devon TQ13 8NF

Tel: 01647 440406
Fax: 01647 440565

Fully licensed; 20 bedrooms, all with private bathrooms; Historic interest; Children over 10 years welcome; Exeter 11 miles; £££.

Moretonhampstead is the "gateway" to the 365 square miles that make up the Dartmoor National Park, ideal for walking and relaxing. The White Hart, an historic coaching inn, has stood in the town square for over 350 years. It has 20 de-luxe en suite bedrooms, with colour television, courtesy trays, hairdryers and telephones; bathrooms have power showers, big fluffy towels and complimentary toiletries. The restaurant is famous for good food (and plenty of it!), using local meat, fresh fish, vegetables, and cream from Devon farms. Bar snacks are served in our cosy lounge and in the oak-beamed bar which has a selection of real ales. "The most famous coaching inn on Dartmoor." Recommended by leading food and travel guides of the world. ♛♛♛♛ *Highly Commended, AA and RAC **, Egon Ronay, Minotel.*

VENN OTTERY BARTON HOTEL,
Venn Ottery, Ottery St Mary,
Devon EXII IRZ

Tel: 01404 812733
Fax: 01404 814713

Restaurant and residential licence; 17 bedrooms, 12 with private bathrooms; Historic interest; Children and pets welcome; Ottery St Mary 3 miles; £.

In lush gardens of 2½ acres, this lovely and historic place we greet as a mature old friend, our acquaintance spanning merely a fraction of its nigh on 500 years. We are happy to acknowledge it unreservedly as a superb country hotel which supplements its 16th century charm and character with a high standard of home comforts and magnificent food. Listed as a building of special architectural interest, the house retains many fascinating original features although requirements of the modern day have been skilfully introduced. Enjoying fine views over the Otter Valley, the hotel is an excellent centre for touring Dartmoor and the East Devon coast and there are numerous historic and sporting attractions near at hand. ♛♛♛ *Commended, AA and RAC.*

HEDDONS GATE HOTEL,
Heddons Mouth, Parracombe, Devon EX31 4PZ

Tel: 01598 763313*
Fax: 01598 763363

Restaurant and residential licence; 14 bedrooms, all with private bathrooms; Children over 10 years and pets welcome; Lynton 4 miles; ££.

Just inland from the Exmoor coast, we discovered this gem looking more like a grand Swiss chateau than an English country house — but then, from its lofty perch, it blends perfectly with its surroundings high above Heddon Valley, with views so phenomenal one should see and marvel in person. This is real escape from the daily grind, bidding one relax, and enjoy all the magic world that is Exmoor. Superb accommodation with a Victorian influence benefits from the finest contemporary appointments and appetites sharpened by clean, open air are more than satisfied by the outstanding cuisine. Complimentary afternoon tea, served daily, is a thoughtful and well-appreciated bonus. Exmoor 'par excellence'. ♛♛♛ *Highly Commended.*

PRESTON HOUSE HOTEL,
Saunton, Braunton, Devon EX33 lLG

Tel: 01271 890472
Fax: 01271 890555

Restaurant and residential licence; 15 bedrooms, all with private bathrooms; Children welcome; Leisure facilities; Barnstaple 7 miles; £/££.

Two minutes from a magnificent, uncrowded sandy beach and with far-reaching sea views, this fine, upstanding hotel we regard as one of the best in the seaside-cum-country category that we have seen. Victorian in origin, it has been beautifully updated, its rooms bright, sunny and sumptuously furnished. Stroll along the flower and shrub-lined cliff paths, enjoy a swim and, maybe, return to the hotel for a cream tea, remembering to leave room for a delicious dinner served later in the elegant restaurant. Sleep is easily induced in this relaxed atmosphere thanks to en suite guest rooms with colour television, direct-dial telephone and tea and coffee-makers; some have the added luxury of four-poster beds, jacuzzis and balconies. Terms represent excellent value. ♛♛♛♛ *Commended, AA, Les Routiers.*

WHITECHAPEL MANOR,
South Molton, Devon EX36 3EG

Tel: 01769 573377
Fax: 01769 573797

Licensed; 10 bedrooms, all with private bathrooms; Historic associations; Children welcome; Conference facilities; Barnstaple 11 miles; £££.

On the edge of the Exmoor National Park, this beautiful Elizabethan manor house, a Grade I Listed building, stands in 14 acres of lovely terraced gardens and woodland. Full of architectural interest, the house has rich panelling, and a magnificent Jacobean oak screen separates the reception hall from the impressive Great Hall. Flowers, log fires and gracious paintings stimulate the atmosphere of a typical old English country house and the hospitality shown by Proprietor, Patricia Shapland, is perfectly placed. An historic retreat offering a high standard of good living, Whitechapel Manor is renowned for its superb award-winning cuisine, here an art form, with wines to match. *AA Two Red Stars and Three Rosettes, RAC Blue Ribbon, Egon Ronay.*

POLTIMORE,
Ramsley, South Zeal, Okehampton,
Devon EX20 2PD

Tel: 01837 840209

Licensed; Children and pets welcome; Okehampton 4 miles; £.

This delightful thatched house is set on the fringe of Dartmoor in three acres of grounds with breathtaking views, and is a lovely place to relax, with a warm and friendly atmosphere. Bedrooms are very comfortable, with television and drinks trays, and there is an oak-beamed lounge with an inglenook fireplace, a cosy, well-stocked bar and a panelled dining room. Good English home cooking is served, with a choice of menu at every meal, and there is an extensive wine list. With direct access to Dartmoor, this is a walkers' paradise, and many West Country attractions are only a short drive away. It is also ideally placed for fishing, horse riding and golf. Charming self catering accommodation is also available — please send for details. ♛♛♛ *Approved, AA QQQ.* **See also Colour Advertisement on page 4.**

CHERRYBROOK HOTEL,
Two Bridges, Yelverton,
Devon PL20 6SP

Tel and Fax: 01822 880260

Fully licensed; 7 bedrooms, all with private bathrooms; Historic interest; Children and pets welcome; Conference facilities; Tavistock 8 miles; £.

Cherrybrook is a family-run 19th century hotel, set in the heart of Dartmoor National Park. Originally a farmhouse, it is comfortably furnished, with a cosy beamed lounge and bar. It provides a good base for walking, touring, riding, golf or fishing. There is always a good choice on the menu, which reflects the high quality produce of the area; Devon cheeses a speciality. Members of "Taste of the West" and Vegetarian Society. ♛♛♛ *Commended, AA QQQQ Selected.* **See also Colour Advertisement on page 4.**

PRINCE HALL HOTEL
Two Bridges, Dartmoor,
Devon PL20 6SA

Tel: 01822 890403
Fax: 01822 890676

Residential licence; 9 bedrooms, all with private bathrooms; Historic interest; Dogs welcome; Tavistock 8 miles, Yelverton 7; £.

The Prince Hall Hotel is a small, friendly and relaxed country house hotel, in a peaceful and secluded setting, commanding glorious views over open moorland. Nine en suite bedrooms, with two four-posters; all rooms have colour television, direct-dial telephone and refreshment tray. The hotel offers peaceful surroundings, a warm welcome, log fires, good books, gourmet cooking by the owner-chef, and an excellent wine list. Marvellous walks from the hotel; fishing, riding and golf nearby. *ETB ♛♛♛ Commended, AA **, Ashley Courtenay and Johansens Recommended, Good Hotel Guide, The Hidden Places Series.*

Dorset

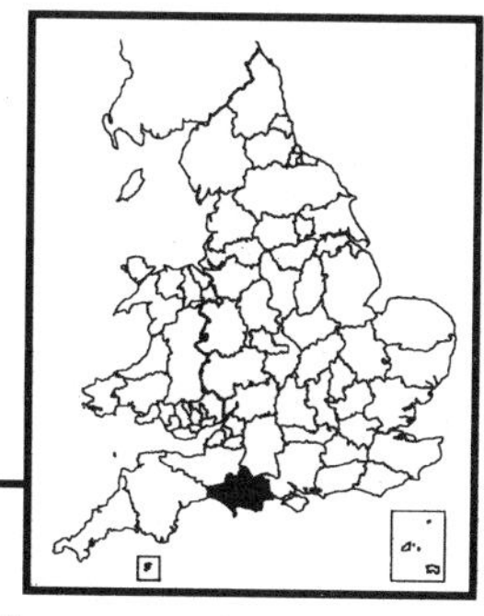

THE LODGE COUNTRY HOUSE HOTEL,
Beaminster,
Dorset DT8 3BL

Tel: 01308 863468

Residential licence; 3 bedrooms with private facilities, plus 2 in cottage; Historic interest; Children over 8 years and pets welcome; Leisure facilities; Bridport 5 miles; £/££.

An unspoilt hideaway set in 4 leafy acres on the fringe of an unspoilt little town, The Lodge is a Grade II Listed Georgian house with all the prerequisites for a relaxing holiday featuring excellent English home cooking. There is a swimming pool in the walled garden and two all-weather tennis courts to attract enthusiasts, especially as the owner is a tennis coach! The house interior boasts fine examples of original wood, plasterwork and fireplaces and the spacious bedrooms all have their own bathroom, colour television and tea and coffee-making facilities; guests may also avail themselves of room service. The beautiful Dorset coastline is only 7 miles away. This wonderful Hardy Country is waiting to be explored! 👑👑👑 *Highly Commended.*

ANVIL HOTEL,
Salisbury Road, Pimperne, Blandford,
Dorset DT11 8UQ

Tel: 01258 453431/480182

Fully licensed free house; 10 bedrooms, all with private bathrooms; Historic interest; Leisure and conference facilities; Children and pets welcome; London 107 miles, Salisbury 24, Bournemouth 26, Poole 16; ££.

A long, low, thatched building set in a tiny village deep in the Dorset countryside two miles from Blandford – what could be more English? And that is what visitors to the Anvil will find – a typical old English hostelry offering good, old-fashioned English hospitality. A mouthwatering full à la carte menu with delicious desserts is available in the charming beamed and flagged restaurant, and a wide selection of bar meals in the attractive, fully licensed bar. All bedrooms have private facilities. Ample parking. Clay pigeon shooting and tuition for individuals. 👑👑👑 *Commended, Good Food Pub Guide, Les Routiers.*

EYPE'S MOUTH COUNTRY HOTEL,
Eype, Bridport,
Dorset DT6 6AL

Tel: 01308 423300
Fax: 01308 420033

Fully licensed; 18 bedrooms, all with private bathrooms; Children and pets welcome; Conference facilities; Dorchester 14 miles; £.

We first discovered this quiet and comfortable retreat some while ago and our opinion of it has grown with the years. A country lane off the A35, a mile or so to the west of Bridport, leads down to the hotel and the sea, a delectable and tranquil spot. There is everything here for a relaxing and memorable holiday; a fine old-world cellar bar with garden patio overlooking the sea, an attractive restaurant presenting gourmet-acclaimed à la carte and table d'hôte fare with an extensive wine list, and accommodation in the multi-starred class. All rooms have en suite facilities, colour television, telephone and tea and coffee makers, as well as superb views. *RAC***

CHEDINGTON COURT HOTEL,
Chedington, Beaminster, Dorset DT8 3HY

Tel: 01935 891265*
Fax: 01935 891442

Restaurant licence; 10 bedrooms, all with private bathrooms; Children welcome, pets not allowed in public rooms; Leisure and conference facilities; Beaminster 5 miles, Crewkerne 4; £££.

High in the Dorset hills and surrounded by 10 acres of exquisite gardens, this superb house has a fascinating history that goes back to the 14th century. Imposing and impressive, yet warmly welcoming in its role as a country house hotel of distinction, the excellent facilities developed by proprietors, Hilary and Philip Chapman, now present elegant and spacious rooms which are furnished to a very high standard whilst retaining many reminders of unhurried days gone by. Attractive furnishings grace lounges and private rooms and an atmosphere of relaxed contentment prevails with log fires contributing to the mood in chilly weather. Wind down in a well stocked library, enjoy a friendly game of snooker, a nap in a snug armchair or a stroll past a massive, sculptured hedge down paths leading to sweeping lawns, ponds, grotto and water garden, taking in the large variety of wildlife. There are magnificent views to be had over the Dorset, Somerset and Devon countryside. Return to the house to consider, with eager anticipation, the forthcoming pleasure of a memorable dinner. Menus tend to be short but they are changed daily and are of the highest calibre, while the wine list offers a choice of over 500 vintages from all over the world. Vegetarians and special diets are willingly catered for. Golf enthusiasts will be interested to learn of the hotel's newly extended (now 18-hole) golf course built on 140 acres of beautiful parkland; yet another reason to consider this fine retreat for an unforgettable break. *Highly Commended, Egon Ronay, Good Hotel Guide, Good Food Guide, Which? Hotel Guide.*

KEMPS COUNTRY HOUSE HOTEL,
East Stoke, Wareham, Dorset BH20 6AL

Tel: 01929 462563
Fax: 01929 405287

Residential licence; 15 bedrooms, 14 with private bathrooms; Children welcome, pets by arrangement; Conference facilities; Wareham 3 miles; ££.

Originally built as a Victorian rectory, Kemps is situated in its own grounds rising from the valley of the River Frome, with lovely views of the Purbeck Hills. The Victorian atmosphere is faithfully preserved and the spacious new bedrooms are tastefully decorated and equipped with everything required for comfort and relaxation. Superior rooms are also available, with either four-poster or half-tester beds and corner whirlpool baths — ideal for an extra special celebration. The attractive restaurant, acclaimed for the high standard of food and service, has been enhanced by the addition of a Victorian conservatory extension which overlooks the garden and hills. *Commended, AA Rosette for Food, Egon Ronay, Johansens.*

THE DOWER HOUSE HOTEL,
Rousdon, Near Lyme Regis,
Dorset DT7 3RB

Tel: 01297 21047
Fax: 01297 24748

Fully licensed; 9 bedrooms, all with private bathrooms; Children and pets welcome; Leisure facilities; Lyme Regis 3 miles; ££.

This beautiful, family-run country house hotel stands in its own lawned and wooded grounds, which ensures safe and convenient parking. All rooms are en suite, with central heating, colour television, radio, telephone, beverage tray and hairdryer. Guests can enjoy open fires, fine cuisine and old-fashioned courteous service; amenities include an indoor heated swimming pool and sauna. There are many lovely walks in the area, as well as the bracing coastal footpath, and golf can be played nearby. Special Winter and Spring Breaks. Colour brochure, sample menu and tariff on request. ♛♛♛♛ *Highly Commended, RAC and AA ***, Ashley Courtenay Highly Recommended.*

PLUMBER MANOR,
Sturminster Newton,
Dorset DT10 2AF

Tel: 01258 472507*
Fax: 01258 473370

Fully licensed; 16 bedrooms, all with private bathrooms; Historic interest; Children and pets welcome; Leisure and conference facilities; Blandford 8 miles; £££.

Set in tranquil and lovely grounds and surrounded by all the delights of Hardy's Dorset countryside. this is very much a family home, being owned by the Prideaux-Brunes dynasty since the early 17th century. A real "away fom it all" gem, it prefers to be styled as a restaurant with bedrooms, the emphasis, naturally enough, being on the excellent dinners served here. However, the standard of accommodation is just as high, guest rooms in the main house, converted barn and courtyards being charmingly apppointed. There is a hard tennis court and croquet lawn in the grounds and there are numerous opportunities for country sports in the vicinity. Free stabling is available on a do-it-yourself basis with a full livery service nearby. *SETB* ♛♛♛.

KNOLL HOUSE HOTEL,
Studland, Near Swanage,
Dorset BH19 3AZ

Tel: 01929 450450

Fax: 01929 450423

Restaurant and residential licence; 80 bedrooms, 56 with private bathrooms, including 30 family suites; Children and dogs welcome; Leisure facilities; Corfe Castle 6 miles, Sandbanks Ferry 3; Full Board £££/ ££££.

On the Dorset Heritage coast this delightful hotel is surrounded by National Trust land and some of the prettiest scenery in the West Country. Knoll House is an independent country house hotel under the personal management of its owners. It overlooks three miles of beach from an attractive setting in pine trees and pleasant gardens, and offers facilities for sport and relaxation that must be counted amongst the finest in the country – two hard tennis courts, a pitch and putt course and a swimming pool. The Health Spa offers a sauna, steam room, jacuzzi and other leisure pursuits. Young children are catered for in their own dining room. **See advertisement Inside Back Cover.**

WORGRET MANOR HOTEL,
Worgret Road, Wareham,
Dorset BH20 6AB

Tel: 01929 552957

Fax: 01929 554804

Fully licensed; Historic interest; Children and pets welcome; Dorchester 17 miles.

The Georgian Worgret Manor Hotel lies between the ancient Wessex towns of Wareham and Wool and dates back some 250 years. Here you can relax deep in the heart of Thomas Hardy country and enjoy the unique holiday opportunities of Dorset. Recently refurbished, the hotel retains the country manor charm for which it is renowned. All bedrooms have colour television, radio, tea and coffee making facilities, direct-dial telephones and baby listening. Family rooms are available and rooms on the ground floor are suitable for disabled visitors. Home-made bar meals are served and the restaurant offers a full à la carte menu and an extensive wine list. Poole, Bournemouth and Swanage are within easy reach, as well as many excellent beaches. All major credit cards accepted. ♛♛♛ *Commended, AA**, RAC**.*

CROMWELL HOUSE HOTEL,
Lulworth Cove, Wareham,
Dorset BH20 5RJ

Tel: 01929 400253/400332

Fax: 01929 400566

Residential and restaurant licence; 14 bedrooms, all with private bathrooms; Children welcome; Leisure and conference facilities; Wareham 8 miles; £.

Catriona and Alistair Miller welcome guests to their comfortable family-run hotel, set in secluded gardens with spectacular sea views. It is situated 200 yards from Lulworth Cove, with direct access to the Dorset Coastal Footpath. A heated swimming pool is available for guests' use from May to October. There are 14 en suite bedrooms, with television, direct-dial telephone, radio, and tea/coffee making facilities; most have wonderful sea views. There is a popular restaurant and bar. ♛♛♛ *Commended, AA and RAC **.*

SHIRLEY HOTEL,
West Lulworth,
Dorset BH20 5RL

Tel: 01929 400358*
Fax: 01929 400358

Restaurant and residential licence; 18 bedrooms, all with private bathrooms; Children and pets welcome; Leisure facilities; Weymouth 20 miles; £.

A short stroll from the village of West Lulworth, Lulworth Cove is one of the most romantic beauty spots on the south coast. The Shirley Hotel has all the attributes and more to ensure an unforgettable holiday in tranquil surroundings with Dorset's coastal path running close by. The public and private rooms are a joy to behold with the sunny dining room presenting cuisine of the highest standard with special diets catered for on request. Guest rooms compose a symphony of delicate colour schemes and fine appointments include en suite facilities, colour television, direct-dial telephone and tea and coffee-makers. The *pièce de résistance*, perhaps, is the magnificent heated indoor swimming pool. Real Dorset delight. ♛♛♛ *Highly Commended, AA***.

MOONFLEET MANOR HOTEL,
Moonfleet, Near Weymouth,
Dorset DT3 4ED

Tel: 01305 786948
Fax: 01305 774395

Fully licensed; 38 bedrooms, all with private bathrooms; Historic interest; Children welcome; Leisure and conference facilities; Weymouth 5 miles; £.

A (breathtaking!) concept of what family holidays should all be about, this superb complex is almost ahead of its time in inspiration. As romantic as its name, with its origins back in the mid-16th century, Moonfleet is to be found by one of nature's wonders — Chesil Bank. Its outstanding features include a first-class hotel with superior en suite accommodation (with a four-poster available) and a reputation for interesting and attractively-presented cuisine; a number of self-catering, two-bedroom cottages and the Blue Lagoon Centre which comprises three separate pools, a gymnasium, sauna and sunbed. To say that we were impressed would be an understatement. As if this was not enough, nearby is a children's paradise in the form of a sandpit, swing and play area, mini-golf and short tennis court. Passing the entrance to the Blue Moon Cellar restaurant and bar, one comes to the Ball Park with fabulous facilities for bowls, squash, tennis (two hard courts), snooker and skittles, to say nothing of an indoor playroom and — such excitement for the young — Blackbeard's Moonfleet Adventures (smugglers' tunnel, secret passages, haunted house, et al). Table tennis, pool and darts are also available. See what we mean by breathtaking? Fantastic family funtime and the kids won't want to go home! ♛♛♛♛, *RAC***.

Durham

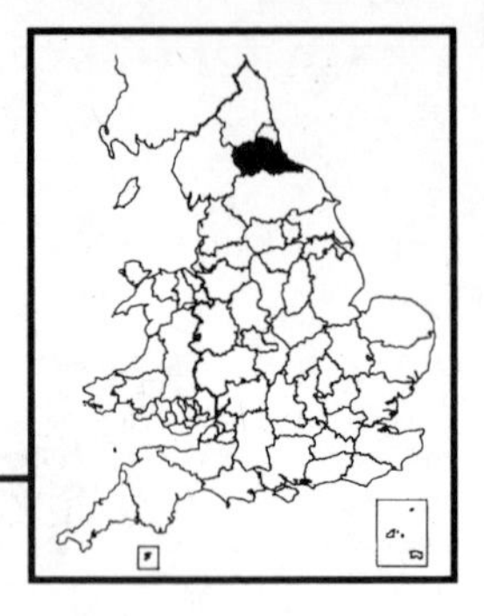

including Hartlepool, Middlesbrough, Stockton, Redcar & Cleveland (formerly Cleveland).

LUMLEY CASTLE HOTEL, Chester-le-Street, Co. Durham DH3 4NX

Tel: 0191-389 1111
Fax: 0191-387 1437

Fully licensed; 62 bedrooms, all with private bathrooms; Historic interest; Children welcome; Durham 6 miles; ££££.

Well known for its superb conference, banqueting and social function facilities, this magnificently preserved castle dates back in part to the 14th century. Today it offers guests an exciting blend of historic charm and modern luxury. Constantly keeping in touch with modern requirements, this internationally famous hotel presents the most sumptuous accommodation in exquisite bedrooms of individual style, ranging from the magnificent 20ft high four-poster in the King James Suite to the cottage-style charm of the courtyard quarters. Dining is a pleasure to consider whilst enjoying an aperitif in the elegant Library Bar where one may browse through book-lined shelves. And so to dine in the romantic candlelit restaurant with its medieval pillars and domed ceiling. The cuisine is outstanding, the wines carefully selected, and the service unobtrusive and efficient. A highlight here is the award-winning Elizabethan Banquet where the Court Chamberlain and the Ladies of the Court are waiting to present a show full of colour and merriment. Special Weekend rates offer an opportunity to sample the unique flavour of this very special hotel.

HEADLAM HALL,
Headlam, Near Gainford, Darlington, Co. Durham DL2 3HA

Tel: 01325 730238/730691
Fax: 01325 730790

Fully licensed; 26 bedrooms, all with private bathrooms; Historic interest; Children and pets welcome; Leisure and conference facilities; Piercebridge 3 miles; £££.

Of direct interest to guests seeking a relaxing holiday with a high degree of individual attention, this elegant and luxuriously furnished house has accommodation of a really excellent standard. Tastefully modified from its Jacobean origins, this mellow creeper-clad establishment provides first class food, in keeping with its other facilities. Bedrooms and suites, whether in the main house or the adjacent Coach House, are traditionally furnished and fully equipped with the amenities expected by today's discerning visitor. The extensive grounds are secluded and incorporate a small trout lake, tennis court, golf practice area and croquet lawn; leisure amenities include an indoor heated swimming pool, sauna, and snooker room. ♛♛♛♛ *Highly Commended, AA Rosette.*

RAVEN COUNTRY HOTEL
Broomhill, Ebchester, Co. Durham DH8 6RY

Tel: 01207 560367
Fax: 01207 560262

Licensed; 28 bedrooms, all with private bathrooms; Conference facilities; Children welcome; Consett 3 miles; ££.

In a quiet rural setting but within easy reach of Newcastle, Gateshead Metro Centre and Durham, this spruce, relaxing hotel combines stylish comfort with a flair for tasteful colour schemes. Its main components are arranged in contiguous single-storey fashion, yet a very English ambience shines through for which the friendly and efficient staff deserves much credit. Each en suite bedroom enjoys fine views and incorporates facilities in the best comtemporary mode with a choice of twin, double or family rooms. The attractive lounge bar is a popular meeting place and an interesting selection of bar meals is on offer. For more formal dining, the Conservatory Restaurant is well known for its excellent standard of luncheon and dinner dishes. ♛♛♛♛, *AA*** and Rosette for Cuisine.*

STANHOPE OLD HALL,
Stanhope, Weardale, Bishop Auckland, Co. Durham DL13 2PF

Tel: 01388 528451
Fax: 01388 527795

Bedrooms with private bathrooms; Historic interest; Leisure facilities; Wolsingham 5 miles.

This 12th century fortified manor house, reputedly the oldest hotel and restaurant in England, is steeped in history. It provides comfortable, characterful rooms with en suite facilities, and superb food. Situated in the North Pennines, Britain's largest Area of Outstanding Natural Beauty, Stanhope Old Hall is a central point from which to explore the counties of Durham, Northumberland, North Yorkshire and Cumbria. There is an abundance of wildlife, country walks, fishing, shooting and horse-riding, as well as four-wheel drive safaris, off-road quad biking — or just simple relaxation.

NOTE

All the information in this book is given in good faith in the belief that it is correct. However, the publishers cannot guarantee the facts given in these pages, neither are they responsible for changes in policy, ownership or terms that may take place after the date of going to press. Readers should always satisfy themselves that the facilities they require are available and that the terms, if quoted, still apply.

Essex

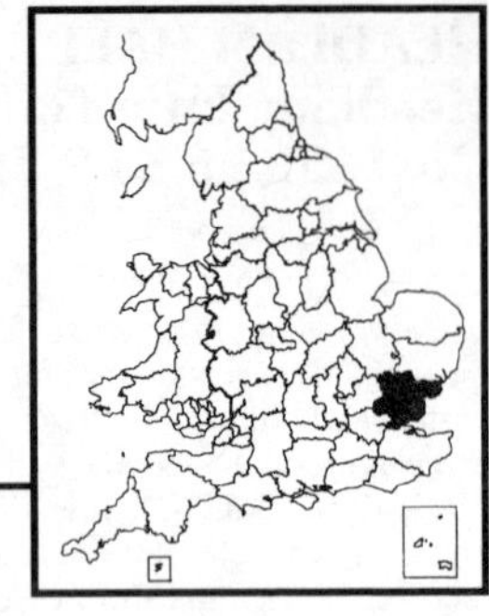

PONTLANDS PARK COUNTRY HOTEL,
West Hanningfield Road, Great Baddow, Near Chelmsford, Essex CM2 8HR

Tel: 01245 476444
Fax: 01245 478393

Licensed; 17 bedrooms, all with private bathrooms; Children welcome; Leisure and conference facilities; Conference facilities; London 30 miles; ££££.

A grand Victorian mansion built on the site of a mid-16th century building, Pontlands Park attracts discriminating guests by reason of its luxurious hotel facilities and superb leisure centre in the grounds. Here, the indoor and outdoor swimming pools, jacuzzis and sauna may be enjoyed free of charge by residents. Guest rooms are spacious and individually appointed to a very high standard and incorporate bathrooms en suite, colour television, radio, direct-dial telephone and many thoughtful extras. The outstanding cuisine deserves special mention: the restaurant offers a wide variety of menus throughout and is open from Tuesday to Friday for lunch and from Monday to Saturday for dinner. 👑👑👑👑 Highly Commended, AA****.

THE BELL INN AND HILL HOUSE,
High Road, Horndon-on-the-Hill, Essex SS17 8LD

Tel: 01375 673154/642463
Fax: 01375 361611

Fully licensed; 14 bedrooms, all with private bathrooms; Historic interest; Children welcome; Conference facilities; Basildon 5 miles; ££/£££ (double).

At first sight an attractive private house, closer inspection reveals this 17th century building to have been discreetly transformed into a charming little coutry hotel. The facilities, too, would shame many a multi-starred establishment although the atmosphere here is far more friendly and relaxed. Guest rooms are all of individual character, have bathrooms en suite (some with spa baths), teletext television and direct-dial telephone, whilst, in the courtyard, a stable block has been converted into a self-contained unit with a spiral staircase leading to a bedroom that was originally a hayloft. A delightful restaurant with a huge fireplace offers enjoyment of an interesting and imaginative cuisine, popular with non-residents as well. Good news spreads fast.

Gloucestershire

including South Gloucester, and Bristol (formerly Avon).

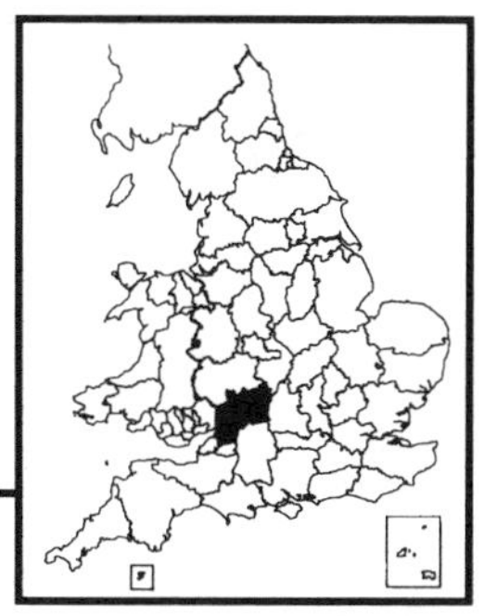

CHARLTON KINGS HOTEL, Cheltenham, Gloucestershire GL52 6UU

Tel: 01242 231061
Fax: 01242 241900

Restaurant and residential licence; 14 bedrooms, all with private bathrooms; Children and dogs welcome; Bourton-on-the-Water 12 miles, Tewkesbury 10, Winchcombe 8; £££.

The ideal venue for Cheltenham and the Cotswolds situated in an acre of garden in an area of outstanding natural beauty on the edge of town. Newly opened in 1991 after extensive refurbishment. All rooms (some reserved for non-smokers) have views of the Cotswold Hills, which are easily reached on foot – there is a footpath right alongside the hotel leading onto the famous Cotswold Way. There is plenty to do and see (our room information folder lists over 200 sights/activities), or simply watch the world go by from the conservatory. During your stay you will be tempted to try our cosy restaurant offering an imaginative and varied menu. Above all, we offer a standard of service only a small hotel can provide. *ETB* ♛♛♛♛ *Highly Commended, Johansens Recommended.*

WYNDHAM ARMS, Clearwell, Near Coleford, Gloucestershire GL16 8JT

Tel: 01594 833666
Fax: 01594 836450

Fully licensed; 17 bedrooms, all with private bathrooms; Historic interest; Children and pets welcome; Coleford 2 miles; ££.

Set in a valley on the edge of the Royal Forest of Dean, the splendid 600-year-old Wyndham Arms is full of old-world charm and offers excellent hotel facilities. The delicious food served in the busy restaurant and bar is renowned for miles around, home-grown produce and fresh local salmon (in season) figuring prominently on the imaginative menus. Elegant guest rooms are delightfully furnished; all have bathroom en suite, colour television, direct-dial telephone and beverage making facilities among their thoughtful appointments. There are ground floor rooms for the less physically able and flat access to bar and restaurant; for children there are cots, high chairs and baby-listening intercom. ♛♛♛♛ *Highly Commended, AA and RAC ***.*

HALEWELL CLOSE,
Withington, Near Cheltenham, Gloucestershire GL54 4BN

Tel: 01242 890238
Fax: 01242 890332

Residential licence; 6 bedrooms, all with private bathrooms; Historic interest; Children and pets by arrangement; Leisure facilities; Northleach 5 miles; ££.

This lovely old Cotswold-stone house, dating in part from the early 15th century, is very much in the benefice of its Owner, Elizabeth Carey-Wilson who, over the past few years, has adapted it with style, imagination and considerable pride to cater for guests. And beautifully appointed it is with individually furnished and delightfully decorated bedrooms, all with bathrooms en suite plus colour television, clock radio, tea and coffee-making facilities and several much appreciated extras: some have showers as well, and two inter-communicating rooms are ideal for family parties. Incidentally, there is no need to worry about knees in the back or who is hogging the bedclothes for the double beds are 6ft wide! One twin-bedded room on the ground floor has been arranged with disabled guests in mind. The atmosphere is that of a convivial house party with mealtimes flexible according to popular arrangement. There is a drinks licence for visitors and their friends. Magnificent grounds extend to 50 acres, incorporating formal and informal gardens, stone terracing leading to a swimming pool (heated end-May to September) and a 5-acre trout lake. Fishing in the River Coln and pony trekking may also be arranged. Mrs.Carey-Wilson's magnificent private sitting room, the Solar, is used after dinner and there is a sitting room for guests' use with colour television, video and games table. An absolute gem!

TUDOR FARMHOUSE HOTEL & RESTAURANT,
Clearwell, Near Coleford, Gloucestershire GL16 8JS

Tel: 01594 833046*
Fax: 01594 837093

Restaurant and residential licence; 13 bedrooms, all with private bathrooms; Historic interest; Children and pets welcome; Coleford 2 miles; £/££.

If you go down to the woods today, you're in for a big surprise. For 'woods' substitute the Royal Forest of Dean and the surprise — and a delightful one it is too — is this cosy retreat from the shackles of everyday life. Deborah and Richard Fletcher have wrought wonders at this character-filled haven. Oak beams, original oak panelling and a large roughstone fireplace provide evidence of the house's 13th century beginnings but the modern facilities that have been sympathetically introduced are there to marvel at even now. Reached by way of the ancient oak spiral staircase, the bedrooms in the main house, including two with four-poster beds, have bathrooms en suite, colour television, direct-dial telephone and tea and coffee-makers. Other rooms with a similarly high standard of appointment, are situated in charming, stone, former cider-makers cottages with their own patios and entrances. With great play being made of subtle colour shades and quality fabrics, it is easy to understand why the amenities at this gem of a place have been so widely acclaimed. Last but by no means least, consider the cuisine: varied and imaginative fare, chef-inspired and served by candlelight in the most romantic setting. There is an excellent vegetarian choice and a comprehensive wine list to add the perfect finishing touch. You may gather we rather like the place! ♛♛♛ *Highly Commended, AA QQQQQ, AA Red Rosette.*

SEVERN BANK,
Minsterworth, Near Gloucester, Gloucestershire GL2 8JH

Tel and Fax: 01452 750357

Unlicensed; 6 bedrooms, 4 with private bathrooms; Gloucester 4 miles; £.

Severn Bank is a fine country house standing in six acres of grounds on the banks of the Severn, four miles west of Gloucester. It is ideally situated for touring the Cotswolds, the Forest of Dean and the Wye Valley, and is the recommended viewpoint for the Severn Bore tidal wave. It has a friendly atmosphere and comfortable rooms with superb views and full central heating. The en suite, non-smoking bedrooms have tea and coffee making facilities and colour television. Ample parking. ♛♛ *Commended.*

LOWER SLAUGHTER MANOR,
Lower Slaughter,
Gloucestershire GL54 2HP

Tel: 01451 820456
Fax: 01451 822150

Fully licensed; 14 bedrooms, all with private bathrooms; Historic interest; Children welcome; Leisure and conference facilities; Stow-on-the-Wold 3 miles; ££££.

Pride of the Slaughters, twin villages of honey-coloured cottages and tinkling streams, this gracious country manor dates from the mid-17th century.Flowers abound in all the elegant public rooms, where fine antiques, works of art and blazing log fires in winter add to the very special atmosphere. The Manor is the perfect base for leisurely exploration of the Cotswolds. We recall it has a reputation second to none for its award-winning cuisine and the accommodation may be fairly described as romantically regal. A detailed brochure is available direct from the hotel. *AA Three Red Stars and Three Rosettes, Egon Ronay Recommended.*

WYCK HILL HOUSE HOTEL,
Burford Road, Stow-on-the-Wold,
Gloucestershire GL54 lHY

Tel: 01451 831936
Fax: 01451 832243

Fully licensed; 31 bedrooms, all with private bathrooms; Historic interest; Children and pets welcome; Conference facilities; Chipping Norton 8 miles; ££££.

With rich but tasteful furnishings, this imposing, 18th century manor house is elegance personified. Built of mellow Cotswold stone, it lies back from the road in 100 acres of landscaped gardens. Many are the architectural delights, including the gracious galleried staircase, library and sumptuously appointed bedrooms, all equipped with bath and shower, remote-control colour television, direct-dial telephone and a number of thoughtful extras. Some rooms are available with four-poster or king-size beds with those in the Orangery and Coach House annexes offering seclusion and every modern comfort. A most impressive feature of the hotel is the dining room where the international, award-winning cuisine has acquired a peerless reputation. ♛♛♛♛♛ *De Luxe, AA Three Rosettes.*

BURLEIGH COURT HOTEL,
Burleigh, Minchinhampton, Near Stroud,
Gloucestershire GL5 2PF

Tel: 01453 883804
Fax: 01453 886870

Fully licensed; 17 bedrooms, all with private bathrooms; Historic interest; Children welcome, pets by arrangement; Leisure and conference facilities; Stroud 3 miles; £££.

At this warm and welcoming 18th century manor house, all the talk was about the superb cuisine. Inspired chatter as it turned out and inspired skills exhibited by an enthusiastic cadre of chefs beavering away to produce culinary gems, with vegetarian and special diets also well catered for. However, there are other notable facets to attract visitors to the charming house which is set in 3½ acres of lovely grounds. As a centre from which to explore the delights of the Cotswolds, Burleigh Court provides a plethora of reasons to recommend it. Each guest room has its own character and many thoughtful touches complement the appointments which include a private bathroom, direct-dial telephone, colour television and radio. AA***.

---

* The appearance of an asterisk after the telephone number indicates that the hotel in question is closed for a period during the winter months. Exact dates should be ascertained from the hotel itself.

TEWKESBURY PARK HOTEL COUNTRY CLUB RESORT,
Lincoln Green Lane, Tewkesbury, Gloucestershire GL20 7DN

Tel: 01684 295405
Fax: 01684 292386

Fully licensed; 78 bedrooms, all with private bathrooms; Historic interest; Children welcome; Leisure and conference facilities; Gloucester 10 miles, Cheltenham 9; ££££.

Supreme comfort and care await guests at Tewkesbury Park, 176 acres of picturesque parkland which surround a magnificent 18th century country house, which, in company with a newly added wing, provides spacious, well-planned accommodation with a full range of modern amenities and leisure opportunities that include a fine 18-hole golf course. In addition there is an indoor heated swimming pool, squash and tennis courts, fitness studio, and the option to take it easy in a health and beauty salon, sauna, solarium and steam room. This elegant and hospitable mansion also boasts the well regarded Garden Restaurant with its mouth-watering selection of à la carte and table d'hôte dishes. Several purpose equipped meeting rooms are avaialble for conferences and special occasions. *HETB* ♛♛♛♛.

HATTON COURT HOTEL,
Upton Hill, Upton St Leonards, Gloucestershire GL4 8DE

Tel: 01452 617412
Fax: 01452 612945

Fully licensed; 45 bedrooms, all with private bathrooms; Historic interest; Children welcome; Leisure and conference facilities; Gloucester 3 miles; ££££.

Set in 37 acres of beautifully maintained gardens and pastures, Hatton Court gazes proudly over the Severn Valley to the distant slopes of the Malvern Hills. For those wishing to explore this glorious part of the English landscape, this makes an ideal base — the splendid city of Gloucester lies close by; Bath, Bristol, Worcester and Stratford-upon-Avon are all within comfortable reach, as are delightful historic Cotswold towns and villages. Recently extensively and luxuriously refurbished, Hatton Court offers all one would expect of a superior country hotel, plus those thoughtful little extras which lift this elegant establishment into a class of its own. In a class of its own too is the renowned Carringtons Restaurant where a wide choice of modern French, classic and traditional dishes are prepared the freshest of ingredients. ♛♛♛♛ *Highly Commended, AA***, RAC*** and Merit Awards, Egon Ronay.*

Lower Slaughter, Gloucestershire

Hampshire

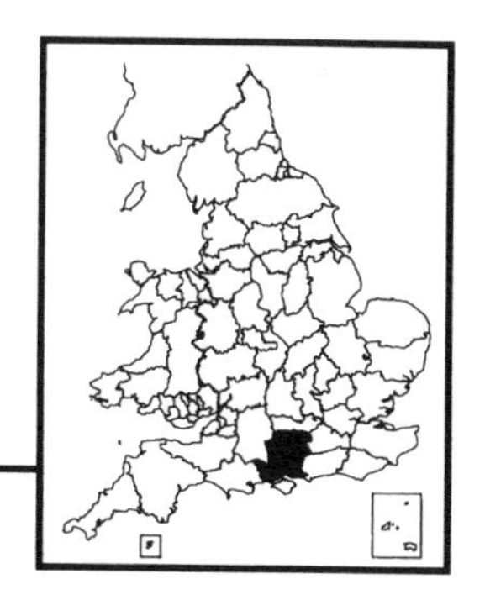

WOODLANDS LODGE HOTEL,
Bartley Road, Ashurst, Woodlands,
Hampshire SO4 2GN

Tel: 01703 292257
Fax: 01703 293090

Licensed; 16 luxury bedrooms and suites, all with private bathrooms; Historic interest; Conference facilities; Dogs and horses welcome by arrangement; Totton 3 miles; £££.

This beautiful Georgian building, originally a Royal hunting lodge, has been extensively renovated and refurbished to offer the highest standards of luxury and comfort, while retaining the welcoming, informal atmosphere the hotel has always enjoyed. All of the individually designed bedrooms are en suite (all with whirlpool baths), and have remote-control colour television, direct-dial telephone, trouser press etc; the spacious suites have the additional luxury of a fully furnished sitting room. Set in its own grounds in the heart of the New Forest, Woodlands Lodge is ideal for walking or riding. **See also Colour Advertisement on page 5.**

WHITLEY RIDGE COUNTRY HOUSE HOTEL,
Beaulieu Road, Brockenhurst,
Hampshire SO42 7QL

Tel: 01590 622354
Fax: 01590 622856

Residential licence; 13 bedrooms, all with private bathrooms; Historic interest; Children and pets welcome; Leisure facilities; Lyndhurst 4 miles, Lymington 4; ££/£££.

Whitley Ridge is a beautiful Georgian country house hotel set in spacious grounds surrounded by the New Forest. Ponies and deer can be seen from the hotel and there is direct access into the Forest. The charming bedrooms include Georgian rooms and a Four-Poster room, and all are very well appointed with private facilities, television and telephone. Imaginative and reasonably priced dishes are served in the candlelit dining room where a log fire burns on cooler evenings. A cosy bar and a charming drawing room are adjacent. Turn off the A337 before entering or leaving Brockenhurst and look for the sign of the two acorns beside the B3055 road to Beaulieu. Go up the drive to this old hunting lodge set well away from the road. *ETB ♛♛♛♛ Highly Commended, AA** and Rosettes for Good Food.*

NEW PARK MANOR,
Lyndhurst Road, Brockenhurst, Hampshire S042 7QH

Tel: 01590 623467
Fax: 01590 622268

Fully licensed; 24 bedrooms, all with private bathrooms; Historic interest; Children over 7 years welcome; Leisure and conference facilities; Lyndhurst 4 miles; £££/££££.

Set in New Forest parkland midway between Lyndhurst and Brockenhurst, this fine country house hotel was formerly a Royal Hunting Lodge. The hotel has an historical ambience, with log fires. Luxury suites and bedrooms, some with four-poster or half tester beds, include en suite facilities, satellite television, radio, telephone and tea and coffee-makers. The innovative, French-influenced cuisine is served in the charming, candlelit Stag Restaurant. The hotel has its own splendid equestrian centre with a qualified B.H.S. stablecrew, catering for cross-forest rides, training and liveries. Other diversions on hand include an outdoor heated swimming pool, a tennis court and biking, whilst clay pigeon shooting and golf may be arranged. ♛♛♛♛ *Highly Commended, AA*** and Two Rosettes, RAC* **.*

ASHBURN HOTEL,
Damerham Road (B3078), Fordingbridge, Hampshire SP6 lJP

Tel: 01425 652060
Fax: 01425 652150

Fully licensed; 20 bedrooms, all with private bathrooms; Children and pets welcome; Leisure and conference facilities; Ringwood 6 miles; £.

On the northern margin of the New Forest, this comfortable Victorian country house has been skilfully converted into an hotel of some standing by the addition of a modern wing comprising spacious and superbly-appointed bedrooms and a functions suite. Standing in landscaped gardens which lead to a heated open-air swimming pool, the hotel is not only attractively furnished but has acquired an enviable reputation for its outstanding, award-winning cuisine. The area has a variety of leisure possibilities quite apart from the lure of the forest glades: golf, fishing and horse riding may be enjoyed locally and there are numerous historic houses to visit. ♛♛♛♛ *Commended, AA Red Rosette, RAC Merit Awards.*

LIONS COURT RESTAURANT AND HOTEL,
29 The High Street, Fordingbridge, Hampshire SP6 1AS

Tel: 01425 652006
Fax: 01425 657946

Licensed; 6 bedrooms, all with private bathrooms; Historic interest; Children welcome; Bournemouth 18 miles, Salisbury 11, Ringwood 5; £/££.

This charming 17th century family hotel is set on the edge of the New Forest, with all its amenities and rural pursuits. Fordingbridge is centrally situated for the cathedral city of Salisbury, Bournemouth, Stonehenge and many other places of interest. There are six en suite bedrooms, one with a four-poster. The à la carte restaurant has a reputation for excellent cuisine in a relaxed, intimate atmosphere. Favouring fresh local produce, specialities include Salad of Smoked Venison and Grilled Calves' Liver with a Bacon and Mushroom Concasse flavoured with Basil; unusual fish dishes and an extensive vegetarian selection are also available. This is a classic English setting with gardens extending to the River Avon. Fishing, golf, horse riding available locally. ♛♛♛ *Commended, AA, Les Routiers, Logis.*

ESSEBORNE MANOR HOTEL,
Hurstbourne Tarrant, Andover, Hampshire SPll OER

Tel: 01264 736444
Fax: 01264 736725

Residential licence; 12 bedrooms, all with private bathrooms; Children and pets welcome; Leisure and conference facilities; Andover 5 miles; ££££.

Imaginative cooking in the classic tradition is just one of the attractions of this stylish yet unpretentious country house set amidst rolling downland. A good touring centre, the house is within easy reach of such historic places as Winchester, Salisbury, Stonehenge and Highclere Castle and racing enthusiasts are well catered for at Newbury and Salisbury's courses. Nearby attractions also include motor sport at Thruxton, golf and fishing. The hotel has its own all-weather tennis court. Of delightful decor throughout, the house has six splendidly appointed guest rooms in the main house and six in a new wing adapted from an adjacent former barn; all have en suite facilities. ♛♛♛♛, *AA/RAC ***.*

BRAMBLE HILL HOTEL,
Bramshaw, Near Lyndhurst, Hampshire SO43 7JG

Tel: 01703 813165

Fully licensed; 10 bedrooms, all with private bathrooms; Historic interest; Pets welcome; Conference facilities; Cadnam 2 miles; ££.

Peacefully located in tranquil surroundings, this country house hotel is only three miles from Junction 1 of the M27. Set in ancient woodland with 30 acres of glades, lawns and shrubbery to enjoy, this is an ideal place for country walks and horse riding. The hotel is just a short drive from many places of interest including Salisbury, Stonehenge, Winchester and Beaulieu. All bedrooms have en suite bathrooms, and some have antique four-poster beds. There is a cosy public bar and restaurant. Guests are assured of a warm friendly welcome and good home cooking. Please telephone for details of Special Breaks. **See also Colour Advertisement on page 6.**

The **£** symbol when appearing at the end of the italic section of an entry shows the anticipated price, during 1997, for single full Bed and Breakfast.

Under £40	**£**	**Over £55 but under £70**	**£££**
Over £40 but under £55	**££**	**Over £70**	**££££**

This is meant as an indication only and does not show prices for Special Breaks, Weekends, etc. Guests are therefore advised to verify all prices on enquiring or booking.

PASSFORD HOUSE HOTEL,
Mount Pleasant Lane, Near Lymington, Hampshire SO41 8LS

Tel: 01590 682398
Fax: 01590 683494

Fully licensed; 50 bedrooms, all with private bathrooms; Children welcome, pets by arrangement; Leisure and conference facilities; Bournemouth 15 miles; ££££.

All that one could wish for in a country house hotel, Passford House stands in 10 acres of well-tended grounds, its long Georgian facade overlooking peaceful lawns. The informal charm of the panelled lounge and cocktail bar is matched by the de luxe bedrooms, all with private bathroom, television, telephone, radio, baby listening, trouser press, hairdryer and tea/coffee making facilities. The restaurant and the catering are, of course, of the highest standard. For indoor and leisure facilities, the Dolphin Centre offers a heated swimming pool, sauna, solarium, gym and games room, while outdoors, guests can enjoy petanque, putting, croquet, heated swimming pool (in season) in the idyllic setting of a sunken garden, alongside a hard tennis court. There is a choice of at least eleven golf courses within easy driving distance, horse-riding stables within half a mile, the glorious New Forest on the very doorstep, and sailing at Lymington. *ETB ♕♕♕♕ Highly Commended, AA***, RAC *** and Merit Award, Ashley Courtenay, Johansen, Egon Ronay.*

BUSKETTS LAWN HOTEL,
Woodlands Road, Woodlands, New Forest, Near Southampton, Hampshire SO40 7GL

Tel: 01703 292272
Fax: 01703 292487

Restaurant and residential licence; 14 bedrooms, all with private bathrooms; Children and pets welcome; Leisure and conference facilities; Totton 3 miles; £.

Busketts Lawn is a delightful Victorian country house hotel in quiet New Forest surroundings, ideal for visiting Beaulieu and Broadlands. It is set in large gardens with a swimming pool (heated in season), putting, croquet and mini football pitch. The hotel offers excellent food, service and comfort, all rooms being en suite, with colour television, direct-dial telephone, tea making facilities, hair dryers and trouser press; some rooms with mini-fridges. Dinner dances some weekends. Established 1968. Colour brochure on request. *ETB ♕♕♕♕ Commended, AA and RAC **.*

PLEASE MENTION THIS GUIDE WHEN YOU WRITE
OR PHONE TO ENQUIRE ABOUT
ACCOMMODATION.
IF YOU ARE WRITING, A STAMPED,
ADDRESSED ENVELOPE IS ALWAYS APPRECIATED.

BOTLEY PARK HOTEL, GOLF & COUNTRY CLUB,

Boorley Green, Botley, Southampton, Hampshire SO32 2UA

Tel: 01489 780888
Fax: 01489 789242

Licensed; 100 bedrooms, all with private bathrooms; Children and pets welcome; Leisure and conference facilities; Southampton 6 miles; ££££.

Your first impression of Botley Park is likely to be one of space. Surrounded by the rolling hills of Hampshire, the estate stretches across 176 acres of parkland which includes an 18-hole golf course. Guest rooms have ample space to stretch out and unwind, and you will appreciate thoughtful touches such as the complimentary decanter of sherry, bottles of mineral water and basket of fruit which await you. Many rooms overlook the golf course, and each has a private bathroom, colour satellite television, hairdryer, hospitality tray and direct-dial telephone; 24 hour room service is available. An evening in the Winchester Restaurant is memorable for the quality of the food, the excellence of the wine, and the highly agreeable atmosphere. The Plus Fours Lounge offers a lighter selection in an informal atmosphere, and there are two friendly bars in which to enjoy an aperitif or nightcap. The superb leisure complex offers a full range of facilities, and as well as the golf course, there is a tennis court, croquet lawn and petanque terrain. ♛♛♛♛♛ *Highly Commended, AA**** and Rosette, RAC****.*

FIFEHEAD MANOR,

Middle Wallop, Stockbridge, Salisbury, Hampshire SO20 8EG

Tel: 01264 781565
Fax: 01264 781400

Fully licensed; 15 bedrooms, all with private bathrooms; Historic interest; Children and pets welcome; Conference facilities; Andover 7 miles; ££.

This gracious country manor, parts of which date from the 11th century, has seen a varied history, and was at one time a nunnery. It now serves equally well as a haven for those who appreciate high standards of food, wine and accommodation, as well as courteous and friendly service. Various sizes of guest rooms cater for all requirements and are charmingly decorated and well equipped; each has its own private bathroom. The dining room, in which the remains of a minstrels' gallery may be seen, is warmly welcoming, especially by candlelight. The manor stands in several acres of lovely gardens, and is most conveniently situated for visiting Winchester, Salisbury and Stonehenge. ♛♛♛♛ *Commended, AA** and Two Rosettes, RAC*** and Merit Award, Egon Ronay, Good Food Guide.*

STRING OF HORSES,
Mead End Road, Sway, Near Lymington,
Hampshire SO41 6EH

Tel and Fax: 01590 682631

Residential and restaurant licence; 7 bedrooms, all with private facilities; Leisure facilities; Bournemouth 15 miles, Southampton 15; ££.

Unique secluded, exclusive hotel set in four acres in the heart of the New Forest, with a friendly relaxed atmosphere. Seven luxurious double bedrooms are available, each with its own fantasy bathroom with spa bath and shower. Every facility is offered including colour television, direct-dial telephone, radio and tea-making facilities. Several four-poster bedrooms, making this an ideal honeymoon setting. Dine in our intimate candlelit "Carriages" restaurant. For relaxation there is a heated outdoor swimming pool. This is superb riding country, and the hotel is close to excellent yachting resorts and several good golf courses. *ETB* ♛♛♛♛ *Highly Commended, AA** and Rosette.* **See also Colour Advertisement on page 6.**

Hereford & Worcester

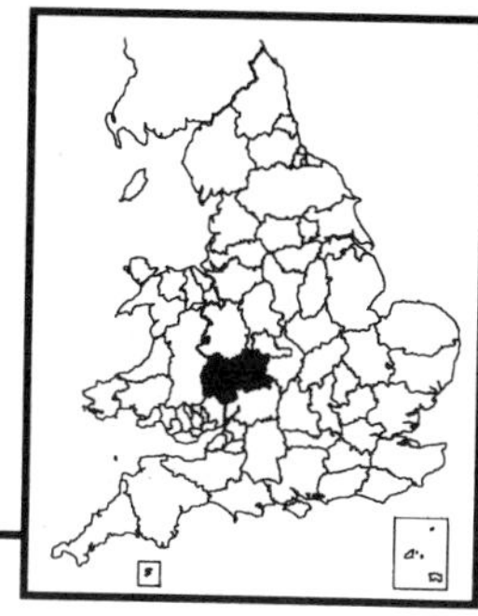

COLLIN HOUSE HOTEL,
Collin Lane, Broadway,
Hereford & Worcester WR12 7PB

Tel: 01386 858354

Residential and restaurant licence; 7 bedrooms, all with private bathrooms; Historic interest; Children welcome; Leisure facilities; Evesham 5 miles; ££.

Only one mile from the centre of picturesque Broadway, this homely, 16th century Cotswold-stone house has immense character evinced by mullioned windows, solid oak beams and inglenook fireplaces where log fires crackle in cool weather. The guest rooms are furnished to the most exacting standards; two of them have four-poster beds and terms for accommodation are extremely reasonable. Traditional English fare is served by candlelight in a beamed dining room and there are two comfortable lounges in which to relax. A quiet and well-run base from which to explore the delightful Cotswold countryside, Collin House stands in 8 acres of meadow, orchard and garden with a small open air swimming pool available for guests. *Commended, AA Red Rosette.*

DUMBLETON HALL,
Dumbleton, Near Evesham,
Hereford & Worcester WR11 6TS

Tel: 01386 881240
Fax: 01386 882142

Licensed; 38 bedrooms, all with private bathrooms; Historic interest; Children welcome; Conference facilities; Evesham 7 miles.

Dumbleton Hall Hotel is a superb mansion set in 16 acres of breathtaking grounds. Built in the 1830s from Cotswold stone, the hotel contains 38 quality bedrooms, all en suite. There is also a large restaurant serving many mouthwatering dishes, a comfortable bar, and lounge with spectacular views of the beautiful grounds. A new conference suite will cater for every need. **See also Colour Advertisement on page 6.**

THE BOWENS COUNTRY HOUSE,

Fownhope,

Hereford & Worcester HR1 4PS

Tel and Fax: 01432 860430

Residential and restaurant licence; 12 bedrooms, all en suite or with shower; Historic interest; Children welcome, pets by arrangement; Leisure facilities; Ross-on-Wye 7 miles, Hereford 6; £.

Peacefully situated on the edge of Fownhope village on the B4224 in the Wye Valley (an Area of Outstanding Natural Beauty), midway between Hereford, with its cathedral and the Mappa Mundi, and Ross-on-Wye. Ideal for touring, walking and exploring the Welsh Borders, Malverns, Cotswolds, Brecon Beacons and the rolling wooded countryside of Herefordshire with its many black-and-white villages. This tastefully restored 17th century former farmhouse is set in two acres of immaculate gardens. Bedrooms are comfortable and well-appointed; each has television, central heating and tea/coffee facilities and four are on on the ground floor. There is an oak-beamed lounge with inglenook fireplace and honesty bar, and an attractive dining room where a choice of superb home-cooked meals (including vegetarian dishes), using local and home produce, and an excellent wine list have gained acclaim for many years. ♕♕♕ *Commended, AA QQQ Recommended.*

FOLEY ARMS HOTEL,

14 Worcester Road, Malvern,

Hereford & Worcester WR14 4QS

Tel: 01684 573397
Fax: 01684 569665

Fully licensed; 28 bedrooms, all with private bathrooms; Children and pets welcome; £££.

A Regency Coaching Inn with the style and ambience of a Country House Hotel, the Foley Arms was built in 1810 and has 28 bedrooms, some with spectacular views over the Severn Valley. It is situated in the centre of Great Malvern with its own gardens and car parking. This family-run hotel has been awarded AA***RAC with Merit Awards for hospitality and its restaurant. The elegant Elgar's Restaurant serves fine English cuisine and the Foley Tavern adjoining the hotel offers a pub-style bar with real ales and an interesting choice of bar meals. Malvern is conveniently located for touring the Cotswolds, Wales, Hereford and Cheshire; M5 and M50 motorways are only 15 minutes away. ♕♕♕♕.

RECOMMENDED SHORT BREAK HOLIDAYS IN BRITAIN

Introduced by John Carter, TV Holiday Expert and Journalist

Specifically designed to cater for the most rapid]y growing sector of the holiday market in the UK. Illustrated details of hotels offering special "Bargain Breaks" throughout the year.

Available from newsagents and bookshops for £4.25 or direct from the publishers for £4.80 including postage (UK only).

FHG PUBLICATIONS LTD
Abbey Mill Business Centre, Seedhill,
Paisley, Renfrewshire PAI ITJ

THE MILL AT HARVINGTON,
Anchor Lane, Harvington, Evesham, Hereford & Worcester WR11 5NR

Tel and Fax: 01386 870688

Restaurant and residential licence; 15 bedrooms, all with private bathrooms; Historic interest; Leisure facilities; Evesham 3 miles; ££.

Beautifully placed on the banks of the peaceful Avon as its winds its way from Stratford to the Severn, the enchanting Mill at Harvington has served the community in a variety of guises since it was built in 1750. It has been, in turn, a malting mill, brewery and bread mill before embarking on its present distinctive career as a first-class country hotel. Sensitively modernised, the hotel stands in almost eight acres of wooded parkland with 600ft of river frontage from which guests may enjoy excellent fishing and boating. Other sporting attractions in the grounds include a hard tennis court and heated swimming pool; and in addition, for nature lovers, there is a fascinating variety of wildlife to be viewed. Guest rooms are bright and cheerful and delightfully appointed with bathrooms en suite, colour television, radio, telephone, and tea and coffee making facilities. Special provision has been made for wheelchair access in certain bedrooms and bathrooms. With views across the garden, the elegantly decorated restaurant is an attractive setting for contemplation and enjoyment of dishes from an interesting and frequently changed menu, much use being made of local produce. If one can tear oneself away from this idyllic retreat, there are numerous places of historic interest within easy reach, including Stratford-upon-Avon, only 10 miles away. ♛♛♛♛ *Highly Commended.*

NEW PRIORY HOTEL,
Stretton Sugwas, Hereford, Hereford & Worcester HR4 7AR

Tel: 01432 760264
Fax: 01432 761809

Licensed; 10 bedrooms, doubles with private bathrooms, singles with shower/toilet adjacent; Children welcome; Conference facilities; Hereford 2 miles; £.

Deep in the heart of Cider Country, just outside the cathedral city of Hereford, lies the pretty little village of Stretton Sugwas and this elegant hotel. The tastefully decorated bedrooms (including two four-poster rooms) offer far-reaching views over the unspoiled countryside and provide an excellent range of up-to-date facilities. The same high standards are maintained in the restaurants, which offer a choice of à la carte and table d'hôte menus, as well as good value four-course traditional Sunday lunches; a comprehensive range of bar snacks is also available. Set in 3½ acres of landscaped grounds and gardens, this is a popular venue for weddings, business meetings and other functions. ♛♛♛ *Approved.*

PENRHOS COURT HOTEL,
Penrhos Court, Kington, Hereford & Worcester HR5 3LH

Tel: 01544 230720
Fax: 01544 230754

Fully licensed; 19 bedrooms, all with private bathrooms; Historic interest; Children welcome; Conference facilities; Leominster 11 miles; ££/£££.

For more than 700 years a farm on the turbulent English-Welsh border, Penrhos has been adapted with skill into a delectable country hotel with many fascinating features. The main house covers three periods in the medieval Cruck hall with stone-flag floors, a snug corner with a roaring log fire, and an Elizabethan wing with vast oak beams. Delightfully converted bedrooms have infinite character and spectacular views. Two have four-poster beds. Those on the ground floor lead out on to a pretty garden whilst, at the front, is a farm pond brimming with life. The cuisine is exceptional and has acquired a peerless reputation for its variety, imagination and quality in the hands of Chef, Daphne Lambert. ♛♛♛.

PENGETHLEY MANOR HOTEL,
Pengethey Park, Near Ross-on-Wye, Hereford & Worcester HR9 6LL

Tel: 01989 730211
Fax: 01989 730238

Fully licensed; 25 bedrooms, all with private bathrooms; Historic interest; Children and pets welcome; Leisure and conference facilities; Monmouth 9 miles; £££.

15 acres of well-tended parkland and lawns, incorporating a challenging 9-hole golf improvement course, croquet lawn and trout lake, form the tranquil setting of this lovely Georgian manor house where character, style and elegance are watchwords by which this recommended retreat prospers. Hospitality and informality will endear Pengethley to family parties, for the young and not-so-young are cared for with equal attention. There are numerous amenities provided to meet the needs of children, and special facilities are on hand for disabled guests. Light and airy bedrooms are beautifully furnished in a manner reminiscent of a bygone age, to which such contemporary practicalities as bathrooms en suite, colour television, direct-dial telephone and hairdryers have been added. Rooms with four-poster and canopied beds are also available. The imaginative cuisine has achieved a reputation for its excellence and generosity, with such delicacies as Wye salmon and tender Welsh lamb featuring regularly in company with home-grown produce. The surrounding countryside is ideal for walking or exploring numerous places of historic interest and sporting venues, whilst, alternatively, evenings "at home" may be spent relaxing with a novel before a log fire in the panelled library or playing a few frames in the snooker room. Understandably, Pengethley is also in great demand for conferences, receptions etc. *AA ***, RAC.*

THE STEPPES COUNTRY HOUSE HOTEL,

Ullingswick, Near Hereford,
Hereford & Worcester HR1 3JG

Tel: 01432 820424
Fax: 01432 820042

Residential licence; 6 bedrooms, all with private bathrooms; Historic interest; Children over 12 years and dogs welcome; Hereford 8 miles; £.

Sometimes the traveller has to wander off the beaten track to find something truly original, and "The Steppes", peacefully resting in the tiny Wye Valley hamlet of Ullingswick, will more than repay those who visit it. This charming creeper-clad country hotel is furnished and decorated entirely in keeping with its seventeenth-century character. Beamed en suite bedrooms are located in a restored courtyard barn and stable, and are complete with television, clock/radio, tea/coffee making facilities and mini-bar. The cordon bleu cuisine is personally prepared by Mrs Tricia Howland, for whom each dinner served is a special occasion, appealing particularly to those with more adventurous tastes, and deserving of the best locally grown vegetables. And what better, after an ample breakfast, than to tour the area's ancient villages, walk in the Black Mountains and Malvern Hills, visit the porcelain works in Worcester or a local cider mill. See also our advertisement on the Outside Back Cover. ♛♛♛♛ *Highly Commended. AA** and Two Food Rosettes, Johansens Most Excellent Value Hotel 1996, Ashley Courtenay, Good Hotel Guide.* **See also advertisement Outside Back Cover.**

Hertfordshire

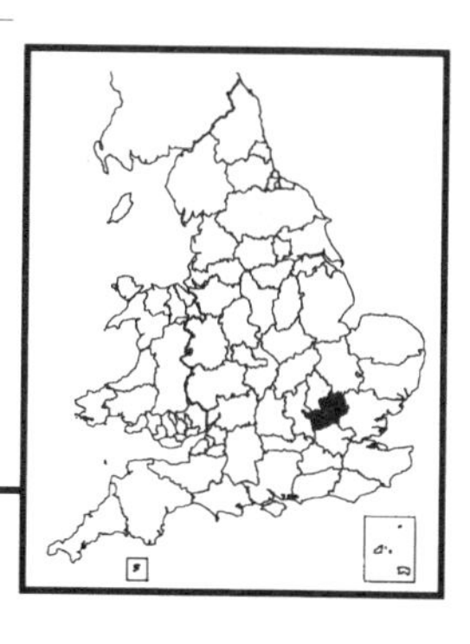

BRIGGENS HOUSE HOTEL,

Briggens Park, Stanstead Abbotts,
Near Ware, Hertfordshire SG12 8LD

Tel: 01279 829955
Fax: 01279 793685

Fully licensed; 54 bedrooms, all with private bathrooms; Historic interest; Children and pets welcome; Leisure and conference facilities; Ware 3 miles; ££££.

The wish to escape into a world of elegance and tranquillity need not involve an arduous journey, for it can be found in this most elegant 17th century country house. Set in 80 acres of softly rolling Hertfordshire countryside, Briggens House is an oasis of good living in the true traditions of yesteryear. Public and guest rooms have been meticulously and tastefully restored and are lavish in their luxurious appointments. The kitchens are under the expert supervision of a master chef, the cuisine being both beautifully presented and imaginative. A peaceful retreat this may be, but there are opportunities for active pursuits such as golf, tennis, swimming, croquet, boules and fishing. ♛♛♛♛♛, *AA and RAC ****.*

WEST LODGE PARK HOTEL,
Cockfosters Road, Hadley Wood,
Hertfordshire EN4 0PY

Tel: 0181 440 8311
Fax: 0181 449 3698

Fully licensed; 45 bedrooms, all with private bathrooms; Children welcome, guide dogs only; Leisure and conference facilities; London 11 miles, Potters Bar 3; ££££.

Georgian in character and set in a 35-acre gloriously wooded park, the charming and historic mansion has been extended and refurbished to provide outstanding facilities for tourists and businessmen. Conveniently placed only one mile off the M25 at Junction 24 and within 30 minutes of Luton Airport, the grand house is sumptuously furnished with a perceptive eye to harmonious colour schemes and graced with numerous attractive paintings. The individually-designed bedrooms range from cottage-style single rooms to luxury four-posters; all have private facilities, satellite television, direct-dial telephone, tea and coffee-makers and several thoughtful extras including a complimentary teddy bear! In the matter of cuisine, there is an impressive choice of imaginative dishes on offer in the Cedar Restaurant: a small tip — remember to leave room for a delicious sweet. Recently, the John Evelyn and Coventry Rooms have been extended by the addition of two Regency-style conservatories which provide extra space for the private functions for which the hotel is noted. Fine opportunities for leisure pursuits in the grounds include putting, croquet and golf practice net with clay pigeon shooting and archery available by prior arrangement. Within half-a-mile is Hadley Wood Golf Club where guests may play. The hotel is ideally placed for sight-seeing excursions to London, whilst within 20 minutes' drive are Jacobean Hatfield House and historic St.Albans with its fascinating abbey. ♛♛♛♛♛ *Highly Commended, AA**** and Rosette, RAC **** and Three Merit Awards, Egon Ronay, Which? Hotel Guide 1995 Hotel of the Year Hertfordshire.*

Isle of Wight

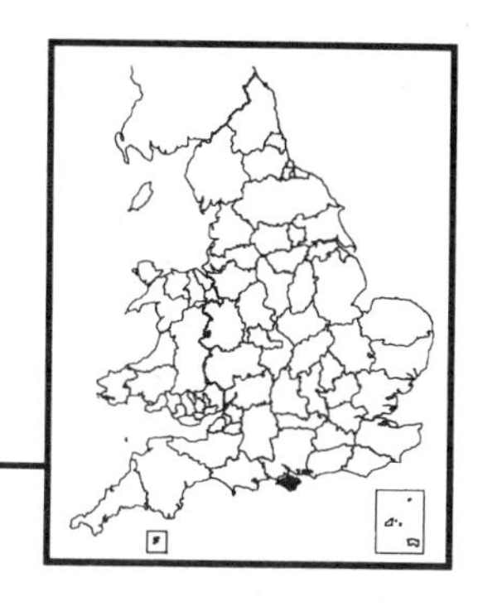

COUNTRY GARDEN HOTEL,
Church Hill, Totland Bay,
Isle of Wight PO39 0ET

Tel: 01983 754521*
Fax: 01983 754421

Residential and restaurant licence; 16 bedrooms, all with private bathrooms; Pets welcome; Yarmouth 3 miles; £.

Tucked away behind the gentle curve of Totland's golden sands and lovely walks, yet overlooking the sea, this really does offer the best of both worlds. Ashley Courtenay sums it up perfectly as "...A really superb hotel set in beautiful gardens", adding that here too "you will relish the superb cuisine" in one of the island's finest restaurants. All rooms have bath and shower, television, radio, fridge, telephone, hairdryer and hospitality tray. Single, double, and twin rooms are available, as well as suites and ground floor rooms. Special Spring and Autumn Break rates. 👑👑👑👑 *Commended, RAC *** and Hospitality Award.*

LAKE HOTEL,
Shore Road, Lower Bonchurch,
Isle of Wight PO38 1RF

Tel and Fax: 01983 852613*

Residential licence; 21 bedrooms, all with private bathrooms; Historic interest; Children over 3 years and pets welcome; Shanklin 3 miles, Ventnor ½ mile; £.

"Truly unbeatable value for money". This lovely country house hotel is set in a beautiful quiet two-acre garden on the seaward side of the olde worlde village of Bonchurch. Run by the same family for over 30 years, the hotel offers first class food and service, all in a relaxed and friendly atmosphere. All rooms are en suite with complimentary tea/coffee facilities and television, and are decorated in the "Laura Ashley" style. We can offer an Isle of Wight car ferry inclusive price of just £120.00 for four nights' half board during March/April/May and October, and we really do believe that you will not find better value on our beautiful island. *Commended, AA QQQQ Selected, RAC Highly Acclaimed.*

FRENCHMAN'S COVE COUNTRY HOTEL,
Alum Bay Old Road, Totland,
Isle of Wight PO39 0HZ

Tel: 01983 752227
Fax: 01983 755125

Residential licence; 12 bedrooms, 8 with private bathrooms; Children welcome; Yarmouth 3 miles; £.

Our delightful family-run country hotel is set amongst National Trust downland, not far from the Needles and safe sandy beaches. Ideal for ramblers, birdwatchers, cyclists and those who enjoy the countryside. Children are welcome and we have almost an acre of grounds with outdoor play equipment; cots and high chairs are available. Most rooms are en suite, all with colour television and tea/coffee making facilities. Guests can relax in the cosy bar or in the attractive lounge. Also available is the Coach House, a delightfully appointed apartment for two adults and two children. Please contact Sue and Chris Boatfield for details. *AA QQ.* **See also Colour Advertisement on page 13.**

WINDCLIFFE MANOR HOTEL & RESTAURANT,
Sandrock Road, Niton Undercliffe,
Isle of Wight PO38 2NG

Tel and Fax: 01983 730215

Residential and restaurant licence; 14 bedrooms, all with private bathrooms; Children welcome, pets by arrangement; Leisure facilities; Ventnor 4 miles; £.

The hotel is situated in its own grounds at the most southerly part of the island overlooking the English Channel and offers lovely walks along the coastal paths and through unspoilt countryside. The many places of interest are all within an easy drive, and after a day out, guests can enjoy a dip in the heated outdoor pool before dinner. Windcliffe dining is of the highest standard, with à la carte and vegetarian menus and excellent breakfasts; light lunches and afternoon teas are served. Our well stocked bar and extensive wine list complement the food. All rooms are en suite with colour television, video and tea/coffee making facilities. Fishing, golf and horse riding are all available locally. Colour brochure. *Highly Commended.*

Please mention
Recommended COUNTRY HOTELS
when seeking refreshment or accommodation
at a Hotel mentioned in these pages.

Isles of Scilly

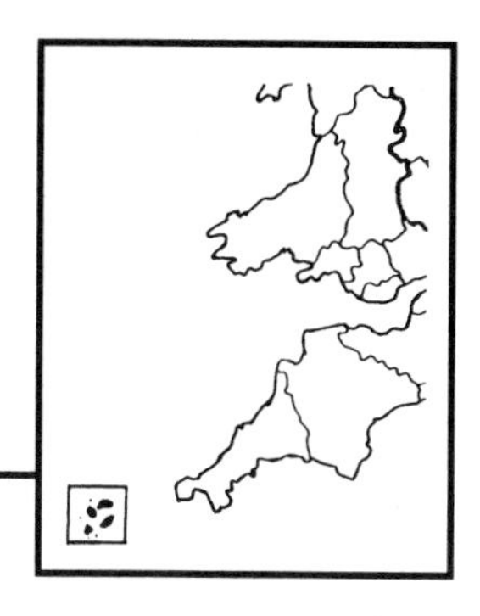

ST MARTIN'S ON THE ISLE,
St Martin's,
Isles of Scilly TR25 0QW

01720 422092*
Fax: 01720 422298

Fully licensed; 24 bedrooms, all with private bathrooms; Children and pets welcome; Leisure and conference facilities; Land's End 28 miles; ££££.

The third largest island of the Scillies,this is most people's idea of paradise on earth — the ultimate escape: long white beaches, clear blue water, shetered coves, fascinating flora and fauna, and, best of all, peace and quiet. The hotel complex has been imaginatively designed as a cluster of cottages nestling into the hillside, and the harmonious blend of colour and style in the decor and furnishings enhances one's appreciation of the magnificently appointed rooms and suites. The cuisine presented in the newly refurbished Tean Restaurant is superb, and naturally features locally caught seafood. Call FREEPHONE 0800 834056 for free 7-minute video. ♛♛♛♛ *Highly Commended, AA Three Red Stars and Three Rosettes.*

Kent

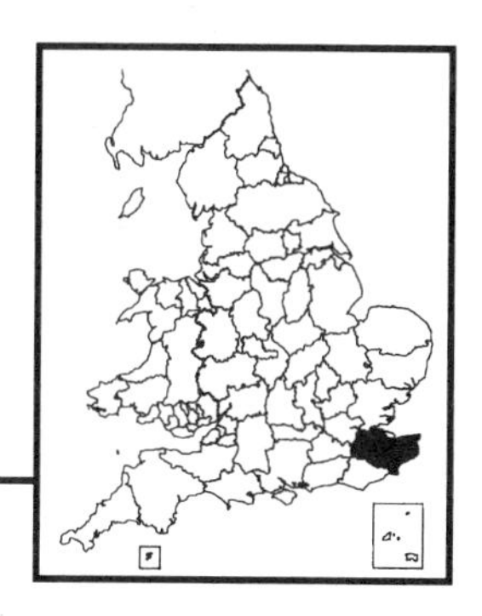

GARDEN HOTEL,
167 The Street, Boughton, Faversham,
Kent ME13 9BH

Tel: 01227 751411
Fax: 01227 751801

Fully licensed; 10 bedrooms, all with private bathrooms; Historic interest; Children and well-behaved pets welcome; Conference facilities; Faversham 3 miles; £££.

In the heart of Kent's fertile hop country, this charming hotel and restaurant is a 17th century Grade II building with a restored 19th century frontage. It has had a varied career, having been a general store, soup kitchen during World War II, school canteen and antique shop prior to its present distinguished function. Landscaped gardens lead to the Conservatory Restaurant where excellent à la carte and table d'hôte menus feature traditional English fare at its best. Set in tranquil countryside within easy reach of Canterbury, the hotel provides first-rate accommodation in bedrooms appointed with en suite facilities, television, direct dial telephone, tea and coffee-makers, hair dryer and trouser press. ♛♛♛♛ *Highly Commended.*

EASTWELL MANOR HOTEL,
Eastwell Park, Boughton Lees, Ashford, Kent TN25 4HR

Tel: 01233 219955
Fax: 01233 635530

Fully licensed; 23 bedrooms, all with private bathrooms; Historic interest; Children and pets welcome; Leisure facilities; Ashford 3 miles; ££££.

For sheer quality of service and traditional English and French cuisine in the gourmet class, this lovingly restored country house hotel and restaurant stands supreme. Conveniently placed for Canterbury, the coast and Channel Tunnel, the house stands in 62 acres of grounds surrounded by 3000 acres of private parkland. With a fascinating history, the manor is elegantly furnished with its public rooms featuring huge open fireplaces with stone mantles, carved panelling and fine antique pieces. Guest rooms offer every modern facility, including private bathrooms and showers. Tennis, croquet and pitch and putt may be enjoyed within the grounds and activities such as golf, squash, horse riding and fishing can be arranged locally. ♛♛♛♛♛ *De Luxe.*

BRANDSHATCH PLACE,
Fawkham Valley Road, Fawkham, Kent DA3 8NQ

Tel: 01474 872239
Fax: 01474 879652

Licensed; 41 bedrooms, all with private bathrooms; Children welcome, pets by arrangement; Leisure and conference facilities; Farningham 3 miles; ££££.

Set in 12 acres of parkland, this spacious and elegant Georgian house has graduated into an exclusive country club and hotel with accommodation and leisure facilities that are in the top echelon of their particular field. The handsomely appointed guest rooms form part of the main house. Each bedroom (including a four-poster suite) has its own private bathroom, colour television, direct-dial telephone and trouser press whilst the lounges, bars and restaurant are beautifully equipped. The cuisine here attracts a great deal of attention, a recommendation in itself. The imaginative menus make interesting reading and may be studied when enjoying a leisurely pre-luncheon or dinner drink in the library or lounge. ♛♛♛♛, *AA*** and Two Rosettes for Food.*

WALLETT'S COURT HOTEL,
Westcliffe, St Margarets-at-Cliffe, Dover, Kent CT15 6EW

Tel: 01304 852424*
Fax: 01304 853430

Residential and restaurant licence; 10 bedrooms, all with private bathrooms; Historic interest; Children welcome; Leisure facilities; Canterbury 15 miles, Eurotunnel 11, Dover Docks 3; £/££.

Wallett's Court is a seventeenth century manor house with wood carvings, beams and ornate fireplaces. It is set in rolling countryside above the White Cliffs of Dover. The ten bedrooms are all en suite and the restaurant, presided over by chef/proprietor Chris Oakley, is noted in major guides. The hotel is close to Dover Harbour, championship golf courses and the historic towns of Canterbury and Sandwich. *SEETB* ♛♛♛♛ *Highly Commended.*

COLLINA HOUSE HOTEL,
East Hill, Tenterden,
Kent TN30 6RL

Tel: 01580 764852/764004
Fax: 01580 762224

Fully licensed; 17 bedrooms, all with private bathrooms; Children welcome, pets by arrangement only; Ashford 10 miles; £.

This charming hotel is quietly situated in the country town of Tenterden, yet is only a few minutes' walk from the Leisure Centre. There are many National Trust properties and places of interest in the area, including Sissinghurst Castle, Leeds Castle, Scotney Castle Gardens and the Kent and East Sussex steam engines. Personal attention is assured by the Swiss-trained owners of this comfortable hotel, who provide home cooking of the highest standard, enhanced by the use of home-grown produce. All the well-appointed bedrooms, including five family rooms, have private bathrooms, central heating and colour television. Further details on request. ♛♛♛.

Lancashire

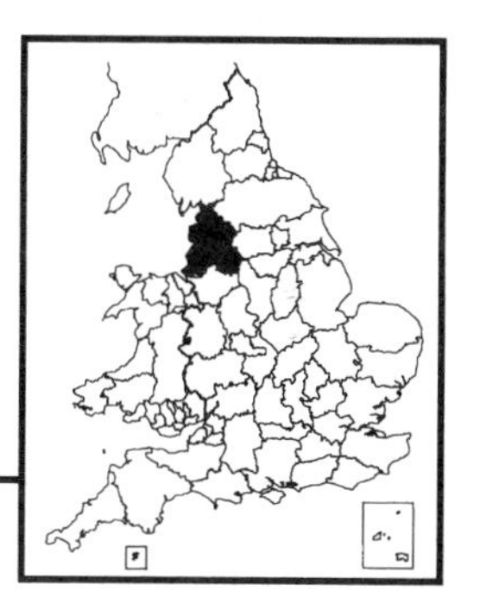

including Greater Manchester, and Merseyside.

NORTHCOTE MANOR,
Northcote Road, Langho, Blackburn,
Lancashire BB6 8BE

Tel: 01254 240555
Fax: 01254 246568

Restaurant licence; 14 bedrooms, all with private bathrooms; Children welcome; Conference facilities; Blackburn 4 miles; ££££.

Hidden away in glorious countryside between the beautiful Trough of Bowland and the Ribble Valley, this Victorian manor house is well known for its imaginative kitchen. Under the guidance of joint owner Nigel Haworth (Egon Ronay Chef of the Year), dining is an experience to be cherished. No less worthy of the highest praise is the delightful accommodation. Reached by means of the original oak staircase, guest rooms are sumptuously appointed. Another new extension has recently been added and the handsome decor is complemented by en suite facilities, colour television with satellite channels, direct-dial telephone, trouser press and tea and coffee makers. Sporting arrangements may be made for game and clay pigeon shooting, horse riding, cycling, fishing and golf. ♛♛♛♛ *Highly Commended.*

SHAW HILL HOTEL, GOLF & COUNTRY CLUB,
Whittle-le-Woods, Near Chorley,
Lancashire PR6 7PP

Tel: 01257 269221
Fax: 01257 261223

Licensed; 30 bedrooms, all with private bathrooms; Historic interest; Children and pets welcome; Leisure facilities; Leyland 2 miles; £££.

This magnificent Georgian hotel retains many of its original features, and is well known for its fine cuisine and excellent wine list. All bedrooms have private bathrooms, and suites are also available. This is an ideal spot for a golfing break, and lessons are available from the Professional. Please ring for a brochure and details of all-year-round mini-breaks. ♛♛♛♛ *Highly Commended, AA***.*

WOOLTON REDBOURNE HOTEL,
Acrefield Road, Woolton,
Liverpool L25 5JN

Tel: 0151 428 2152/421 1500
Fax: 0151 421 1501

Licensed; 25 bedrooms, all with private bathrooms; Historic interest; Children and pets welcome; Conference facilities; Liverpool 5 miles; ££££.

Classically Victorian in atmosphere and opulent comfort, this grand country house was built in 1884 by Sir Henry Tate (of sugar fame) as a wedding present for his daughter, Katherine. Skilfully converted into a country house hotel of infinite character, it lies resplendent in beautiful gardens just 5 minutes from the M62 and Liverpool International Airport. Good food in a refined setting is assured with the interesting Settle Bar a convivial place prior to dining by candlelight in the elegant Lady Katherine Restaurant. Luxury bedrooms are enhanced by antique furnishings, yet blending in subtle fashion are the finest modern facilities. The magnificent Redbourne Suite, with its timbered arched beam, has a four-poster bed and jacuzzi. 👑👑👑 *Highly Commended, City of Liverpool Vase Award Winner 1995/96.*

HOLLAND HALL HOTEL,
Lafford Lane, Upholland,
Lancashire WN8 0QZ

Tel: 01695 624426
Fax: 01695 622433

Fully licensed; 34 bedrooms, all with private bathrooms; Historic interest; Children welcome; Conference facilities; Wigan 4 miles; ££/£££.

Experience luxury and quality at historic Holland Hall Hotel where the emphasis is on comfort and style. Situated in the heart of Lancashire adjacent to Dean Wood golf course, this is the perfect home from home for the business executive seeking a tranquil haven. 34 tastefully furnished bedrooms all have en suite facilities, television and direct-dial telephones. The hotel offers the choice of two restaurants: experience unique classic cuisine in the elegant Churchill's Restaurant with the emphasis on individually prepared fresh food, or taste award-winning pizza in Winston's Restaurant and Bar. There are banqueting and conference facilities for up to 200, and promotional events, sales seminars, personalised corporate golf days etc can be catered for. The hotel has a large car park and sumptuous gardens and grounds. 👑👑👑👑, *AA*** and Two Rosettes, RAC***.*

MAINS HALL,
Mains Lane, Singleton,
Lancashire FY6 7LE

Tel: 01253 885130
Fax: 01253 894132

Fully licensed; 10 bedrooms, all with private bathrooms; Historic interest; Children and pets welcome; Conference facilities; Poulton-le-Fylde 2 miles; ££/£££.

Of impeccable style and elegance, this lovely Grade II listed house has a romantic history and much of its period detail remains. Ideally placed for those who hanker after the tranquillity of the countryside yet appreciate the entertainments of a lively seaside resort, Mains Hall graces 4 acres of secluded grounds overlooking the River Wyre but only 10 minutes' drive from the M55. The cuisine to be enjoyed in either of two sophisticated restaurants is imaginative and of the highest quality as befits a Member of the North-West Culinary Circle. The accommodation comprises beautifully appointed bedrooms, some with antique four poster or half-tester beds, en suite facilities, colour television, radio, tea and coffee-makers, hair dryer and trouser press.

Leicestershire

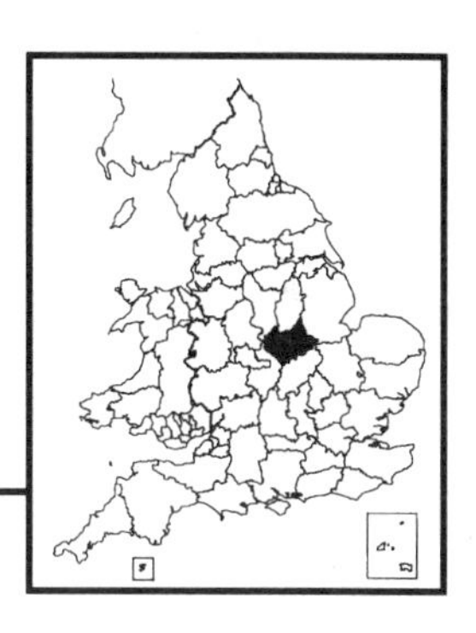

THE PRIEST HOUSE,
Kings Mills, Castle Donington,
Leicestershire DE74 2RR

Tel: 01332 810649
Fax: 01332 811141

Fully licensed; 45 bedrooms, all with private bathrooms; Historic interest; Children and pets welcome; Leisure and conference facilities; Nottingham 16 miles, Derby 11; ££££.

This unusual and attractive hotel was originally a water-mill mentioned in the Domesday Book, and today stands in over 50 acres of mature parkland on the banks of the River Trent. All bedrooms have a full range of modern amenities, and those which have been converted from the cottages of the 17th century mill-workers incorporate the old fireplaces and oak beams. The Malt Bar features a fine selection of real ale and malt whiskies, perhaps to be sampled before dining in the elegant Mille Fleame Restaurant which has gained a reputation far beyond the immediate neighbourhood for its imaginative cuisine and excellent wine list. With its central sitcentral situation and easy access by road, rail and air, the hotel is ideal for business meetings as well as comfortable country house holidays and short breaks.

PUBLISHER'S NOTE

While every effort is made to ensure accuracy, we regret that FHG Publications cannot accept responsibility for errors, omissions or misrepresentations in our entries or any consequences thereof. Prices in particular should be checked because we go to press early. We will follow up complaints but cannot act as arbiters or agents for either party.

BARNSDALE LODGE HOTEL,
The Avenue, Rutland Water North Shore, Exton, Leicestershire LE15 8AB

Tel: 01572 724678
Fax: 01572 724961

Fully licensed; 29 bedrooms, all with private bathrooms; Children and pets welcome; Conference facilities; Oakham 4 miles; ££.

Graduating from 17th century farmhouse to a warm and welcoming country house on the shore of man-made Rutland Water, Barnsdale Lodge is an ideal base for fishing and all kinds of watersports with beautiful countryside all around. A reputation has been earned for its comfort and superb traditional English fare which is served in an Edwardian-style dining room or Conservatory Restaurant. The excellent accommodation comprises rooms with private bathrooms, television, telephones, radio alarms and tea and coffee-makers. Children are especially welcome with several facilities provided for them including a safe playground area, cots, special menus and a baby sitting service. ♛♛♛, *AA/RAC ****

HAMBLETON HALL,
Hambleton, Oakham, Rutland, Leicestershire LE15 8TH

Tel: 01572 756991
Fax: 01572 724721

Fully licensed; 15 bedrooms, all with private bathrooms; Historic interest; Children and pets welcome; Leisure facilities; Melton Mowbray 9 miles.

Rutland, which has been re-instated as a county, is verdant, undulating, and largely unspoilt, making it an ideal place to spend a tranquil vacation. No better venue for such an excursion into the relatively unknown exists than this fine hotel, perched in the very centre of man-made Rutland Water. Beautifully furnished in subtle shades, elegant and profoundly comfortable, Hambleton Hall is within easy reach of numerous places of historic interest, and there are good opportunities locally for tennis, swimming (in the outdoor heated pool), golf, horse riding, boating and fishing. We cannot speak too highly of the superb cuisine which exhibits flair and refreshing originality. *AA Three Red Stars, Egon Ronay, Johansens, Relais & Chateaux.*

NORMANTON PARK HOTEL,
Rutland Water South Shore, Oakham, Leicestershire LE15 7HG

Tel: 01780 720315
Fax: 01780 721086

Fully licensed; 23 bedrooms, all with private bathrooms; Historic interest; Children and pets welcome; Conference facilities; Stamford 6 miles; ££.

With a broad and impressive facade, this fine hotel has been skilfully fashioned out of the stable block and coach house of former Normanton Hall. A recommended retreat known for its comfort and cuisine, the hotel stands in 5 acres of parkland convenient for all the watersport opportunities provided by Rutland Water. Furnishings are cheerful throughout and warm in off-season months. Tempting and imaginative dishes may be enjoyed in the stylish two-tier Sailing Bar or on the Courtyard Patio or, more formally, in the attractive Orangery which has a direct lake view. The hotel has a high standard of service and care, with five stars awarded for the full, traditional English breakfast. *Which? Hotel of the County 1996.*

NOTE

All the information in this book is given in good faith in the belief that it is correct. However, the publishers cannot guarantee the facts given in these pages, neither are they responsible for changes in policy, ownership or terms that may take place after the date of going to press. Readers should always satisfy themselves that the facilities they require are available and that the terms, if quoted, still apply.

Lincolnshire

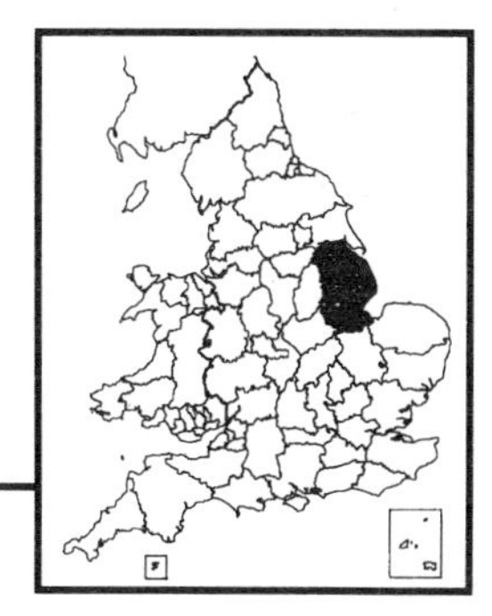

including North Lincolnshire, and North East Lincolnshire, formerly Humberside (Immingham).

WASHINGBOROUGH HALL, Church Hill, Washingborough, Lincolnshire LN4 1BE

Tel: 01522 790340
Fax: 01522 792936

Fully licensed; 12 bedrooms, all with private bathrooms; Children and pets welcome; Leisure and conference facilities; Lincoln 3 miles; ££.

Impressive Lincoln and its splendid hilltop cathedral may be the motivating reason for acquainting oneself with Washingborough Hall which is only 3 miles away; as solidly British as the square tower of the adjacent village church, this delightful country house is also ideally placed for quiet holidays, with the Lincolnshire Wolds, Nottinghamshire and even the East Coast within easy reach. Beautifully furnished public rooms and well equipped, comfortable bedrooms await discerning guests, and the à la carte cuisine is varied and imaginative. The house stands in three acres of lawns and woodland where one may swim in the outdoor heated pool; opportunities for fishing, golf, riding and squash exist close by. 👑👑👑👑 *Commended.*

EAGLE LODGE HOTEL, The Broadway, Woodhall Spa, Lincolnshire LN10 6ST

Tel: 01526 353231
Fax: 01526 352797

Fully licensed; 23 bedrooms, all with private bathrooms; Children and pets welcome; Conference facilities; Horncastle 6 miles; £.

Dating from the end of the last century, the Eagle Lodge has been restored to its former glory and now offers a modern range of facilities. Situated just one mile from the famous Woodhall Spa championship golf course, it is an ideal holiday centre for touring Lincolnshire and visiting the unspoiled East Coast. All the superbly equipped bedrooms have en suite bathrooms, remote-control satellite television and telephone, while, for that special occasion, the Stanhope Suite offers four-poster luxury and a private spa bath. Table d'hôte and à la carte menus to suit all tastes and pockets can be enjoyed in the Kestrel Suite Restaurant; alternatively, a daily changing menu is available in the new Osprey Bar and Brasserie, along with a full range of refreshments. 👑👑👑 *Commended.* **See also Colour Advertisement on page 7.**

PETWOOD HOUSE, Woodhall Spa, Lincolnshire LN10 6QF

Tel: 01526 352411
Fax: 01526 353473

Fully licensed; 45 bedrooms, all with private bathrooms; Historic interest; Children welcome; Leisure and conference facilities; Horncastle 6 miles; £££.

Many notable persons have graced the rooms of this charming country house, including King George V, his son (later George VI), two daughters of Queen Victoria, and Lady Louis Mountbatten. During World War II it became the Officers' Mess of several squadrons, including 617 Squadron known as the "Dambusters". Today it is a country house hotel of unique charm, offering a high standard of comfort and hospitality in elegant surroundings. All bedrooms are fully equipped to meet the needs of today's discerning guests, and the highly recommended Tennysons Restaurant offers the very best of English and Continental cuisine. There are ample leisure opportunities available locally as well as tranquil villages and historic market towns to explore. 👑👑👑👑.

Norfolk

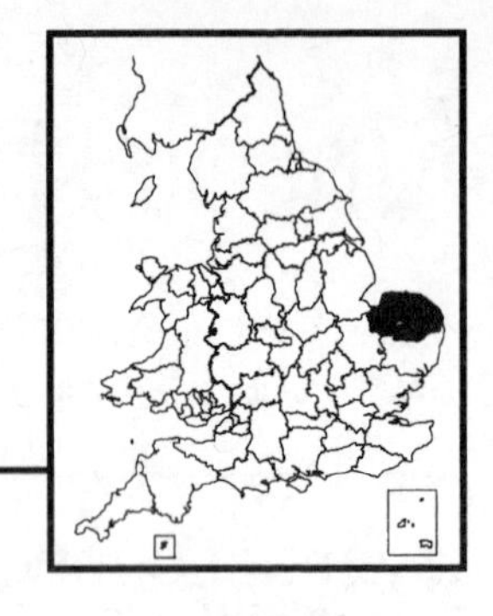

THE OLD RECTORY,
Great Snoring, Fakenham,
Norfolk NR21 OHP

Tel: 01328 820597
Fax: 01328 820048

Restaurant and residential licence; 6 bedrooms, all with private bathrooms; Historic interest; Children by arrangement; Conference facilities; Fakenham 3 miles; ££/£££.

Architecturally fascinating with stone mullioned windows, oak beams and carving and several other unusual features, this old manor house is believed to date back to 1500 but was much changed in Victorian times. It stands in a large walled garden in a quaint and aptly-named location; a peaceful and secluded retreat close to Walsingham and within easy reach of Norwich, King's Lynn and the coast. Just the place for a relaxing holiday. Guest rooms are en suite and have colour television and direct-dial telephone. From the full breakfast to table d'hôte dinner, the food is traditionally English in character, meals being served in a pleasant period dining room. *Good Hotel Guide, Egon Ronay, Johansens, Which? Hotel Guide etc.*

PARK FARM COUNTRY HOTEL,
Hethersett, Norwich,
Norfolk NR9 3DL

Tel: 01603 810264
Fax: 01603 812104

Fully licensed; 38 bedrooms, all with private bathrooms; Children welcome; Leisure and conference facilities; Norwich 5 miles; £££.

A tree-lined drive through beautiful landscaped gardens leads the way to pure, unashamed luxury. Conveniently situated for the Broads, coast and City of Norwich, this spruce and welcoming gem of a holiday venue has fabulous leisure facilities and accommodation in the multi-starred class. Guest rooms, several with four-poster beds and jacuzzis, are attractively arranged, some in the renovated barn, others in the original Georgian farmhouse. They are magnificently appointed with en suite facilities, colour television, telephone and beverage-makers. One dines in some style here, the superb à la carte and table d'hôte cuisine setting the seal on a really memorable holiday. ♛♛♛♛ *Highly Commended, AA*** and Rosette.*

NORFOLK MEAD HOTEL & RESTAURANT,
Coltishall, Norwich,
Norfolk NR12 7DN

Tel: 01603 737531
Fax: 01603 737521

Residential and restaurant licence; 10 bedrooms, all with private bathrooms; Historic interest; Children welcome, pets by arrangment; Leisure and conference facilities; Norwich 6 miles; ££.

"Paradise Found" — *Vogue* magazine. Providing all facilities with personal service, this privately owned beautiful country house hotel is located in 8 tranquil riverside acres. With a 900ft River Bure frontage and private mooring, it also offers secluded gardens with a 60ft swimming pool, a well stocked fishing lake, boating, and abundant birdlife. The renowned restaurant offers superb cuisine and a comprehensive wine list. On one of the most peaceful parts of the Norfolk Broads yet ideally located for East Anglia's finest golf courses and only 6 miles from the centre of Norwich and 15 miles from the coast. ♛♛♛, *Johansens, Broads Award for Care.*

CATTON OLD HALL,
Lodge Lane, Old Catton, Norwich,
Norfolk NR6 7HG

Tel: 01603 419379
Fax: 01603 400339

Fully licensed; 5 bedrooms, all with private bathrooms; Historic interest; Children welcome, pets by arrangement; Norwich 3 miles; £.

A short bus journey from Norwich city centre, this lovely old house is the family home of Roger and Anthea Cawdron. Built in 1632 and sympathetically restored, it now offers luxury accommodation for both holidaymaker and businessman. The dining room and delightfully furnished lounge encourage easy relaxation and the spacious en suite bedrooms are charmingly decorated and appointed to a very high specification with satellite television, radio, direct-dial telephone and tea and coffee-making facilities. There is also a special Honeymoon Suite. A full English breakfast is served; evening meals are available if booked in advance and may be taken with the family if desired. ♛♛♛ *Highly Commended.*

PARK HOUSE,
Sandringham, King's Lynn,
Norfolk PE35 6EH

Tel: 01485 543000
Fax: 01485 540663

Residential licence; 16 bedrooms, all with private bathrooms; Historic interest; Guide dogs only; Leisure and conference facilities; King's Lynn 7 miles; ££.

This delightful country hotel, presented to the Leonard Cheshire Foundation by HM The Queen, has been specially adapted for people with physical disabilities and their partners, carers or companions (and families). Situated in its own picturesque grounds on the Sandringham Estate near Sandringham House, Church and Visitor Centre, it offers first-class accommodation. Single and twin-bedded rooms each have their own toilet, bath or shower, colour television, radio, telephone, tea/coffee making facilities and staff intercom. The hotel provides outings to local places of interest every weekday afternoon. After-dinner entertainment is available most evenings. Guests with physical disabilities can be assured of an exceptionally high standard of assistance from the care staff.

KINGFISHER HOTEL,
High Street, Stalham,
Norfolk NR12 9AN

Tel: 01692 581974
Fax: 01692 582544

Fully licensed; 18 bedrooms, all with private bathrooms; Children and dogs welcome; Conference facilities; North Walsham 7 miles; £.

A short stroll from Stalham Staithe where boats may be hired and close to the nature reserve of Hickling Broad, this is one of Broadland's brightest jewels. Serious, peak-capped boating enthusiasts, those who just like messing about in boats, hopeful anglers and birdwatchers join those merely captivated by the bucolic charm of rural Norfolk in contributing to the mood of happy informality here. The restaurant presents an extensive à la carte menu specialising in local seafood dishes (the coast is only 20 minutes distant). An excellent hotel in which to stay, the accommodation comprises en suite bedrooms with colour television, direct-dial telephone, radio and tea and coffee-making facilities. A Broads beauty. ♛♛♛ *Commended, RAC** and Hospitality Award, AA**.*

BRIARFIELDS HOTEL,
Main Road, Titchwell, King's Lynn,
Norfolk PE31 8BB

Tel: 01485 210742
Fax: 01485 210933

Fully licensed; 17 bedrooms, all with private bathrooms; Hunstanton 5 miles.

Briarfields is a delightful country hotel located in an area rich in wildlife, overlooking the sea and Titchwell RSPB Reserve. Quiet sandy beaches can be found close by and there is a wealth of local places of interest to visit. For golf enthusiasts, Briarfields is a short distance from the Royal West Norfolk course at Brancaster or the links at Hunstanton. The hotel has 17 twin or double bedrooms, all individually furnished; two include four-poster beds for that extra touch of luxury. There are also two family suites, one of which has its own lounge/dining area. Briarfields Restaurant has an enviable reputation for its extensive menus and dessert trolley. Traditionally home-cooked dishes prepared from fresh daily ingredients are certain to satisfy the most discerning diner! ♛♛♛ *Commended, AA**.* **See also Colour Advertisement on page 7.**

The **£** symbol when appearing at the end of the italic section of an entry shows the anticipated price, during 1997, for single full Bed and Breakfast.

Under £40	**£**	**Over £55 but under £70**	**£££**
Over £40 but under £55	**££**	**Over £70**	**££££**

This is meant as an indication only and does not show prices for Special Breaks, Weekends, etc. Guests are therefore advised to verify all prices on enquiring or booking.

Northumberland

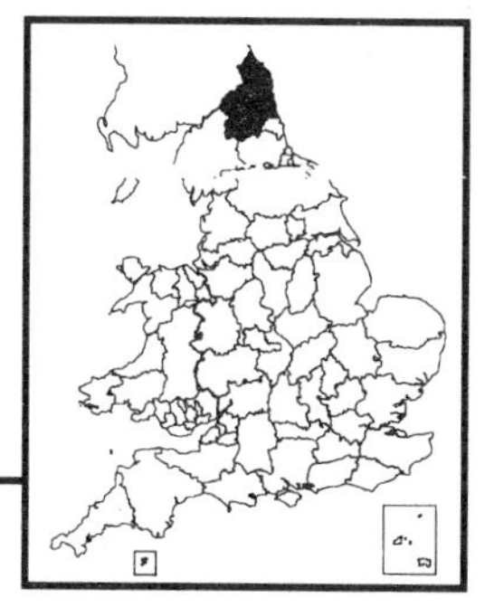

RIVERDALE HALL HOTEL & RESTAURANT,
Bellingham,
Northumberland NE48 2JT

Tel: 01434 220254
Fax: 01434 220457

Fully licensed; 20 bedrooms, all with private bathrooms; Children and pets welcome; Leisure and conference facilities; Hexham 17 miles; ££.

Set in Northumberland National Park, this is the nearest hotel to Kielder Water and Forest. Popular with the sporting enthusiast, Riverdale Hall has its own indoor swimming pool, games room, sauna, cricket field, and salmon and trout river, and just opposite is Bellingham's golf course. The Pennine Way and National Trust walks pass through the town, and Hadrian's Wall is nearby. The hotel is centrally heated throughout, and much character is added by log fires and four-poster beds. The restaurant has an RAC Merit Award for its high standard of cuisine. ♛♛♛♛ *Commended, RAC Merit Awards for Hospitality and Restaurant.* **See also Colour Advertisement on page 7.**

LINDEN HALL HOTEL & HEALTH SPA,
Longhorsley, Morpeth,
Northumberland NE65 8XF

Tel: 01670 516611
Fax: 01670 788544

Licensed; 50 bedrooms, all with private bathrooms; Historic interest; Children and pets welcome; Leisure and conference facilities; Morpeth 6 miles; ££££.

With its richly furnished rooms combining tranquil elegance with the best of modern comforts, this magnificent Georgian country house is situated in 450 acres of splendid park, woodland and landscaped gardens. Stylish twin, double, four-poster beds and executive suites are available, each fully equipped with private bathroom and shower, colour television, radio, direct-dial telephone, mini-bar, trouser press, hair dryer and baby listening service. The restaurant offers excellent cuisine and panoramic views to the distant coastline, whilst the Linden Pub has the atmosphere of a traditional country inn. ♛♛♛♛♛ *De Luxe, AA**** and Rosette, Silver England for Excellence 1993.*

Nottinghamshire

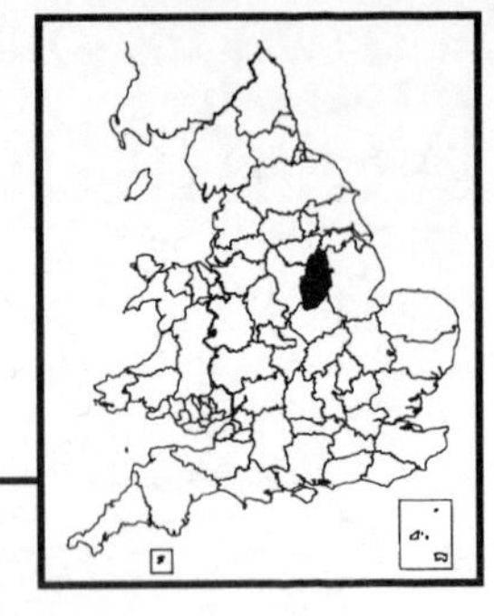

OLD ENGLAND HOTEL,
High Street, Sutton-on-Trent, Near Newark,
Nottinghamshire NG23 6QA

Tel: 01636 821216

Restaurant licence; 10 bedrooms, all with private facilities; Historic interest; Children and dogs welcome; London 133 miles, Nottingham 28, Newark-on-Trent 8; £££.

Appropriately named, the Old England Hotel, owned and run by the Pike family for over fifty years, epitomises traditional hospitality, charm and courtesy, together with the modern amenities we expect from a first-class establishment. All bedrooms are individually appointed, with private facilities and colour television, and the hotel is graced with a large collection of antique furniture, delightfully displayed in its old world setting. The menu too is selected from the very best of traditional fare, using locally produced meat and fresh vegetables. Extensive grounds invite the stroller, and Sherwood Forest and Southwell Minster are readily accessible.

Oxfordshire

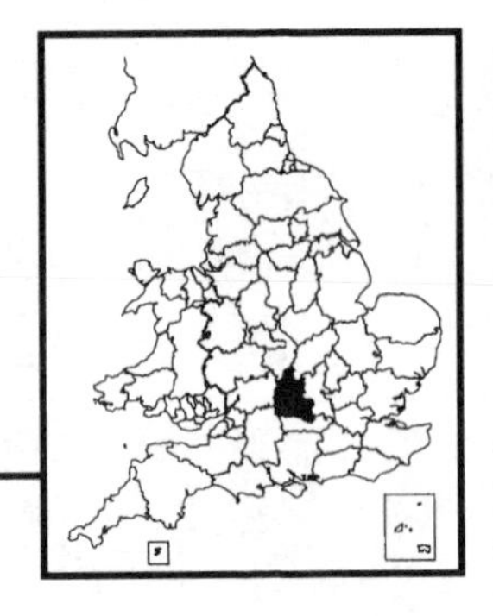

THE SPRINGS HOTEL,
Wallingford Road, North Stoke,
Wallingford, Oxfordshire OX10 6BE

Tel: 01491 836687
Fax: 01491 836877

Licensed; 30 bedrooms, all with private bathrooms; Historic interest; Children welcome; Leisure and conference facilities; Wallingford 2 miles; ££££;

Taking its name from springs that feed a lake that graces attractive grounds of 30 acres, this fine Mock Tudor house offers remarkable amenities indoor and out. Guest rooms are delightfully decorated and have private bathrooms, colour television, trouser press and direct-dial telephone, whilst executive suites have jacuzzi spas. Dining in the romantic atmosphere of the Lakeside Restaurant is an experience to savour; the menu is imaginative and changed regularly. In the grounds, floodlit at night, is a tennis court, croquet lawn, putting green, heated swimming pool and sauna; riding, golf, boating and other activities may be enjoyed nearby.This is a lovely place in which to unwind and it is easy to understand its popularity for conferences and functions. *AA and RAC ***, Egon Ronay.*

WESTWOOD COUNTRY HOTEL, Hinksey Hill Top, Oxford, Oxfordshire OX1 5BG

Tel: 01865 735408
Fax: 01865 736536

Fully licensed; 22 bedrooms, all with private bathrooms; Children welcome; Leisure and conference facilities; Gloucester 49 miles, Reading 26; ££.

The leafy grounds of this fine hotel are a bonus for nature-lovers, for the four acres are frequented by many species of wildlife, and are surrounded by a further 400 acres of woodland nature reserve opened by David Bellamy. Guests return again and again to sample the excellent accommodation and superb cuisine. Single, double and family rooms all have private facilities, television, radio, baby listening, and tea and coffee makers. There is a comfortable lounge and a convivial bar; sauna, jacuzzi and mini-gym are available free to guests. Good facilities exist for conferences, meetings and weddings. 👑👑👑 *Commended, Winner of Oxfordshire Environmental Section Business of the Year Award 1996.*

STUDLEY PRIORY HOTEL, Horton-cum-Studley, Oxford, Oxfordshire OX33 1AZ

Tel: 01865 351203/351254
Fax: 01865 351613

Residential and restaurant licence; 19 bedrooms, all with private bathrooms; Children welcome; Leisure and conference facilities; Oxford 7 miles; ££££.

In the 12th century a Benedictine nunnery, this fine building was converted into a hotel in 1961 and now provides splendid contemporary comforts which blend in subtle fashion with the gracious aura of unhurried days gone by. The Priory has changed little in external appearance since the days of Queen Elizabeth I and it retains its imposing presence. Log fires in the main reception room and oak panelled bar augment the central heating to provide a real warmth of welcome to present-day guests. Standing in 13 acres of wooded grounds and within easy reach of Oxford and numerous places of historic interest, the hotel has exceptionally fine accommodation with en suite facilities and is also a most popular venue for conferences and functions. 👑👑👑👑, *AA *** and Two Rosettes.*

FOR THE MUTUAL GUIDANCE OF GUEST AND HOST

Every year literally thousands of holidays, short breaks and overnight stops are arranged through our guides, the vast majority without any problems at all. In a handful of cases, however, difficulties do arise about bookings, which often could have been prevented from the outset.

It is important to remember that when accommodation has been booked, both parties – guests and hosts – have entered into a form of contract. We hope that the following points will provide helpful guidance.

GUESTS: When enquiring about accommodation, be as precise as possible. Give exact dates, numbers in your party and the ages of any children. State the number and type of rooms wanted and also what catenng you require – bed and breakfast, full board etc. Make sure that the position about evening meals is clear – and about pets, reductions for children or any other special points.

Read our reviews carefully to ensure that the proprietors you are going to contact can supply what you want. Ask for a letter confirming all arrangements, if possible.

If you have to cancel, do so as soon as possible. Proprietors do have the right to retain deposits and under certain circumstances to charge for cancelled holidays if adequate notice is not given and they cannot re-let the accommodation.

HOSTS: Give details about your facilities and about any special conditions. Explain your deposit system clearly and arrangements for cancellations, charges etc. and whether or not your terms include VAT.

If for any reason you are unable to fulfil an agreed booking without adequate notice, you may be under an obligation to arrange suitable alternative accommodation or to make some form of compensation.

While every effort is made to ensure accuracy, we regret that FHG Publications cannot accept responsibility for errors, omissions or misrepresentations in our entries or any consequences thereof. Prices in particular should be checked because we go to press early. We will follow up complaints but cannot act as arbiters or agents for either party.

Shropshire

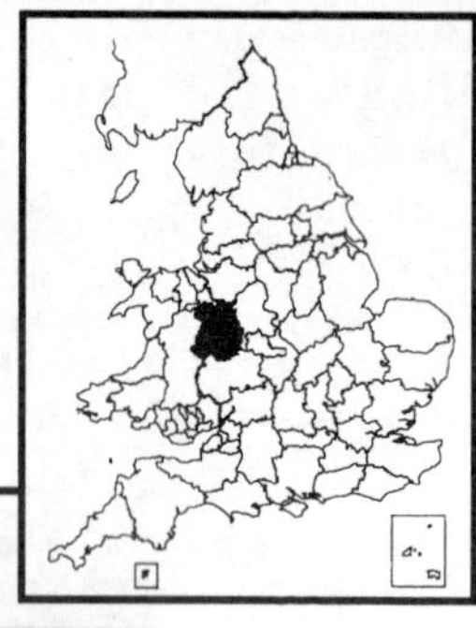

JINLYE,
Castle Hill, All Stretton, Church Stretton, Shropshire SY6 6JP

Tel and Fax: 01694 723243

Residential licence; 8 bedrooms, all with private bathrooms; Historic interest; Children over 12 years welcome; Church Stretton 1 mile; £.

Jinlye is a beautifully situated country guest house standing in 15 acres of grounds set in the lovely Shropshire Highlands immediately adjoining 6000 acres of National Trust land, ideally situated for Ironbridge museums and Cadfael Country. A stroll from the house can provide some of the most stunning views in England and the cottage gardens abound with rare plants. The house is delightfully furnished in period decor, offering luxurious and peaceful accommodation, with inglenook fires and comfortable lounges. The spacious en suite rooms all have magnificent views, and for a romantic interlude our wedding suite is furnished around a splendidly carved 17th century French wedding bed. Ground floor rooms suitable for disabled guests available. We are renowned for our excellent home cooking — desserts a speciality! Winter breaks and traditional Christmas breaks: colour brochure on request. *HETB* ♛♛♛ *Highly Commended, AA QQQQ.*

LONGMYND HOTEL,
Church Stretton, Shropshire SY6 6AG

Tel: 01694 722244
Fax: 01694 722718

Fully licensed; 50 bedrooms, all with private bathrooms; Historic interest; Children and dogs welcome; Leisure and conference facilities; Ludlow 15 miles, Shrewsbury 13; £££.

Perched high above the pleasant town of Church Stretton in grounds of ten acres, this fine hotel enjoys sweeping views over the beautiful Welsh border country. A subtle mixture of superb modern and period rooms, the hotel possesses outstanding amenities. Luxury suites and bedrooms are equipped with every refinement demanded by the discerning guest of today, an outdoor heated swimming pool (covered in winter months), 9-hole pitch-and-putt course, trim gym, sauna and solarium. Riding, fishing, shooting and gliding may also be arranged nearby. The cuisine is noteworthy for its excellence and variety and there are superb facilities for conferences and other functions. There are also self-catering lodges in the hotel grounds. ♛♛♛, *RAC***, Johansens, Ashley Courtenay.* **See also Colour Advertisement on page 8.**

THE REDFERN HOTEL,
Cleobury Mortimer,
Shropshire DY14 8AA

Tel: 01299 270395; Fax: 01299 271011
e-mail/jon@red-fern.demon.co.uk

Licensed; 11 bedrooms, all with private bathrooms or showers; Conference facilities; Children and dogs welcome; Ludlow 11 miles, Bewdley 8; ££.

For centuries past travellers have stayed in the old market town of Cleobury Mortimer. Now a conservation area on the edge of the 6000-acre Forest of Wyre, it forms a perfect centre for exploring the Welsh Marches, Ironbridge Industrial Museum and 2000 years of English history. The shire horses at Acton Scott Farm Museum and the steam engines on the Severn Valley railway will conjure up nostalgia of times past. After a day's adventuring or walking in the Shropshire hills, what better place to relax than in this warm and comfortable hotel, where good fresh food, fine wines and friendly service will make your stay one to remember. All bedrooms have tea/coffee making facilities, baby-listening, hairdryer and direct-dial telephone. Bargain breaks available throughout the year. ♛♛♛♛ *Commended, AA ** and Rosette, RAC **.*

THE MOOR HALL,
Stoke St Milborough, Near Ludlow,
Shropshire SY8 3EG

Tel: 01584 823209/333
Fax: 01584 823387

Residential and restaurant licence; 3 bedrooms, all with private bathrooms; Historic interest; Children welcome, pets by arrangement; Leisure and conference facilities; Ludlow 4 miles; £.

Handsome Moor Hall has an unusual claim to fame: it was built in splendid Palladian style in 1789, a year that saw the outbreak of the French Revolution and the Mutiny on the Bounty. There any similarity ends for this is a peaceful holiday retreat in the ancient Marches, one of Britain's most beautiful and comparatively unfrequented areas calculated to stimulate the spirit of the laid-back explorer, for there is much of sporting and historic interest to be discovered in this enchanting county. Elegantly decorated, the house stands in five acres of verdant grounds, and accommodation and cuisine conform to the highest ideals of the traditional country house lifestyle. The result — utter contentment. ♛♛♛ *Highly Commended, AA Selected, RAC Acclaimed, Johansens.* **See also Colour Advertisement on page 7.**

DINHAM HALL HOTEL,
By the Castle, Dinham, Ludlow, Shropshire SY8 lEJ

Tel: 01584 876464
Fax: 01584 876019

Fully licensed; 12 bedrooms, all with private bathrooms; Historic interest; Children and pets welcome; Leisure and conference facilities; Shrewsbury 24 miles; £££.

Delectable Ludlow has many attractions both historic and practical. The imposing Norman castle, picturesque old inns, Georgian houses and antique shops come into the first category; in the second, this enlightened hotel, itself a fine Georgian building, certainly deserves its place. A mere 40 metres from the castle and bathed in an aura hallowed by time, the hotel has numerous attributes, including picturesque views of the Teme Valley. We were particularly impressed by the scope and balance of the à la carte menu, imaginative, varied and reasonable in price. The guest rooms are sheer delight, achieving a happy amalgam of period design and such modern facilities as bathrooms en suite, colour television, direct-dial telephone, mini-bar and tea/coffee making facilities. 👑👑👑👑, *AA *** and Two Rosettes.*

DINHAM WEIR HOTEL,
Dinham Bridge, Ludlow,
Shropshire SY8 1EH

Tel: 01584 874431

Fully licensed; 8 bedrooms, all with private bathrooms; Historic interest; Children over 5 years welcome; Shrewsbury 24 miles; ££££.

To visit lovely Ludlow is to step back into history, with its imposing Norman castle, old houses and inns to fascinate and delight. By the banks of the River Teme we made acquaintance with the delectable Dinham Weir Hotel, certainly a visual attraction in its own right. It occupies the site of the 17th century Castell Myll which was worked as an iron foundry until late Victorian times. For a relaxing holiday in historic surroundings and with the peaceful Shropshire countryside to explore, this splendidly furnished hotel is well recommended. All rooms overlook the garden and river and have en suite facilities, television, telephone, radio and tea and coffee makers. Dining here by candlelight is a special pleasure with full à la carte and table d'hôte menus available. ♛♛♛♛ *Commended, AA**, Ashley Courtenay, Logis.*

BOURTON MANOR,
Bourton, Much Wenlock, Near Telford,
Shropshire TF13 6QE

Tel: 01746 36531
Fax: 01746 36683

Licensed; 8 bedrooms, all with private bathrooms; Historic interest; Children and dogs welcome; Conference facilities; Telford 10 miles; £££.

This 16th century country house has recently been refurbished to offer comfortable hotel facilities. Accommodation comprises eight luxury bedrooms for single, twin and double occupancy, each with radio, colour television and direct-dial telephone. Conference facilities include a room for up to forty delegates; and the hotel restaurant and bars are open to non-residents. Bourton Manor is situated in its own private landscaped grounds and is ideal for walking, riding, or driving in the beautiful Welsh Border countryside. Many places of historic and cultural interest are within easy reach. **See also Colour Advertisement on page 8.**

ROWTON CASTLE HOTEL,
Halfway House, Shrewsbury,
Shropshire SY5 9EP

Tel: 01743 884044
Fax: 01743 884949

Fully licensed; 19 bedrooms, all with private bathrooms; Historic interest; Children and pets welcome; Leisure and conference facilities; Birmingham 48 miles, Shrewsbury 5; ££.

Although set in the tranquil countryside of one of England's most beautiful counties, imposing and picturesque Rowton Castle is only 10 minutes from the historic market town of Shrewsbury. Standing sedately in 17 acres of grounds which include the largest cedar tree in the country, it has been magically transformed into a hotel of distinction blessed with a superb restaurant, spacious and well equipped accommodation and extensive banqueting facilities. The history of this somewhat unusual tourist venue is absorbing. Originally mentioned in the Domesday Book and occupying the site of a Roman fort, the castle was destroyed by Llewellyn, Prince of Wales, in 1282, and although part of the large tower is reputed to be from the original building, the main house dates from the turn of the 17th century with additions made two centuries later. The property was made over to Baron Rowton in 1880, a title created as a reward for serving as Disraeli's private secretary. Still retaining many fascinating historic features, the hotel is delightfully furnished and appointed in keeping with its ornate and opulent origins, yet guests will lack nothing in the way of modern refinements. With its magnificent carved oak fireplace, the restaurant presents an extensive à la carte selection and the 18th century Oak Room can seat up to 20 guests in boardroom style for private functions. The splendid Cardeston Suite is the perfect venue for conferences and receptions. ♛♛♛♛ *Commended, AA and RAC ***.*

Somerset

including Bath and North East Somerset, and North West Somerset

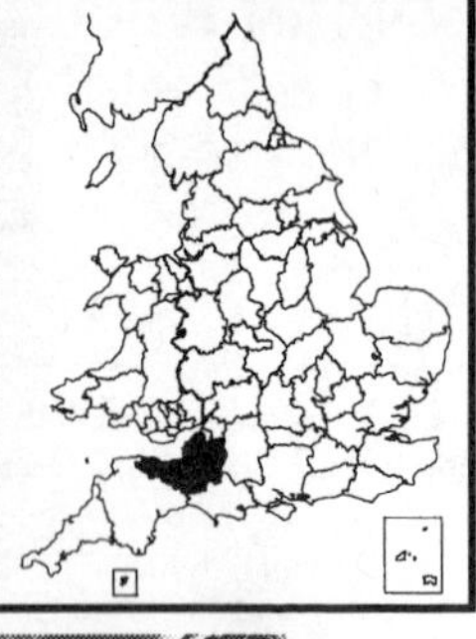

COMBE GROVE MANOR,
Brassknocker Hill, Monkton Combe, Bath, Somerset BA2 7HS

Tel: 01225 834644
Fax: 01225 834561

Fully licensed; 41 bedrooms, all with private bathrooms; Historic interest; Children welcome; Leisure and conference facilities; Bristol 11 miles, ££££.

The magnificent facilities which Combe Grove Manor provides for the leisure interests of their guests perfectly complement the high standards set for bedroom comfort and dining-room quality. If the indoor and outdoor swimming-pools, tennis and squash courts, gymnasium, sauna, golf and other on-site activities leave some energy untapped, clay pigeon shooting, hot-air ballooning or horse-riding can be arranged nearby. Back in your de-luxe bedroom, with a four-poster bed if you wish, watch the news on satellite TV before you bathe. Then down to the Georgian restaurant for a formal dinner or a more casual meal in the Manor Vaults Bistro. Combe Grove has various 'Special Breaks' and the use of leisure facilities is included in all room rates. Why not escape from the busy world into the luxury of this stress-free Hotel with its spectacular surroundings and unrivalled amenities. ♛♛♛♛♛ *Highly Commended, AA ****.* **See also Colour Advertisement on page 9.**

THE BATH TASBURGH HOTEL,
Warminster Road, Bath,
Somerset BA2 6SH

Tel: 01225 425096
Fax: 01225 463842

Residential licence; 12 bedrooms, all with private bathrooms; Historic interest; Children welcome; City centre ½ mile; £.

This family-owned Victorian country house, built for a photographer to the Royal family, is set in an acre of lovely gardens and grounds, with magnificent views across the Avon valley. Extensively refurbished, the house retains many original features, and offers tastefully furnished rooms with all the modern comforts of a good hotel — en suite bath/shower, direct-dial telephone, radio, colour television and tea/coffee facilities in all rooms. Four-poster and ground floor rooms available. The reception rooms are delightful and include a conservatory for guests. One of the important features is the personal care and attention given by David and Susan Keeling, creating a country house atmosphere near and convenient to Bath city centre. *ETB Highly Commended, AA QQQQ Selected, RAC Highly Acclaimed, Les Routiers.* **See also Colour Advertisement on page 10.**

STON EASTON PARK,
Ston Easton, Near Bath,
Somerset BA3 4DF

Tel: 01761 241631
Fax: 01761 241377

Residential and table licence; 20 bedrooms, all with private bathrooms; Historic interest; Children by arrangement, pets not allowed in bedrooms or public rooms; Leisure and conference facilities; Midsomer Norton 3 miles; ££££.

Here is luxury personified, for this grand Listed Grade I Palladian mansion has undergone extensive restoration to recapture the elegance and splendour of the 18th century. It possesses some of the most exceptional architectural and decorative features of its period to be found in the West Country. Under the sympathetic aegis of owners, Peter and Christine Smedley, this is now one of the most distinguished hotels in the country and is well recognised as such. The bedrooms, renowned for their rich and tasteful furnishings, are splendidly appointed and each has a superb bathroom en suite, colour television, radio and telephone. Several rooms have four-poster beds and accommodation is also available in the delightful Gardener's and Riverside Suites set in the beautiful and tranquil grounds, part of the encompassing classical parkland designed by Humphry Repton in 1793. The cuisine is superb; a tempting variety of English and French dishes served in an elegant restaurant that was once the old parlour, whilst the cellars are stocked with a fine selection of rare wines and old vintages. Children of seven years and upwards and babes in arms are welcome but by prior arrangement with the General Manager. Kennelling for dogs is available free of charge subject to prior arrangement but dogs are not allowed in bedrooms or public rooms. *AA Four Red Stars, Egon Ronay Hotel of the Year 1982, Good Food Guide, Good Hotel Guide.*

DASSELS COUNTRY HOUSE,
Dulverton,
Somerset TA22 9RZ

Tel: 01398 341203
Fax: 01398 341561

Restaurant and residential licence; 10 bedrooms, all with private bathrooms; Children and pets welcome; Tiverton 10 miles; £.

Monarch of all it surveys, this fine, Georgian-style house gazes far out over the secret slopes of Exmoor towards Dartmoor in the distance: a haven of tranquillity in 9 acres of glorious grounds with access to a spectacular landscape where fresh air and freedom will soon refresh jaded spirits. The superb, home-cooked food will also play an important part in the rejuvenation process from the full English breakfast to the mouth-watering sweets. A cosy country house with a delightful lounge (with colour television and a log fire in cool weather), Dassels has charmingly appointed guest rooms of single, double, twin and family size, all with en suite facilities, colour television and tea and coffee-makers. The great escape. ♛♛♛ *Commended, AA QQQQ.*

COMBE HOUSE HOTEL,
Holford, Bridgwater,
Somerset TA5 1RZ

Tel and Fax: 01278 741382*

19 bedrooms, 17 with private bathrooms; Restaurant and residential licence; Historic interest; Children welcome, pets by arrangement; Leisure facilities; Nether Stowey 3 miles; £.

Butterfly Combe lies in the lee of a wooded hill in the heart of the Quantocks. In this tranquil and almost secret place nestles this beautifully furnished 17th century house. We state 'almost secret' because it has been our pleasure to sing the praises of Combe House since a number of years back. A delightful retreat, this one-time tannery still retains its water wheel and, in recent years, contemporary conveniences have been added to fine period furniture and antiques; thus a charming mixture of ancient and modern. 3 acres of well-tended grounds surround the house with a hard tennis court and a heated indoor pool for the use of guests. Excellent food, cosy comforts and good, old fashioned service complete a picture of carefree contentment. ♛♛♛ *Highly Commended, AA and RAC **.*

DEVONSHIRE ARMS HOTEL,
Long Sutton, Near Langport,
Somerset TA10 9LP

Tel: 01458 241271
Fax. 01458 241037

Fully licensed; 9 bedrooms, all with private bathrooms; Historic interest; Children welcome; Somerton 2 miles; ££.

Built in 1787 as a hunting lodge for the Duke of Devonshire, this is an old acquaintance we have seen upgraded to luxury hotel class. Its wayside inn character still casts its spell in its traditional bars where an extensive bar menu complements good ale, whilst one may dine formally and well in a neat and tidy restaurant acclaimed for its excellent cuisine. We are always happy to return to this lovely part of the tranquil Somerset countryside with so much of historic, sporting and geographic interest near at hand. Single, double and family rooms provide the most comfortable accommodation, all the centrally heated rooms having en suite facilities, colour television and tea-makers. ♛♛♛ *Commended.*

BATCH COUNTRY HOUSE HOTEL,
Lympsham, Near Weston-super-Mare, Somerset BS24 0EX

Tel: 01934 750371*
Fax: 01934 750501

Restaurant and residential licence; 10 bedrooms, all with private bathrooms; Historic interest; Children welcome; Weston-super-Mare 5 miles, Burnham-on-Sea 4; £.

Set in its own grounds, Batch Country House Hotel is a peaceful haven and is ideally situated for all the local beaches, National Trust properties and five local golf courses (one championship). All 10 bedrooms are en suite with television etc, and are of a high standard with panoramic views of the Mendip Hills or surrounding countryside. In the spacious dining room with its exposed beams guests can choose from either table d'hôte or à la carte menus with an extensive wine list. There are three comfortable lounges, also a well stocked lounge bar. Cheddar, Wells, Longleat and Bath are all within easy reach; easy access from the M5 to Weston-super-Mare and Burnham-on-Sea. Short Breaks available. *AA**, RAC **, Egon Ronay, Ashley Courtenay.* **See also Colour Advertisement on page 9.**

THE BEACON COUNTRY HOUSE HOTEL,
Beacon Road, Minehead, Somerset TA24 5SD

Tel: 01643 703476
Fax: 01643 702668

Residential and restaurant licence; 8 bedrooms, all with private bathrooms; Historic interest; Pets welcome, children by arrangement; Leisure facilities; Dunster 2 miles; £££.

In twenty acres of grounds backing onto the rolling moorland of Exmoor, Beacon Country House Hotel stands high above Minehead with fine views of the coastline. Here is perfect seclusion and tranquillity and the opportunity to study at first hand the area's abundant wildlife — red deer, buzzards and even badgers, who regularly feed on the lawns. The elegant and spacious guest rooms all have en suite bathroom, colour television, radio and direct-dial telephone, and afford splendid views of the surrounding countryside. Dining in the attractive restaurant proves a memorable experience, each dish carefully prepared and complemented by a selection of fine wines, including a notable Australasian range. And if one has over-indulged, a few leisurely lengths in the outdoor swimming pool might help redress the balance, or perhaps a brisk walk along the coastal footpath. Other activities such as riding, fishing and rambling can be arranged with prior notice. Built originally as a hunting lodge for an Edwardian whisky magnate, the Beacon epitomises today the elegance and style of that more gracious era. *Johansens Recommended.*

DANESWOOD HOUSE HOTEL,
Cuck Hill, Shipham, Near Winscombe, Somerset BS25 1RD

Tel: 01934 843145
Fax: 01934 843824

Fully licensed; 13 bedrooms, all with private bathrooms; Historic interest; Children welcome, dogs by arrangement; Conference facilities; Cheddar 3 miles; £££.

High up in the Mendips and only two miles from the Cheddar Caves, this imposing Edwardian building has been transformed into a charming country house hotel under the inspired aegis of proprietors, David and Elise Hodges, who set great store by their first-class and imaginative cuisine. Traditional English and French dishes are combined with more adventurous influences, all admirably supported by a well-chosen list of wines and liqueurs. The accommodation is delightfully modernised without detriment to its original elegance, rooms being decorated to a high standard and featuring private baths and/or showers. Of special note is the magnificent Honeymoon Suite, with a 7ft bed and large bathroom with sunken bath. *WCTB ♛♛♛♛ Highly Commended, AA*** and Two Rosettes.*

HIGHER DIPFORD FARM, Trull, Taunton, Somerset TA3 7NU

Tel: 01823 275770

3 bedrooms, all with private bathroom; Children welcome; Taunton 2½ miles.

This dairy farm is situated two and a half miles from Taunton and accommodation is available in the 600-year old farmhouse, which has many exposed elm beams and inglenook fireplaces. All bedrooms have en suite showers/bathrooms. Guests will enjoy delicious home cooking, with fresh produce from the farm and garden — all helped down by a jug of local cider! Please contact Mrs Maureen Fewings for further details. ♛♛♛ *Commended, AA QQQQ.* **See also Colour Advertisement on page 9.**

DUNKERY BEACON HOTEL, Wootton Courtenay, Somerset TA24 8RH

Tel: 01643 841241

Fully licensed; 20 bedrooms, all with private bathrooms; Children and pets welcome; £.

Dunkery Beacon Hotel enjoys a fabulous unrivalled setting in the beautiful Exmoor National Park, near Dunster and Porlock. The superb views can be absorbed at leisure from the terrace or from the lawns and gardens. All rooms are fully en suite, with colour television and tea and coffee making facilities. Pets are welcome free of charge, and there are lots of lovely "walkies". Special Bargain Breaks are available — write or telephone for details.

* The appearance of an asterisk after the telephone number indicates that the hotel in question is closed for a period during the winter months. Exact dates should be ascertained from the hotel itself.

HOLBROOK HOUSE HOTEL,
Holbrook, Near Wincanton,
Somerset BA9 8BS

Tel: 01963 32377
Fax: 01963 32681

Fully licensed; 22 bedrooms, 17 with private bathrooms; Historic interest; Children and pets welcome; Leisure and conference facilities; Yeovil 12 miles; £.

It is a proud boast of the owners, that this charming house overlooking the Blackmoor Vale has multiplied its clientele over the years by personal recommendation. We first came across this characterful house when visiting Wincanton races. We certainly picked a winner! The hotel stands in splendid grounds of 15 acres. The old orchard is the delightful location of a heated swimming pool and the cider house adjoining is the club house and bar. Adjacent to the house is a grass tennis court and croquet lawn. Behind the pleasing facade lie conveniences, comforts and culinary creations that would flatter a many-starred establishment with the added benefit of a friendly, informal and, even cosy, ambience. 👑👑👑, *AA**, RAC** and Merit Award.*

Staffordshire

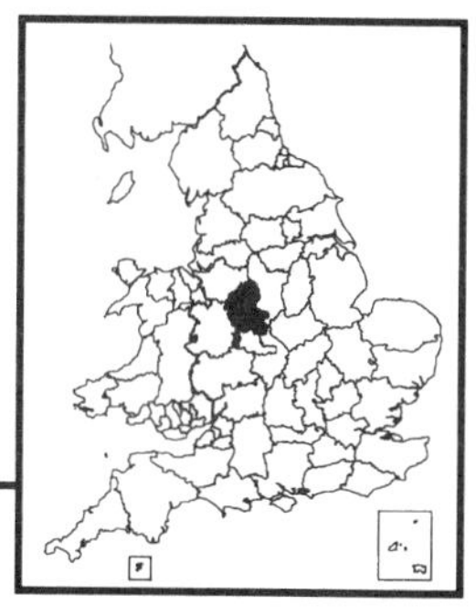

JARVIS NEWTON PARK HOTEL,
Newton Solney, Near Burton-upon-Trent,
Staffordshire DE15 0SS

Tel: 01283 703568
Fax: 01283 703214

Fully licensed; 50 bedrooms, all with private bathrooms; Historic interest; Children and small dogs welcome; Conference facilities; Burton-upon-Trent 3 miles; ££££.

Discerning travellers who expect that little bit more will find everything very much to their satisfaction at Jarvis Newton Park. Of great architectural interest, this fine Grade II Listed property has been sympathetically converted to provide comfortable en suite accommodation in bedrooms and suites with colour television, direct-dial telephone and a choice of hot beverages. Modern English cuisine, carefully prepared from the freshest ingredients, has made the oak-panelled restaurant a popular venue, while lighter appetites are catered for in the Club Bar. Set in carefully tended gardens just three miles from Burton-upon-Trent, Jarvis Newton Park is well placed for access to the road, rail and air networks. 👑👑👑👑 *Commended.*

STONE HOUSE HOTEL,
Stone,
Staffordshire ST15 0BQ

Tel: 01785 815531
Fax: 01785 814764

Fully licensed; 47 bedrooms, all with private bathrooms; Children welcome; Leisure and conference facilities; Stafford 7 miles; ££££.

Easily reached from the M6, this eminently comfortable and convivial hotel is popular with tourists and businessmen alike, whilst refugees from the urban Midlands regularly make it a haven of escape at weekends.The elegant Garden Restaurant overlooks lovely grounds and offers a tempting selection of à la carte dishes, a prior visit to the spruce cocktail bar being an added joy. Charming furnishings betray a gifted eye for colour co-ordination, and guest rooms have private bathrooms, television with satellite channels, direct-dial telephone and beverage makers. Many guests are attracted by the leisure and exercise facilities in the form of mini-gym, swimming pool, sauna and solarium, whist tennis and putting may be enjoyed in the grounds. *AA/RAC* ***.

Key toTourist Board Ratings

The Crown Scheme
(England, Scotland & Wales)

Covering hotels, motels, private hotels, guesthouses, inns, bed & breakfast, farmhouses. Every Crown classified place to stay is inspected annually. *The classification*: Listed then 1-5 Crown indicates the range of facilities and services. Higher quality standards are indicated by the terms APPROVED, COMMENDED, HIGHLY COMMENDED and DELUXE.

The Key Scheme
(also operates in Scotland using a Crown System)

Covering self-catering in cottages, bungalows, flats, houseboats, houses, chalets, etc. Every Key classified holiday home is inspected annually. *The classification*: 1-5 Key indicates the range of facilities and equipment. Higher quality standards are indicated by the terms APPROVED, COMMENDED, HIGHLY COMMENDED and DELUXE.

The Q Scheme
(England, Scotland & Wales)

Covering holiday, caravan, chalet and camping parks. Every Q rated park is inspected annually for its quality standards. The more ✔ in the Q – up to 5 – the higher the standard of what is provided.

Suffolk

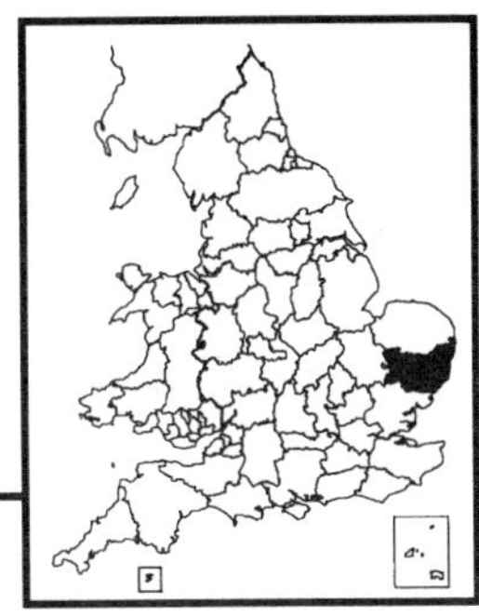

WOOD HALL HOTEL AND COUNTRY CLUB,

Shottisham, Woodbridge, Tel: 01394 411283
Suffolk IP12 3EG Fax: 01394 410007

Fully licensed; 15 bedrooms, all with private bathrooms; Historic interest; Children and pets welcome; Leisure and conference facilities; Woodbridge 4 miles; £££.

Our Elizabethan forebears would still recognise this grand 16th century manor house although its contemporary appointments would occasion no little wonder and delight. Fittingly, for modern Elizabethans, our reactions were the same. Ensconced in magnificent grounds of 10 acres complete with a picturesque lake, the Hall has a serene air about it as befits its idyllic situation in the Suffolk countryside. Now a country hotel of distinction, it boasts guest rooms that are an interior designer's delight, all blessed with en suite facilities, satellite television, direct-dial telephone, radio and tea and coffee-makers. There are no less than three superb restaurants in which one may dine memorably by candlelight. ♛♛♛♛ *Highly Commended, AA***, Les Routiers.*

East Sussex

POWDERMILLS HOTEL,
Powdermill Lane, Battle,
East Sussex TN33 0SP

Tel: 01424 775511
Fax: 01424 774540

Restaurant and residential licence; 35 bedrooms, all with private bathrooms; Historic interest; Children and pets welcome; Leisure and conference facilities; Hastings 6 miles; £££.

This spacious Listed Georgian country house hotel is situated in 150 acres of grounds, formerly part of the Battle Abbey estate, which are a naturalist's delight. The tranquillity of this beautiful setting is completed by a superb seven-acre fishing lake. A large outdoor swimming pool is available for guests, and golf and riding can be arranged locally. All the tastefully decorated bedrooms (two with four-poster beds) have luxury en suite bathrooms, colour television and direct-dial telephone, and in the public rooms crackling log fires in cooler weather and carefully selected antiques create a most relaxing ambience. Fine classical cuisine is served in the Orangery Restaurant, which is open to non-residents.The hotel has large conference facilities and is an ideal venue for weddings.The historic towns of Battle and Rye are close by, and there are many National Trust properties and other places of interest in the area. AA *** and Rosette, RAC *** and Merit Award, *Les Routiers 1996 Hotel of the Year.*

The **£** symbol when appearing at the end of the italic section of an entry shows the anticipated price, during 1997, for single full Bed and Breakfast.

Under £40	**£**	**Over £55 but under £70**	**£££**
Over £40 but under £55	**££**	**Over £70**	**££££**

This is meant as an indication only and does not show prices for Special Breaks, Weekends, etc. Guests are therefore advised to verify all prices on enquiring or booking.

NETHERFIELD PLACE HOTEL, Battle, East Sussex TN33 9PP

Tel: 01424 774455*
Fax: 01424 774024

Fully licensed; 14 bedrooms, all with private bathrooms; Children welcome, small dogs by arrangement; Leisure and conference facilities; Battle 3 miles; £££.

Under the direct supervision of Helen and Michael Collier, Netherfield Place offers luxuries that are simple yet sophisticated — true worth in every aspect, with, perhaps, the superb cuisine claiming pride of place. Fruit and vegetables are culled daily from the walled kitchen gardens and there is a memorable wine list featuring over 250 bins. A pleasant cocktail bar adjoins the dining room and a terrace overlooks beautiful gardens which extend to 30 acres. Here all is tranquillity and good living, and for the active opportunities exist locally for golf, tennis, squash, riding, fishing or just walking. Always there is the promise of sweet repose in magnificently equipped guest rooms at the end of the day. ♛♛♛♛ *De Luxe. RAC Blue Ribbon, AA Three Red Stars and Two Rosettes.*

BEAUPORT PARK HOTEL Battle Road, Hastings, East Sussex TN38 8EA

Tel: 01424 851222
Fax: 01424 852465

Licensed; 16 double bedrooms, 7 single, all with bathrooms; Leisure facilities; Battle 3 miles, Hastings 3; ££.

This fine three-star country house hotel, set amidst 33 acres of woodland and picturesque formal gardens, offers old-fashioned personal service from resident directors Kenneth and Helena Melsom. All guest rooms have private bathrooms and are equipped with remote-control colour television, electric trouser press, direct-dial telephone, hairdryer and tea/coffee making facilities. There is a heated swimming pool in the grounds, country walks, tennis courts, croquet lawn, badminton, outdoor chess, French boules and putting green, with an 18-hole golf course, riding stables and squash courts adjoining. Prospective guests are invited to write or telephone for brochure and tariff, and a country house bargain breaks leaflet. "Country House Getaway Breaks" are available all year. ♛♛♛♛, *AA and RAC****.

CLEAVERS LYNG COUNTRY HOTEL,
Church Road, Herstmonceux,
East Sussex BN27 1QJ

Tel: 01323 833131
Fax: 01323 833617

Fully licensed; 8 bedrooms, Historic interest; Children and pets welcome; Eastbourne, Bexhill and Hastings all 11 miles; £.

For excellent home cooking in traditional English style, comfort and informality, this small family-run hotel in the heart of rural East Sussex is well recommended. It is peacefully set in beautiful landscaped gardens extending to 1.5 acres featuring an ornamental rockpool with waterfall. Adjacent to Hertmonceux Castle West Gate, the house dates from 1577, as its oak beams and inglenook fireplace bear witness. This is an ideal retreat for a quiet sojourn away from urban clamour. The castles at Pevensey, Scotney, Bodiam and Hever are all within easy reach, as are Battle Abbey, Batemans (home of Rudyard Kipling), Michelham Priory, and the seaside resorts of Eastbourne, Bexhill and Hastings. Bedrooms are fully en suite, and all have central heating and tea/coffee making facilities; some have a separate sitting area with colour television. On the ground floor there is an oak-beamed restaurant with a fully licensed bar, cosy residents' lounge with television, and an outer hall with telephone and cloakrooms. Cleavers Lyng does not have any single rooms; however at certain times of the year we offer a reduced single occupancy rate for a double/twin bedroom. At Cleavers Lyng we observe a strict non-smoking policy in our restaurant and television lounge. Smoking is permitted in the lounge bar. Peace, tranquillity and a warm welcome await you. Special attraction: Badger Watch. Amex, Visa and Mastercard accepted. **See also Colour Advertisement on page 10.**

THE ROSE & CROWN INN,
Mayfield,
East Sussex TN20 6TE

Tel and Fax: 01435 872200

Licensed; Bedrooms with private bathrooms; Historic interest; Children over 7 years welcome; Tunbridge Wells 8 miles; ££/£££.

This famous inn sits on the village green of the historic and picturesque village of Mayfield. Dating back to 1546, its unspoilt oak-beamed bars with log fires serve excellent real ales and quality bar meals, or you may choose to dine in the informal candlelit restaurant which serves award-winning food and excellent wines. Each luxury period bedroom has en suite bathroom, central heating, colour television, radio alarm, hairdryer, tea and coffee making facilities and trouser press. ♛♛♛♛ *Commended, AA QQQQ Selected and Rosette for Food, Egon Ronay.*

FAIRSEAT HOUSE,
Newick, Near Lewes,
East Sussex BN8 4PJ

Tel: 01825 722263

Unlicensed; 3 bedrooms, all with private bathrooms; Leisure facilities; Haywards Heath 5 miles, Uckfield 4; £.

This elegant Edwardian house enjoys rural aspects yet is within easy reach of main routes, the South Coast and Gatwick Airport, and is convenient for Glyndebourne Opera, Sussex gardens and the Bluebell Railway. Open fires, buttoned chesterfields, a four-poster bed, ancestral portraits and antique books are just part of the warm welcome that Roy and Carol Pontifex have to offer. On summer evenings, the south-facing terrace is perfect for relaxing, perhaps after a swim in the heated covered swimming pool, while in winter, open fires create a wonderfully cosy atmosphere. Meals are based on the best of local produce, with home-grown vegetables in season. The en suite bedrooms are spacious and prettily decorated, and there is a sitting room for guests. *SEETB Listed Highly Commended, AA QQQQQ Premier Selected.* **See also Colour Advertisement on page 11.**

JEAKE'S HOUSE HOTEL,
Mermaid Street, Rye,
East Sussex TN31 7ET

Tel: 01797 222828
Fax: 01797 222623

Residential licence; 12 bedrooms, 10 with private bathrooms; Historic interest; Children and pets welcome; Hastings 9 miles; £.

Dating from 1689, Jeake's House stands on one of the most beautiful cobbled streets in Rye's medieval town centre. Each stylishly restored bedroom with brass, mahogany or four-poster bed combines traditional elegance and luxury with every modern comfort. A roaring fire greets you on cold mornings in the elegant galleried chapel, which is now the dining room. Choosing either a traditional or vegetarian breakfast, the soft chamber music, airy setting and unhurried atmosphere will provide the perfect start to any day. There is a comfortable sitting room and bar with books and pictures lining the walls. ♛♛ *Highly Commended, AA QQQQQ Premier Selected, RAC Highly Acclaimed, Good Hotel Guide César Award.* **See also Colour Advertisement on page 11.**

RYE LODGE HOTEL,
Hilder's Cliff, Rye,
East Sussex TN31 7LD

Tel: 01797 223838
Fax: 01797 223585

Fully licensed; 15 bedrooms, all with private bathrooms or shower rooms; Children and pets welcome; Hastings 9 miles; ££.

This delightful hotel enjoys superb estuary views, yet is conveniently situated adjacent to the High Street of this ancient Cinque Port town, with the monastery and historic 14th century Landgate nearby. The elegant de luxe rooms, each named after a French wine region, are tastefully furnished; room service is available. Guests can enjoy candlelit dinners, with delicious food and fine wines. Private car park. This is the stylish place to stay when visiting this fascinating area. Short Break packages are available — details on request. ♛♛♛♛ *Highly Commended.* **See also Colour Advertisement on page 11.**

PLEASE MENTION THIS GUIDE WHEN YOU WRITE OR PHONE TO ENQUIRE ABOUT ACCOMMODATION. IF YOU ARE WRITING, A STAMPED, ADDRESSED ENVELOPE IS ALWAYS APPRECIATED.

LITTLE ORCHARD HOUSE,
West Street, Rye,
East Sussex TN31 7ES

Tel: 01791 223831

3 bedrooms, all with private bathrooms; Historic interest; London 67 miles, Canterbury 33, Battle 14, Tenterden 12; ££.

Rye is the most complete small medieval hill town in Britain, and this charming Georgian townhouse is a delightful surprise right at the heart of the Ancient Town, quietly situated in the picturesque cobbled streets with a traditional walled Old English garden and its unique Smugglers Watch Tower. Each bedroom, one with traditional four-poster, has a bathroom en suite, colour television, and hot drinks making facilities. The house is stylishly decorated and furnished with antiques throughout, lots of books, paintings and an open fire in winter. Guests will enjoy a generous country breakfast which features as much local, organic produce as possible, and a good choice of outstanding restaurants are within easy walking distance. ♛♛ *Highly Commended.*

West Sussex

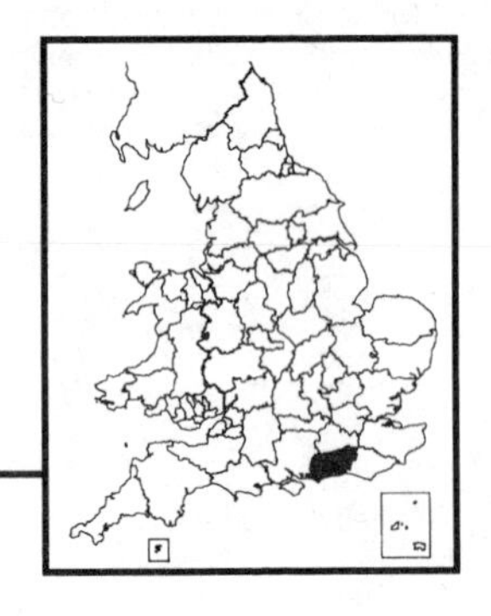

BURPHAM COUNTRY HOTEL,
Old Down, Burpham, Near Arundel,
West Sussex BN18 9RJ

Tel: 01903 882160
Fax: 01903 884627

Residential and restaurant licence; 10 bedrooms, all with private bathrooms; Historic interest; Children over 10 welcome; Conference facilities; Littlehampton 4 miles; ££.

In a picturesque, unspoilt English village complete with historic church, inn and green with cricket pitch, this lovely country house stands in an old world garden enjoying superb views over the South Downs. Reputedly a hunting lodge for the Duke of Norolk, it retains its warm ambience, but to its gracious style modern touches have been added without spoiling its elegance. The spacious en suite bedrooms are delightfully appointed, each having colour television, tea-maker, and direct-dial telephone. The charming licensed restaurant with its splendid table d'hôte menu and excellent wine list is open to non-residents, and vegetarian dishes are available. There are facilities for small functions, business meetings and seminars. ♛♛♛ *Highly Commended, AA** and Rosette, Johansens, Logis of GB.*

MILLSTREAM HOTEL & RESTAURANT,
Bosham, Chichester, West Sussex PO18 8HL

Tel: 01243 573234
Fax: 01243 573459

Restaurant and residential licence; 29 bedrooms, all with private bathrooms; Historic interest; Children welcome, pets in bedrooms only; Chichester 4 miles; £££.

Idyllically situated in a picturesque sailing village on the shores of Chichester Harbour, this homely country house possesses all the credentials for a relaxing holiday in an atmosphere reminiscent of a more leisurely age. For all that, the amenities here lack nothing in terms of modern sophistication and they blend with subtle deference to period style furnishings. Each of the well appointed guest rooms is individually decorated, and public rooms include a sumptuous drawing room with grand piano, and the delightful Malthouse Bar which leads on to a pretty garden complete with its own stream. Dining by candlelight in the restaurant prompts fond memories of exciting and beautifully prepared dishes, exotic sweets and fine vintage wines. ♛♛♛♛ *Highly Commended, AA *** and Food Rosette, RAC ***.*

GHYLL MANOR,
Rusper, Near Horsham, West Sussex RH12 4PX

Tel: 01293 871571
Fax: 01293 871419

Fully licensed; 24 bedrooms, all with private bathrooms; Historic interest; Children and pets welcome; Leisure and conference facilities; Crawley 4 miles; £££/££££.

A superb base from which to explore the South Downs, Sussex coast or the myriad attractions of London, Ghyll Manor combines the elegance of the past with the exacting requirements of the modern age. The accommodation may be termed fairly as luxurious. Suites have been individually furnished and decorated and there is a four-poster apartment which has an inglenook fireplace and magnificent views and which is a favourite with honeymoon couples. Each guest room is equipped to the highest standard with private bathroom, colour television, radio, and direct-dial telephone. The restaurant has an enviable reputation for its fine cuisine, table d'hôte and à la carte menus being available for luncheon and dinner. The Manor has first-class facilities for conferences and private functions. ♛♛♛♛♛, *AA**** and Rosette.*

Midhurst, West Sussex

CHEQUERS HOTEL,
Pulborough,
West Sussex RH20 1AD

Tel: 01798 872486
Fax: 01798 872715

Residential and restaurant licence; 11 bedrooms, all with private bathrooms; Historic interest; Children and dogs welcome; London 49 miles, Brighton 19, Arundel 9; ££.

Tastefully extended over the years, the original Queen Anne house huddles on the edge of Pulborough village, gazing peacefully out over the Arun Valley to the South Downs beyond. Excellent home-cooked dishes using local produce and fresh vegetables have given Chequers its reputation for fine cuisine. Accommodation is comfortable and well appointed with private bathrooms, and also includes colour television, direct-dial telephone, trouser press, hairdryer and tea/coffee facilities. Four-poster bedrooms and ground floor bedrooms also available. Open fires make this as pleasant a holiday venue in winter as it is in summer. Places to visit include Parham, Petworth, Goodwood, Arundel, Chichester and the Weald & Downland Open Air Museum. New garden conservatory. BARGAIN BREAKS are available throughout the year. *ETB ♛♛♛♛ Highly Commended, RAC **, AA ** and Rosette, Ashley Courtenay, Egon Ronay and Johansens Recommended.*

Warwickshire

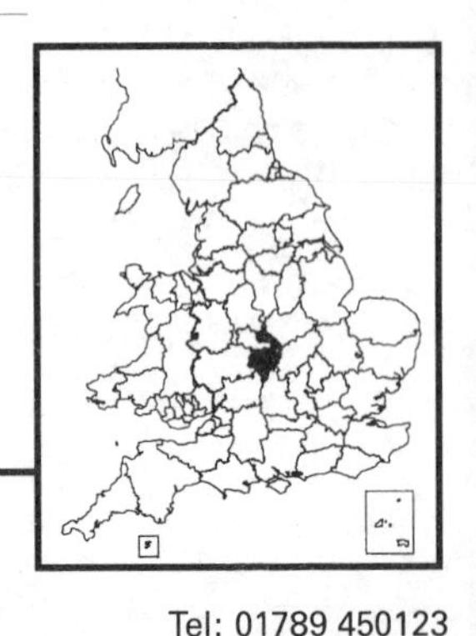

ETTINGTON PARK,
Alderminster, Stratford-upon-Avon,
Warwickshire CV37 8BU

Tel: 01789 450123
Fax: 01789 450472

Licensed; 48 bedrooms, all with private bathrooms; Historic interest; Children welcome; Leisure and conference facilities; Stratford-upon-Avon 7 miles; ££££.

Set in 40 acres of parkland in the heart of the lovely Warwickshire countryside, Ettington Park represents the very epitome of English country house elegance and grandeur. A gracious atmosphere greets guests in all the public rooms, from the imposing Oak Room Restaurant with its hand-carved wooden friezes to the intimate Chapel Room with fine stained glass windows. This sumptuous elegance extends to the individually decorated bedrooms, with their superb views, luxurious bathrooms, antiques and original paintings. Imaginative menus feature French and English cuisine of the highest quality, with accompanying wines to suit every palate. Leisure facilities which include tennis, horse riding and indoor heated pool are of the same high standard. *AA ****, AA Most Haunted Hotel in Britain.*

CHAPEL HOUSE HOTEL & RESTAURANT,
**Friar's Gate, Atherstone,
Warwickshire CV9 lEY**

Tel: 01827 718949
Fax: 01827 717702

Residential and restaurant licence; 10 bedrooms, all with private bathrooms; Historic interest; Children welcome (hotel); Conference facilities; Nuneaton 5 miles; ££.

With a well-deserved reputation for the excellence of its accommodation, food and overall comfort, this one-time Dower House is beautifully furnished and retains the ambience and many of the features of its 18th century origins. A handsome reminder that size isn't everything, this is a fine example of an intimate small English hotel where customer care is the prime consideration. Owners, David and Pat Roberts, extend a warm welcome to guests and are responsible for the appealing decor and imaginative, delightfully presented cuisine. Tucked away in a corner of the Market Square and set in a large walled garden, the lovely old house also provides very good facilities for meetings and private functions. *AA ** and Two Rosettes.*

NAILCOTE HALL HOTEL,
**Nailcote Lane, Berkswell,
Warwickshire CV7 7DE**

Tel: 01203 466174
Fax: 01203 470270

Fully licensed; 38 bedrooms, all with private bathrooms; Historic interest; Children welcome; Leisure and conference facilities; Coventry 6 miles; ££££.

Dating from the sixteenth century, Nailcote Hall has a long and fascinating history— a dwelling has existed on the site since the days of the Norman Conquest. Restoration and alterations have been made over the years, retaining its character while providing all the amenities one would expect in such a superior establishment. Attentive service; comfortable bedrooms, all with private bathroom, colour television and direct-dial telephone; imaginative menus freshly prepared from the finest ingredients, and superb leisure facilities combine to ensure that a stay here, whether on business or relaxing in the beautiful countryside, will be an experience to savour. ♛♛♛♛, *RAC ***, AA **** and Two Rosettes.*

AYLESBURY HOUSE HOTEL,
**Packwood, Near Hockley Heath,
Warwickshire B94 6PL**

Tel: 01564 779207
Fax: 01564 770917

Residential licence; 34 bedrooms, all with private bathrooms; Historic interest; Children and pets welcome; Leisure and conference facilities; Coventry 4 miles; £££.

Built in the time of the Stuarts and with several features added in subsequent centuries, Aylesbury House is not only architecturally fascinating; today it is a supremely comfortable hotel, conveniently located for many places of cultural, sporting and historic interest. In addition, it is of considerable attraction to businessmen. Set in 12 acres of grounds, the hotel has 6 spacious guest rooms in the main house and 28 cottage bedrooms across the courtyard. Each has en suite bath or shower room, satellite television, radio, telephone, hairdryer, trouser press and tea and coffee making facilities. Taking its name from the ancient tree on the croquet lawn, the elegant Mulberry Restaurant is a popular venue for discerning diners. ♛♛♛♛, *AA****.*

PUBLISHER'S NOTE

While every effort is made to ensure accuracy, we regret that FHG Publications cannot accept responsibility for errors, omissions or misrepresentations in our entries or any consequences thereof. Prices in particular should be checked because we go to press early. We will follow up complaints but cannot act as arbiters or agents for either party.

WELCOMBE HOTEL & GOLF COURSE,
Warwick Road, Stratford-upon-Avon, Tel: 01789 295252
Warwickshire CV37 0NR Fax: 01789 414666

Fully licensed; 75 bedrooms, all with private bathrooms; Children welcome; Leisure and conference facilities; Warwick 8 miles; ££££

This magnificent Jacobean-style mansion of late Victorian origin enjoys a tranquil situation just a mile and a half from Shakespeare's Stratford. Cultural attractions vie here with sporting ones, for the hotel boasts a fine 18-hole golf course and two all-weather tennis courts; riding, fishing and boating can all be arranged nearby. High ornate ceilings, chandeliers and a grand period staircase are features of the public rooms, and the bedrooms and suites are furnished with consummate style, incorporating the most up-to-date conveniences. This is a haven of peace and relaxation set in beautiful countryside, with the added blessing of a superb restaurant where the menus present the very best of English and French specialities, augmented by an excellent cellar. 👑👑👑👑👑, *AA **** and Two Rosettes.*

West Midlands

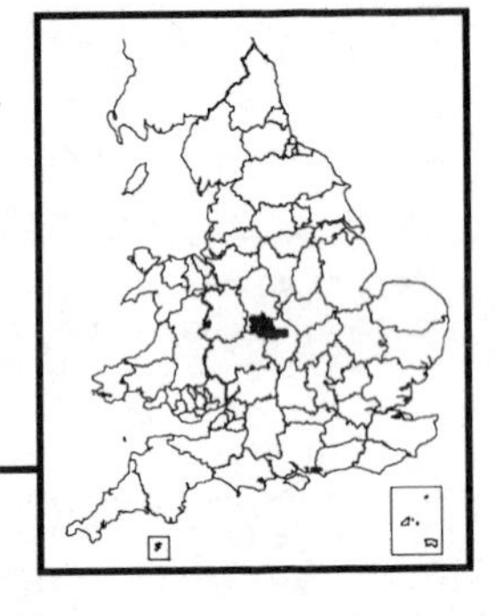

COOMBE ABBEY,
Brinklow Road, Binley, Coventry, Tel: 01203 450450
West Midlands CV3 2AB Fax: 01203 635101

Fully licensed; 63 bedrooms, all with private bathrooms; Historic interest; Children welcome; Conference facilities; Birmingham 17 miles; ££££.

A most unusual holiday venue of considerable historic appeal, this fascinating Cistercian abbey dates from the 11th century. It has a glorious setting in the heart of 500 acres of parkland laid out, in the main, by Capability Brown. The formal gardens and 80-acre lake take the eye and as one crosses the moÂat and passes through the cloistered entrance one is immediately aware of a time-hallowed ambience. Rich furnishings crowd upon each other to pay homage in their efforts to recapture the romance of bygone days. The present owners have left no (flag)stone unturned in exploiting the historic potential. As 'No Ordinary Hotel', the abbey bids one seek repose in flamboyant bedchambers, albeit equipped with the most contemporary facilities. One dines here in some style. The brochure appropriately quotes from Milton - "And pomp and feast and revelry. With mask and antique pageantry", which is brought to life through the Medieval Banquets and Old Time Music Hall performances that are held regularly. The 'everyday' cuisine is worthy of better description for it is certainly of a very high standard. The chef-created menus exhibit originality and meals are made even more memorable by the attentions of a caring staff.

Wiltshire

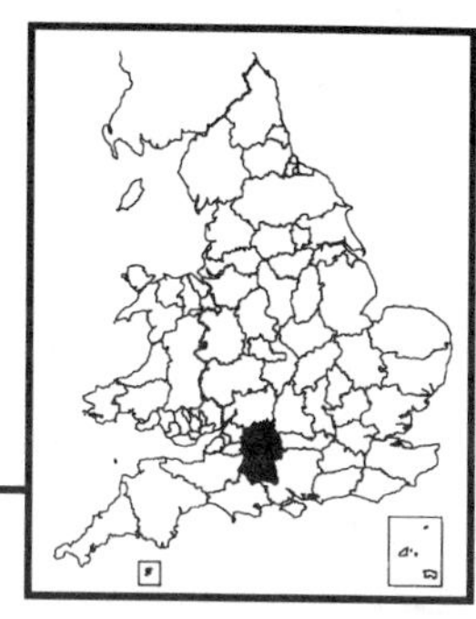

THE MANOR HOUSE HOTEL,
Castle Combe, Chippenham,
Wiltshire SN14 7HR

Tel: 01249 782206
Fax: 01249 782159

Fully licensed; 41 bedrooms, all with private bathrooms; Historic interest; Children welcome; Leisure and conference facilities; Bath 12 miles, Chippenham 6; ££££.

A baronial seat since the fourteenth century, the Manor House is set in 26 acres of lawns and parkland, where the trout-stocked River Bybrook bordering the lawn flows towards the village of Castle Combe, one of the prettiest in England. In this enchanting setting guests may take advantage of modern comforts while revelling in the unhurried atmosphere of days gone by. The elegant restaurant features the best of English and Continental cuisine, accompanied by a selection of fine vintages from the extensive cellars. Accommodation, tastefully furnished in period style with many antiques, is luxurious and boasts all modern appointments. For outdoor relaxation there is an 18-hole championship golf course, heated pool, tennis court and croquet lawn.

CRUDWELL COURT HOTEL,
Crudwell, Malmesbury,
Wiltshire SN16 9EP

Tel: 01666 577194
Fax: 01666 577853

Restaurant and residential licence; 15 bedrooms, all with private bathrooms; Historic interest; Children and pets welcome; Leisure and conference facilities; Malmesbury 4 miles; ££.

This beautifully refurbished 17th century rectory is set in three acres of lovely walled gardens with lily ponds and a heated outdoor swimming pool. Here the resident owner has created a country house atmosphere, with log fires, excellent cooking and an extensive wine list. The fifteen en suite bedrooms enjoy lovely views of the surrounding garden and farmland, and are equipped with colour television, radio, telephone and tea/coffee making facilities. All cooking is freshly prepared to order, and the panelled dining room overlooking the walled garden is open to non-residents for all meals and light lunches. ♛♛♛♛, *Good Food Guide.*

BISHOPSTROW HOUSE,
Warminster,
Wiltshire BA12 9HH

Tel: 01985 212312
Fax: 01985 216769

Fully licensed; 30 bedrooms, all with private bathrooms; Historic interest; Children and pets welcome; Leisure and conference facilities; Trowbridge 8 miles; ££££.

Recently refurbished in magnificent style, this beautiful Georgian mansion is all grace and favour and everything in its place. Walk or drive through the wrought-iron gates, gaze at the warm stone, creeper-clad facade and step into the central hall and a world of ordered elegance. On all sides, antique furniture and oil paintings add to the ambience with log fires adding warmth. Reached via a grand staircase, luxuriously appointed guest rooms all have a private bathroom, satellite television and telephone; some have jacuzzi whirlpools and audio-entertainment systems. Built in 1817 and an hotel since 1978, the house has surroundings well in keeping with the aesthetic pleasures within; parklike grounds lead down to the River Wylye and feature an intriguing pillared temple and ornamental trees. Sporting facilities abound and especially impressive is the recently-introduced Leisure Spa. There is also a golf course just 1½ miles away and guests may enjoy fly-fishing on the hotel's own stretch of river. The cuisine represents traditional English food at its very best. Longleat House and Safari Park and Wilton House are among several places of historic interest that may be reached within half-an-hour's drive. *AA and RAC* ****.

WHATLEY MANOR,
Near Easton Grey, Malmesbury,
Wiltshire SN16 0RB

Tel: 01666 822888
Fax: 01666 826120

Restaurant and residential licence; 29 bedrooms, all with private bathrooms; Historic interest; Children and pets welcome; Leisure and conference facilities; Malmesbury 3 miles; ££££.

A charming stone-built, creeper-clad manor house dating from the early 18th century, Whatley Manor is set in peaceful gardens, with grounds running down to the banks of the Avon. Accommodation is of a luxury standard, whether in the main building or the adjacent Court House. All rooms have private bathrooms, colour television, radio, direct-dial telephone, hairdryer and tea/coffee making facilities. The superb public rooms, including the book-lined Library Bar, provide a marvellous atmosphere for relaxation and some friendly conversation with one's fellow guests after a delicious meal. Recreational and leisure facilities here are truly outstanding, ranging from croquet and tennis to a solarium and sauna.

East Yorkshire

including East Riding, and Kingston-upon-Hull.

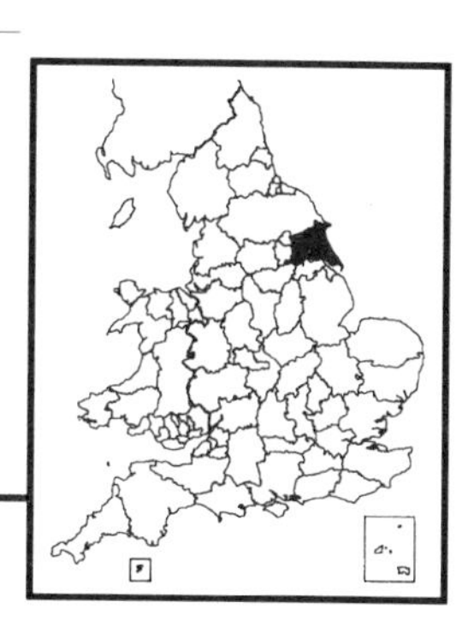

THE MANOR HOUSE,
Northlands, Walkington, Near Beverley,
East Yorkshire HU17 8RT

Tel: 01482 881645
Fax: 01482 866501

Licensed; 7 bedrooms, all with private bathrooms; Children and dogs welcome; Conference facilities; Beverley 3 miles; ££££.

For a quiet, relaxing holiday with a plethora of places of historic and sporting interest near at hand, this distinctive and elegantly furnished late-Victorian house is just the job. It stands on the gentle slopes of the verdant Yorkshire Wolds with York and Lincoln within easy motoring distance and Beverley with its famous minster and racecourse only a canter away. Wining and dining here is a pleasure to savour under the auspices of Derek and Lee Baugh and service is courteous and efficient. The bedrooms are beautifully decorated and appointed with their own luxury bathrooms, colour television, telephone and several other small indulgencies. *Highly Commended, AA**, RAC Small Hotel of the North 1995.*

North Yorkshire

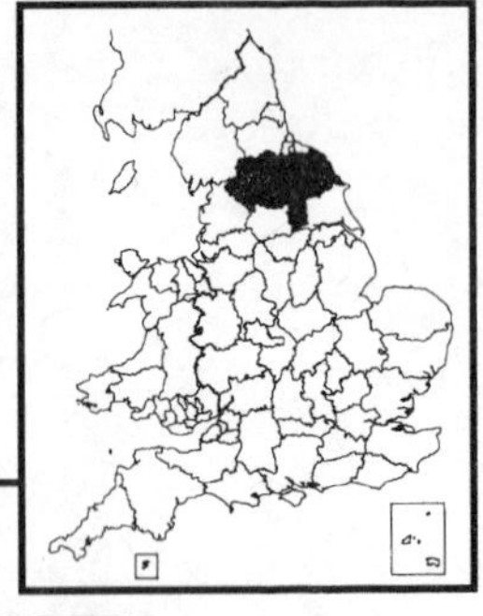

APPLETON HALL COUNTRY HOUSE HOTEL,

Appleton-le-Moors,
North Yorkshire YO6 6TF

Tel: 01751 417227
Fax: 01751 417540

Residential and restaurant licence; 10 bedrooms, all with private bathrooms; Children over 12 years and pets welcome; Pickering 5 miles; ££.

Situated in the North Yorkshire Moors National Park, this elegant Victorian house is set in over two acres of award-winning gardens. The hotel is personally run by the owners, Norma and Graham Davies, and is an ideal base for walking or touring. Offering elegance, comfort and tranquillity at sensible prices, Appleton is a hotel which, having visited, you will certainly wish to return to. ♛♛♛ *Highly Commended, AA Rosette, RAC Merit Award.* **See also Colour Advertisement on page 13.**

ELMFIELD COUNTRY HOUSE,

Arrathorne, Bedale,
North Yorkshire DL8 1NE

Tel: 01677 450558
Fax: 01677 450557

Residential licence; 9 bedrooms, all with private bathrooms; Children welcome; Leisure and conference facilities; Bedale 5 miles; £.

A tranquil oasis far removed from the hurly-burly of urban life, this sprucely-appointed country house, so well run by Jim and Edith Lillie, lies in the heart of Herriot Country. Drink in hand, survey the scenery whilst listening to the calming cadences of the waterfall and all will be right with the world. From full English breakfast to home-cooked evening meal, the cuisine is first-class and the centrally heated bedrooms, all en suite and with colour television, radio/alarm, direct-dial telephone and beverage-making facilities, will ensure comfort, convenience and restful repose. There is a solarium and the young in heart have a games room at their disposal. Not far away is Lightwater Valley Adventure Park with its variety of rides and attractions. ♛♛♛ *Commended, AA QQQQ Selected, RAC Highly Commended.*

PARSONAGE COUNTRY HOUSE HOTEL,

Main Street, Escrick, York,
North YorkshireYO4 6LE

Tel: 01904 728111
Fax: 01904 728151

Fully licensed; 13 bedrooms, all with private bathrooms; Historic interest; Children welcome; Conference facilities; York 6 miles; £££/££££.

Quietly situated off the A19 and only four miles from York, this ivy-festooned early 19th century parsonage is reached via a sweeping drive through exquisite formal gardens and woodland. Full of character as befits its history, this tranquil retreat is sumptuously furnished with living rooms and bedrooms having splendid modern appointments. Each has a private bathroom, colour television, radio, telephone, trouser press and tea and coffee-making facilities; two of the larger rooms boast magnificent four-poster beds. With lovely views on all sides, the hotel has a renowned reputation for its Anglo-French cuisine; for visiting historic York, genteel Harrogate and the incomparable Yorkshire Dales, this is a highly recommended base. ♛♛♛♛ *Highly Commended, AA Red Rosette, RAC Merit Awards.*

BOAR'S HEAD COUNTRY HOTEL, Ripley Castle Estate, Near Harrogate, North Yorkshire HG3 3AY

Tel: 01423 771888
Fax: 01423 771509

Fully licensed; 25 bedrooms, all with private bathrooms; Historic interest; Children and pets welcome; Leisure and conference facilities; Harrogate 3 miles; ££££.

Part of the Ripley Castle Estate, the elegant ancestral home of the Ingilby family for nearly 700 years, this former coaching inn is surrounded by hundreds of acres of deer park, woodland and lakes, walled gardens and tropical palm houses, all designed by Capability Brown. Re-opened by Lord and Lady Ingilby a few years ago after a 'drought' of 75 years, the hotel has been subject to substantial renovation that has provided many pieces of antique furniture and paintings that formerly graced the castle itself, some 100 yards away down the cobbled village street. Nevertheless, there is nothing antique about the modern country house facilities now on offer at the Boar's Head. Bedrooms are beautifully appointed; the majority have king-size beds and all have a private bathroom, colour television, direct dial telephone and refreshment tray. Conveniently placed within 10 minutes of Harrogate, the popular Boris Bar and Bistro serves traditional ales from the wood, whilst the restaurant has earned fulsome praise for its award-winning cuisine. Menus are changed regularly and the wine list boasts more than 200 bins from around the world. Having played a leading role in England's history, the 16th century castle is a fascinating place having associations with many famous personages, including Oliver Cromwell. Period furniture and an atmosphere reflecting its turbulent history form the receptive background for specially arranged Super Sleuth Weekends when a lavish banquet precedes the skulduggery. ♛♛♛ *Highly Commended, AA Two Rosettes.*

ROOKHURST GEORGIAN COUNTRY HOUSE, Gayle, Near Hawes, North Yorkshire DL8 3RT

Tel: 01969 667454*
Fax: 01969 667454

Restaurant and residential licence; 5 bedrooms, all with private bathrooms; Historic interest; Children over 12 years welcome; Kirkby Stephen 14 miles; ££.

A small, friendly and comfortable country house in wonderful Wensleydale, Rookhurst offers a charming mixture of accommodation: the Georgian bedrooms are cosy and oak-beamed whilst the Victorian rooms are spacious and grand. All, however, are handsomely appointed, with two four-poster beds available. The views from the windows are fabulous and for close acquaintance with the scenic splendour of the Yorkshire Dales, there can be few more enchanting places. Special mention, too, must be made of the heavily-beamed Bridal Suite with its superb brass half-tester bed and luxurious Edwardian bathroom suite. After a day's excursions, guests may look forward to returning to a drink in the intimate bar, a splendid dinner and convivial conversation by a log fire. *AA **.*

Sawley, near Ripon, North Yorkshire

WRANGHAM HOUSE HOTEL,
Stonegate, Hunmanby, North Yorkshire YO14 ONS

Tel: 01723 891333
Fax: 01723 891333

Residential licence; 13 bedrooms, all with private bathrooms; Historic interest; Children over 12 years welcome, guide dogs only; Filey 3 miles; £.

This lovely Georgian house offers the graciousness and elegance of a bygone age combined with modern comforts, a warm welcome and fine food. Delightfully placed between the Wolds and the sea, of which some rooms have a dramatic view, this former vicarage has been skilfully converted to offer facilities of the highest order. Lounges, one with an intimate bar, overlook the wooded gardens; central heating is installed and log fires counteract winter chill. Traditional home cooking is a prime attraction here from the generous English breakfast to the excellent five-course dinner and the fixed-price menu represents fine value for money, a comment that also applies to the well-appointed accommodation.

BEANSHEAF HOTEL,
Malton Road, Kirby Misperton, Malton, North Yorkshire YO17 0UE

Tel: 01653 668614
Fax: 01653 668370

Fully licensed; 20 bedrooms, all with private bathrooms; Children and pets welcome; Leisure facilities; Pickering 3 miles; £.

Recently refurbished, the Beansheaf is ideally placed for touring the North York Moors and the East Yorkshire coast. All rooms are en suite, with colour television, telephone and tea/coffee making facilities; a special four-poster suite is also available. The pleasantly appointed restaurant offers English and Continental cuisine, with excellent light meals, and table d'hôte and à la carte lunches and dinners. Relax after one's meal in the bar or coffee lounge. There are large pleasant gardens and a sauna. ♛♛♛ *Commended.*

LIME TREE FARM,
Hutts Lane, Grewelthorpe, Near Ripon, North Yorkshire HG4 3DA

Tel: 01765 658450

Unlicensed; 3 bedrooms, all with private bathrooms; Historic interest; Children and well-behaved pets welcome; Masham 3 miles; £.

The farmhouse is almost 200 years old, with exposed beams, oak panelling, open fires, clipped rugs, grandfather clocks, etc, and is situated on a secluded Dales farm near Ripon, ideal for touring and visiting Yorkshire's many attractions. All bedrooms are en suite and have colour television and tea/coffee making facilities; the dining room has separate tables; guests have their own lounge with access to books and games. There is central heating throughout. A full English breakfast is served, and good traditional home cooking is a feature of the four-course evening meals (optional). Open all year. ♛♛♛

RED HALL,
Great Broughton, Stokesley,
North Yorkshire TS9 7ET

Tel and Fax: 01642 712300

3 bedrooms, all with en suite bathrooms; Historic interest; Children welcome; Conference facilities; Stokesley 3 miles; £.

Red Hall offers the calm and elegance of the small country house. Our family-run business with spacious centrally heated en suite bedrooms provides personal service in a friendly, caring atmosphere. Join us in our lovely Queen Anne Grade II Listed country house set in tranquil meadows and woodland at the foot of the rugged North Yorks Moors National Park, with access to some of England's most dramatic and beautiful scenery, also superb in autumn and winter. The country's largest area of open heather connects the picturesque fishing resorts of Staithes, Whitby and Robin Hood's Bay to ancient market towns and a rich complement of castles, ancient abbeys and stately homes. **See also Colour Advertisement on page 13.**

STAKESBY MANOR HOTEL,
Manor Close, High Stakesby, Whitby,
North Yorkshire YO21 1HL

Tel: 01947 602773
Fax: 01947 602140

Fully licensed; 8 bedrooms, all with private bathrooms; Children welcome; Conference facilities; ££.

In its own well-tended gardens and just a mile or so from the beach, golf course and town centre, Stakesby Manor is an attractively converted Georgian manor which enjoys extensive sea and country views. Public and private rooms have been furnished and decorated with a perceptive eye to form and colour, and the centrally heated guest rooms are appointed with en suite facilities, colour television and tea-making equipment. This is very much a family hotel offering the combined attractions of a sea and country holiday with children of all ages welcomed. The popular Manor Bar features a rare Italian marble fireplace and the panelled Oak Room Restaurant provides an intimate setting in which to savour good food. ♛♛♛♛ *Commended, AA**.*

WELLGARTH HOUSE,
Wetherby Road, Rufforth, York,
North Yorkshire YO2 3QB

Tel: 01904 738592 and 738595

Unlicensed; 7 bedrooms, all with private bathrooms; Children welcome, pets by arrangement; Harrogate 18 miles, York 4; £.

Quietly situated in the village of Rufforth, just five minutes from York, Wellgarth House is ideally situated for exploring this historic city, the breathtaking landscape of the Moors and Dales, and the Heritage Coast with its splendid resorts at Scarborough, Whitby and Filey. Accommodation is spacious, comfortable and well furnished, and all rooms have been decorated to the highest standard, some with four-poster beds. Colour television and tea/coffee making facilities are provided, and thermostatically controlled central heating ensures complete comfort and warmth; ironing facilities and hairdryers are available on request. There is a ground floor bedroom which is ideal for the elderly or for anyone wishing to avoid stairs. On summer days guests can relax and unwind in the colourful gardens which overlook lovely rolling countryside. ♛♛, *AA QQ, FHG Diploma.*

THE MANOR COUNTRY HOUSE,
Acaster Malbis, York,
North Yorkshire YO2 1YL

Tel & Fax: 01904 706723

Residential licence; 10 bedrooms, all with private bathrooms; Historic interest; Children welcome, pets by arrangement; York 4 miles; £.

An atmospheric manor set in rural tranquillity in 5½ acres of beautiful mature grounds with a lake to fish in. Close to the racecourse and only 10 minutes' car journey from the city — or take the leisurely river bus (Easter to October); conveniently situated for trips to Dales, Moors, Wolds and splendid coastline. The hotel is centrally heated, and there are ten en suite bedrooms with full facilities (a four-poster room is available). There is a stair lift. The cosy lounge and lounge bar have an open fire, and the conservatory dining room serves Aga-cooked food. Find The Manor via the A64 exiting for Copmanthorpe-York, Thirsk, Harrogate or Bishopthorpe (Sim Balk Lane). SAE or telephone for details. ♛♛♛ *Highly Commended, FHG Diploma.* **See also Colour Advertisement on page 12.**

OLD FARMHOUSE COUNTRY HOTEL & RESTAURANT,
Raskelf, York,
North Yorkshire YO6 3LF

Tel: 01347 821971*

Residential and restaurant licence; 10 bedrooms, all with private bathrooms; Children welcome, pets by prior arrangement; Easingwold 2 miles; £.

The Old Farmhouse is an award-winning friendly Country Hotel which has retained its original farmhouse character while offering every modern comfort. The ten en suite bedrooms are centrally heated and have colour television, direct-dial telephones and tea and coffee facilities. The food is something special and offers a good choice of dishes, complemented by an extensive wine list and a choice of malts. The area is a haven for many historic houses, magnificent ruined abbeys and castles. For the sporting enthusiast – riding, golf, fishing and swimming are available locally, and several famous racecourses are within driving distance. ♛♛♛ *Highly Commended, AA QQQQ.*

NOTE

All the information in this book is given in good faith in the belief that it is correct. However, the publishers cannot guarantee the facts given in these pages, neither are they responsible for changes in policy, ownership or terms that may take place after the date of going to press. Readers should always satisfy themselves that the facilities they require are available and that the terms, if quoted, still apply.

West Yorkshire

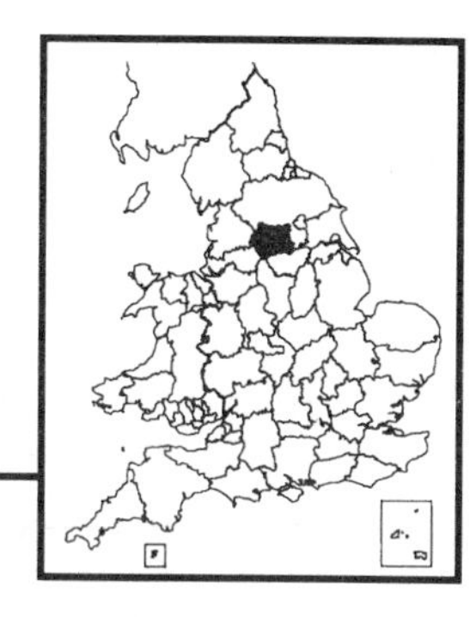

HOLME CASTLE COUNTRY HOTEL,
Holme, Holmfirth,
West Yorkshire HD7 1QG

Tel: 01484 686764
Fax: 01484 687775

Residential licence; 8 bedrooms, 5 with private bathrooms; Children welcome; Conference facilities; Holmfirth 2½ miles; £/££.

Unusual and comfortable Victorian country house with superb views of hills and moorland, situated in a conservation village in the Peak District National Park. There is a splendid oak-panelled drawing room with an open fire. Dinner is prepared to order using fresh food with herbs from the garden and accompanied by world-wide quality wines. Situated on the A6024, this is an ideal business stop, with Manchester, Leeds and Sheffield just 45 minutes away. Local interests include walking, cycling and birdwatching, and the TV series "Last of the Summer Wine" was filmed nearby. Special offer breaks available from October until April. Established in 1983 by the proprietors, Jill Hayfield and John Sandford, winners of the BBC Environment Award for Business 1993. *AA QQQQ Selected, Logis of GB.*

LINTON SPRINGS HOTEL,
Sicklinghall Road, Wetherby,
West Yorkshire LS22 4AF

Tel: 01937 585353
Fax: 01937 587579

Fully licensed; 12 bedrooms, all with private bathrooms; Historic interest; Children welcome; Leisure and conference facilities; Harrogate 8 miles; £££.

Combining all the grace of a late 18th century country house with the latest facilities, Linton Springs nestles on the edge of the beautiful Wharfedale Valley, its 14 acre grounds featuring spacious lawns and well-kept gardens fringed with mature woodland. The busy market town of Wetherby is nearby and the hotel and its restaurant have a high reputation amongst the racegoing and golfing fraternity. Harrogate is but 15 minutes away and Leeds, Bradford and York are all within half-an-hour's drive. Inexpensive luncheons are served and there is an extensive à la carte dinner menu. All rooms have en suite baths and showers, satellite television, direct-dial telephone, refreshments tray, hair dryer and trouser press.

BAGDEN HALL HOTEL,
Wakefield Road, Scissett,
Near Huddersfield, West Yorkshire HD8 9LE

Tel: 01484 865330
Fax: 01484 861001

Fully licensed; 17 bedrooms, all with private bathrooms; Historic interest; Children welcome; Leisure and conference facilities; Denby Dale 2 miles; £££/££££.

15 minutes' driving time from Barnsley, Huddersfield and Wakefield and 30 minutes from Leeds and Sheffield, this captivating and conveniently situated country hotel is a veritable oasis for the urban dweller and businessman, hence its popularity as a venue for conferences and social occasions; moreover, this lovely hotel is a superb holiday retreat in its own right. Retaining all the character of a bygone age, the hall has recently been completely renovated and is now amongst the finest hotels in the country for accommodation, comfort, surroundings, and traditional English and classical French cuisine. The gracious house stands in 40 acres of parkland, only minutes away from Junctions 38 and 39 of the M1. ♛♛♛♛ *Highly Commended, AA Rosette, RAC* ***.

FOR THE MUTUAL GUIDANCE OF GUEST AND HOST

Every year literally thousands of holidays, short breaks and overnight stops are arranged through our guides, the vast majority without any problems at all. In a handful of cases, however, difficulties do arise about bookings, which often could have been prevented from the outset.

It is important to remember that when accommodation has been booked, both parties – guests and hosts – have entered into a form of contract. We hope that the following points will provide helpful guidance.

GUESTS: When enquiring about accommodation, be as precise as possible. Give exact dates, numbers in your party and the ages of any children. State the number and type of rooms wanted and also what catering you require – bed and breakfast, full board etc. Make sure that the position about evening meals is clear – and about pets, reductions for children or any other special points.

Read our reviews carefully to ensure that the proprietors you are going to contact can supply what you want. Ask for a letter confirming all arrangements, if possible.

If you have to cancel, do so as soon as possible. Proprietors do have the right to retain deposits and under certain circumstances to charge for cancelled holidays if adequate notice is not given and they cannot re-let the accommodation.

HOSTS: Give details about your facilities and about any special conditions. Explain your deposit system clearly and arrangements for cancellations, charges etc. and whether or not your terms include VAT.

If for any reason you are unable to fulfil an agreed booking without adequate notice, you may be under an obligation to arrange suitable alternative accommodation or to make some form of compensation.

While every effort is made to ensure accuracy, we regret that FHG Publications cannot accept responsibility for errors, omissions or misrepresentations in our entries or any consequences thereof. Prices in particular should be checked because we go to press early. We will follow up complaints but cannot act as arbiters or agents for either party.

WALES

North Wales

(formerly Clwyd and Gwynedd)

Aberconwy & Colwyn, Anglesey, Denbighshire, Flintshire, Gwynedd and Wrexham.

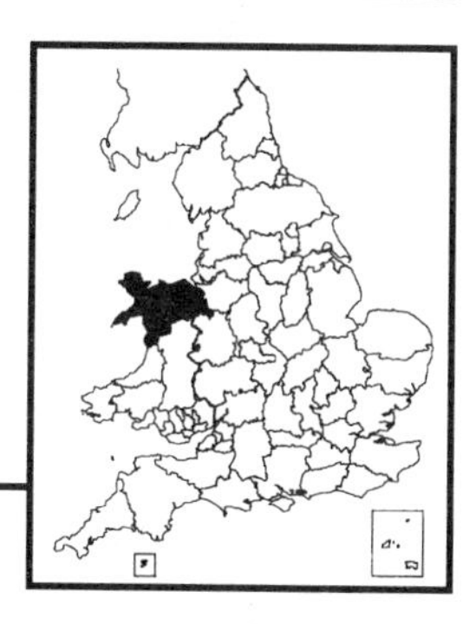

FRON HEULOG COUNTRY HOUSE,
Betws-y-Coed,
North Wales LL24 0BL

Tel/Fax: 01690 710736

Bedrooms with en suite bathrooms; Llandudno 18 miles; £.

"The Country House in the Village". Jean and Peter Whittingham invite you to visit their home where you will enjoy real hospitality. Fron Heulog is an elegant Victorian stone-built house , facing south in quiet, peaceful, wooded riverside scenery. De luxe accommodation is offered (completely non-smoking) in fully equipped en suite bedrooms, spacious lounges, and a pleasant dining room; full central heating. It is highly recommended for its friendly atmosphere, warmth and comfort and guests are assured of excellent home cooking. Situated in Betws-y-Coed in the heart of the wonderfully picturesque Snowdonia National Park, with so much to see and do, Fron Heulog is an ideal centre for touring and walking. Sorry, no pets. Private parking. "More Home than Hotel". WTB ♛♛♛ *Highly Commended*, Guest House Award. Welcome Host.

CASTELL CIDWM HOTEL,
Betws Garmon, Caernarvon,
North Wales LL54 7YT

Tel: 01286 650243

Licensed; 8 bedrooms, all with private bathrooms; Children welcome; Caernarvon 5 miles; £.

In one of the most beautiful settings in Wales on the west side of Snowdon, this delightfully tranquil lakeside hotel offers magnificent views of mountain, forest and water. Private trout fishing, boating and water sports are available from the hotel, with walking, climbing and pony trekking nearby. The hotel offers warm friendly hospitality, eight bedrooms (all en suite), a cosy bar, a bistro snack bar and an à la carte restaurant with a subtly different cuisine. Two and three day breaks available. *WTB* ♛♛♛ *Highly Commended, AA***. **See also Colour Advertisement on page 15.**

MYNYDD EDNYFED COUNTRY HOUSE HOTEL,
Caernarfon Road, Criccieth,
North Wales LL52 OPH

Tel: 01766 523269*

Restaurant and residential licence; 9 bedrooms, all with private bathrooms; Historic interest; Children and pets welcome; Leisure and conference facilities; Caernarfon 15 miles; £.

Overlooking Tremadog Bay and Criccieth Castle, this attractive, 400-year-old Welsh country home has been tastefully refurbished to offer accommodation, food and service of high quality. It stands in 7 glorious acres comprising garden, woods and paddocks, views of which complement the excellent fare served in the restaurant or Victorian conservatory. Guest rooms also benefit from this pleasing panorama, all of them delightfully furnished with en suite facilities, television, radio, direct-dial telephone and tea and coffee-makers; some rooms with handsome four-posters are available. An all-weather tennis court is situated in the long-established walled garden and shooting (game and clay) and golf may be arranged. ♛♛♛♛ *Highly Commended, Which? Hotel Guide, Johansens.*

BORTHWNOG HALL, Bontddu, Dolgellau, North Wales LL40 2TT

Tel: 01341 430271
Fax: 01341 430682

Residential and restaurant licence; 3 bedrooms, all with private bathrooms; Historic interest; Children welcome, pets by prior arrangement; Barmouth 4 miles; ££.

Once described as "a little gem", Borthwnog Hall (a Listed building) is a great favourite of those seeking comfort, relaxation and excellent hospitality, all set in a magnificent location overlooking the beautiful Mawddach estuary in Southern Snowdonia. Uniquely, you will find in your bedroom a personalised guide to the area covering a variety of walks and attractions, with personal comments on each by either your hosts or by previous guests. Couple this with the excellent menu and wine list, and it is not difficut to see why Borthwnog is so popular. Weekly, short break and seasonal special rates are available. ♛♛♛♛ *Highly Commended, AA Premier Selected QQQQQ, RAC Highly Acclaimed, Ashley Courtenay.* **See also Colour Advertisement on page 15.**

PENMAENUCHAF HALL, Penmaenpool, Dolgellau, North Wales LL40 IYB

Tel: 01341 422129
Fax.: 01341 422129

Residential and restaurant licence; 14 bedrooms, all with private bathrooms; Historic interest; Children over 8 years welcome, pets by arrangement; Conference facilities; Dolgellau 2 miles; £££.

To experience gracious living in the most idyllic surroundings, a visit to this welcoming and opulently furnished country house hotel is heartily recommended. Set in its own lovely 21-acre grounds between Cader Idris and the scenic Mawddach estuary, the Hall offers the rare opportunity to relax amidst cossetting splendour provided by oak panelling, blazing log fires, rich drapes and classic comforts which extend to the luxurious en suite bedrooms. High on the list of attractions will be the award-winning cuisine; fine cooking made exceptional by a team of talented chefs. The Hall holds sway over 13 miles of river fishing and other activities available locally include pony trekking, golf, sailing and watersports. ♛♛♛♛ *De Luxe, AA*** and Two Rosettes.*

* The appearance of an asterisk after the telephone number indicates that the hotel in question is closed for a period during the winter months. Exact dates should be ascertained from the hotel itself.

BODYSGALLEN HALL,
Llandudno,
North Wales LL30 1RS

Tel: 01492 584466
Fax: 01492 582519

Fully licensed; 35 bedrooms, all with private bathrooms; Historic interest; Children over 8 years and pets welcome; Leisure and conference facilities; Chester 47 miles; ££££.

Sympathetically restored, this imposing 17th century country house combines the elegance of a sedate past with 20th century comforts. Antiques and fine pictures charm the eye, and each of the comfortable guest rooms has its own Edwardian-style bathroom, colour television, direct-dial telephone and electric trouser press. The house stands in delightful terraced grounds, the setting for several well furnished cottage suites with spectacular views of Snowdonia. This is the ideal centre for those wishing to get away from it all amidst majestic and peaceful surroundings, yet with the amenities of a modern resort nearby. Special mention must be made of the imaginative bill of fare, changed daily and featuring a number of unusual specialities as well as superbly presented traditional dishes. ♛♛♛♛♛ *Commended, AA Three Red Stars and Two Rosettes.*

BRYN BRAS CASTLE,
Llanrug, Near Caernarvon,
North Wales LL55 4RE

Tel and Fax: 01286 870210

Self catering accommodation (some serviced apartments with breakfast); Historic interest; Not suitable for young children; Caernarvon 4 miles.

This romantic Neo-Romanesque castle is set in gentle Snowdonian foothills near North Wales mountains, beaches, resorts and places of historic interest. Built in 1830, on the site of an earlier structure, the Regency castle reflects peace, not war. It stands in 32 acres of tranquil gardens, with delightful views. Bryn Bras offers distinctive and individual apartments for two to four persons within the Castle, each having a suite of spacious rooms radiating comfort, warmth and tranquillity, and providing freedom and independence. There are many inns and restaurants nearby. The welcoming Castle (still a family home) particularly appeals to romantic couples. Short breaks — two nights for two persons from £110 (s/c). Open all year. Brochure sent with pleasure. WTB Grade 5.

PLAS MAENAN COUNTRY HOUSE HOTEL,
Conway Valley, Near Llanwrst,
North Wales LL26 0YR

Tel: 01492 660232
Fax: 01492 660551

Fully licensed; 15 bedrooms, all with private bathrooms; Children and pets welcome; Betws-y-Coed 4 miles; ££.

Situated in 12 acres of grounds in the beautiful Conway Valley, Plas Maenan is within easy travelling distance from the coastal towns of Llandudno and Colwyn Bay, and close to the heart of Snowdonia. Ideally situated for golf, fishing, riding and touring. The world famous Bodnant Garden is five minutes' drive away. The friendly family-run hotel offers excellent cuisine in comfortable surroundings. All bedrooms are furnished to a high standard with tea/coffee facilities, colour television, telephone and hairdryer. During the winter months our real log fire burns. Special Break rates are available all year, including weekends; there are also Christmas and New Year programmes. ♛♛♛♛, *AA/RAC***.*

PLAS BACH,
Glandwr, Near Bontddu, Barmouth,
North Wales LL42 1TG

Tel: 01341 281234

Residential licence; 5 bedrooms, all with private bathrooms; Historic interest; Children over 15 welcome, pets under supervision; Barmouth 4 miles; £.

The views across the Mawddach estuary towards the craggy peaks of Cader Idris are breathtaking from this supremely comfortable little hotel. Nestling in 4 acres of grounds leading to the famous Panorama Walk, homely Plas Bach betrays loving attention to detail in respect of its appointments and food. Days commence with a superb breakfast and the dinners (available most evenings) feature delicious home-made soups, roasts, puddings and pies. The house is scrupulously clean; an enormous sitting room has snug sofas and a log fire adds cheer on chilly evenings. Guest rooms are prettily decorated and have private bath/shower, colour television, clock radio, toiletries and refreshment tray. ♛♛♛ *De Luxe, AA QQQQQ, Finalist 1996 AA Landlady of the Year.*

MINFFORDD HOTEL,
Talyllyn, Tywyn,
North Wales LL36 9AJ

Tel: 01654 761665*
Fax: 01654 761517

Residential and restaurant licence; 6 bedrooms, all with private bathrooms; Historic interest; Car park (12); Machynlleth 10 miles; £.

At last – an opportunity to escape and rediscover lost values set to flight by modern living. At the head of the remote and beautiful Dysynni Valley, this former coaching inn is a scenic gem in itself. Homely, warm and comfortable, the hotel is full of character. Guest rooms are tastefully furnished and each is centrally heated and has private bath and toilet facilities. Beauty spots and places of interest abound in the area, part of the dramatic patterns woven by mountains and streams, Talyllyn Lake, the famous Talyllyn Railway, Cader Idris, Dolgoch Falls amongst them. Always on one's return is the prospect of a sumptuous dinner and the recounting of the day's adventures before a log fire. ♛♛♛♛ *Highly Commended, AA Red Rosette, RAC Merit Awards for Hospitality, Comfort and Cuisine, Good Food Guide.*

Dyfed

Cardiganshire, Carmarthenshire and Pembrokeshire.

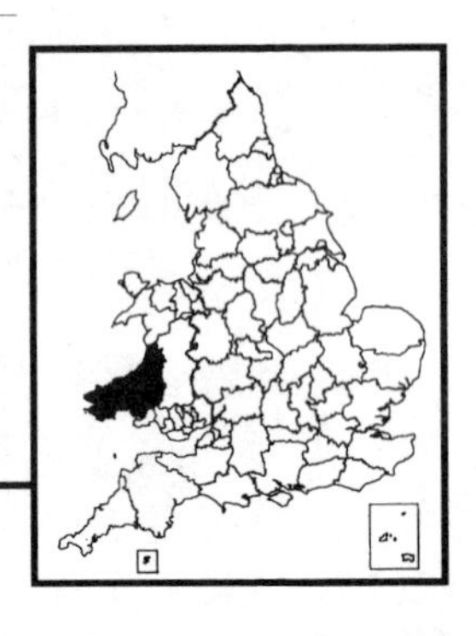

HOTEL PENRALLT,
Aberporth, Cardigan,
Dyfed SA43 2BS

Tel: 01239 810227
Fax: 01239 811375

Fully licensed; 16 bedrooms, all with private bathrooms; Children welcome, pets by arrangement; Leisure and conference facilities; Cardigan 6 miles; £££.

Aberporth, with its two sandy beaches and low sheltering cliffs, is an ideal little resort for family holidays, and children are especially welcome at this comfortable Edwardian hotel. Set in delightful grounds, it commands lovely views over Cardigan Bay and its splendid leisure amenities will appeal to guests of all ages; these include an open-air heated swimming pool with poolside bar and cafeteria, gymnasium, hard tennis court, children's play area, sauna and solarium. Food is a high priority, being varied and generous. Accommodation is exceptionally well appointed, with family rooms available. Business guests are well catered for too, with a small conference room and secretarial services at their disposal. Self catering apartments are also available. ♛♛♛♛ *Highly Commended, AA/RAC****.*

WATERWYNCH BAY HOTEL,
Tenby, South Pembrokeshire
Dyfed SA70 8TJ

Tel: 01834 842464*
Fax: 01834 845076

Restaurant licence; 17 bedrooms, all with private bathrooms; Historic interest; Children over 7 years welcome, pets by arrangement; Leisure and conference facilities; Pembroke 9 miles; ££.

Not only has this supremely comfortable hotel its own secluded, sandy cove but it is set like a jewel in 27 acres of woodland and gardens on the Pembrokeshire Coastal Footpath; an idyllic situation. The hotel has a choice of elegant suites and bedrooms (including two luxury Honeymoon Suites), all of which have en suite facilities, colour television, direct dial telephone and tea and coffee-makers — and fabulous views. With first-class cuisine assured, this is a perfect venue for bird watchers, walkers and artists; indeed, residential painting courses are organised regularly with professional tuition. Fishing and golf may be enjoyed locally as well as gentle diversion in the form of bridge, snooker, croquet, bowls and putting. ♛♛♛♛ *Highly Commended.*

Powys

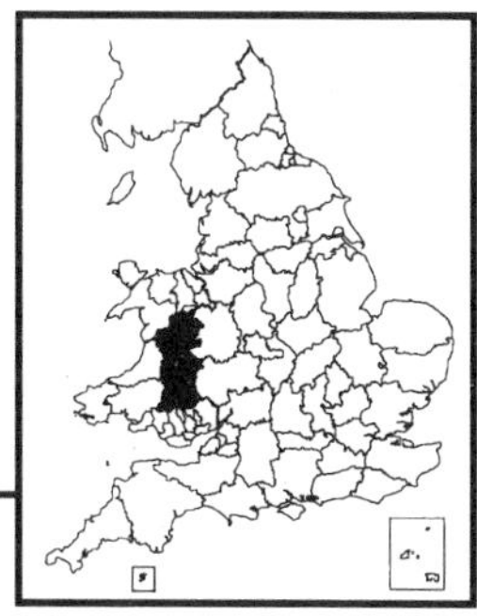

MAESMAWR HALL HOTEL,
Caersws,
Powys SY17 5SF

Tel: 01686 688255
Fax: 01686 688410

Fully licensed; 17 bedrooms, all with private bathrooms; Children welcome; Conference facilities; Newtown 5 miles; ££.

With its handsome black and white facade, this lovely, 16th century period house, Grade I Listed, stands back from the A470 Newtown-Llangurig road. Here, beneath mellow beamed ceilings up-to-date refinements rub shoulders with the ambience of a past age. An unhurried atmosphere predominates, with log fires adding a welcoming touch in cooler weather, especially in the cheerful lounge bar. Fine modern facilities exist in the bedrooms, six of which are situated in the nearby Coach House where ground-floor rooms are available. A la carte and bar food menus specialise in freshly-cooked fare and there is a well-chosen wine list. Opportunities for a variety of country sports abound nearby and the hotel has fishing rights on the River Severn. *WTB* ♛♛♛.

LLANGOED HALL,
Llyswen, Brecon,
Powys LD3 0YP

Tel: 01874 754525
Fax: 01874 754545

Fully licensed; 23 bedrooms, all with private bathrooms; Historic interest; Children over 8 years welcome; Conference facilities; Brecon 8 miles; ££££.

This superb house on the banks of the lovely River Wye has its origins in 1632 when it was built on the foundations of an ancient grange. Redesigned in 1912 by Sir Clough Williams-Ellis, incorporating the beautiful Jacobean porch on the south wing, the elegant Llangoed Hall stands in delightful and well established grounds and now welcomes guests into its exclusive Edwardian country house atmosphere. Grace and gentility mix easily with warm hospitality and opulent comforts. Spacious communal rooms such as the Great Hall, library, morning and dining rooms are furnished with impeccable taste and an eye for harmonious colour schemes; a great carved staircase climbs to an imposing pillared picture gallery and thence to the splendid guest rooms, all of which have a private bathroom, television, radio, and direct-dial telephone. Under the supervision of a highly skilled chef, the cuisine is delicately classical, with emphasis on local specialities such as game, Welsh lamb and Wye salmon, and there is a superb selection of wines to complement each delicious meal. Gentle diversion may be sought playing cards or snooker in the library, and more active pursuits to be enjoyed in the extensive grounds include an all-weather tennis court, croquet , and exploring the walled garden and maze. 👑👑👑👑👑 *De Luxe, AA Four Red Stars, RAC ****.*

GLIFFAES COUNTRY HOUSE HOTEL,
Crickhowell,
Powys NP8 IRH

Tel: 01874 730371
Fax: 01874 730463

Fully licensed; 22 bedrooms, all with private bathrooms; Historic interest; Children welcome, pets by arrangement; Leisure and conference facilities; Abergavenny 6 miles; £/££.

Snug in the lush loveliness of the Usk Valley, this imposing, creeper-clad hotel is approached via a rhododendron-lined drive through the 33 acres of gardens, lawns and woodland. Between the Black Mountains and the Brecon Beacons, the hotel has elegant and delightfully appointed rooms and is of direct appeal to the sporting enthusiast with diversions active and passive. With a variety of runs available on the River Usk, the fishing for wild brown trout and salmon is excellent and the grounds provide facilities for tennis (a hard court with practice wall), putting and croquet and there is also a golf practice net. In the hands of the Brabner family since 1948, the house has all the comforts of a grand country residence and a warm and welcoming ambience ensured by central heating and open log fires in the main reception rooms in cool weather. There are glorious views of the surrounding hills and the splendid guest rooms are individually decorated and appointed with private bathrooms/showers. Dinner is from an imaginative menu covering the best of national dishes as well as Mediterranean specialities created by a talented kitchen team led by Head Chef, Mark Coulton, and the hotel is also renowned for its hot Sunday lunches, light lunches and afternoon teas. Despite its peaceful situation, Gliffaes is easily accessible being just one mile off the main A40 road, 2½ miles west of Crickhowell. ♛♛♛♛

MILEBROOK HOUSE HOTEL,
Milebrook, Knighton,
Powys LD7 ILT

Tel: 01547 528632
Fax: 01547 520509

Table licence; 10 bedrooms, all with private bathrooms; Historic interest; Children welcome; Knighton 2 miles; ££.

Three acres of formal gardens and water meadows cossett this attractive, grey stone house which has been adapted to the standards of a small but distinguished country hotel in the hands of resident owners, Beryl and Rodney Marsden who have 30 years experience in the catering profession. This is reflected in the informal comfort, unobtrusive service and, especially, the imaginative cuisine. Home grown produce features prominently on the 'Prix-Fixe' menus which make interesting reading and represent excellent value. Special diets are willingly catered for. The tranquil Welsh Marches are ideal walking terrain and for a restful, relaxing and rewarding holiday, Milebrook House has much to commend it. Two ground-floor rooms have recently been added. ♛♛♛♛ *Highly Commended.*

ELAN VALLEY HOTEL,
Elan Valley, Rhayader,
Powys LD6 5HN

Tel: 01597 810448

Licensed; 10 bedrooms, all with private bathrooms; Historic interest; Children and pets welcome; Conference facilities; Rhayader 2 miles; £.

Family-run Victorian hotel in spectacular Elan Valley, a perfect base for exploring the beautiful unspoiled countryside of Mid-Wales. This is wonderful walking, cycling, fishing, pony trekking and red kite watching country and the hotel is just two miles from Rhayader with excellent leisure facilities — swimming, golf, tennis, bowls and children's playgrounds. We are renowned for our delicious food, freshly cooked with flair and imagination and served in the cosy Dish-Dash Restaurant; the sunny tearoom is open in summer for home-baked teas and lunches. There is a well-stocked bar with real ales and a varied wine list. Regular music and theatre events are held, and speciality weekends (Birdwatching, Storytelling, etc). Off-season mini-breaks and festive packages are also available. Children are very welcome at special rates. ♛♛♛ *Commended, Taste of Wales.*

South Wales

(formerly Glamorgan and Gwent)

Blaenau Gwent, Bridgend, Caerphilly, Cardiff, Merthyr Tydfil, Monmouthshire, Neath & Port Talbot, Newport, Rhondda Cynon Taff, Swansea, Torfaen, and Vale of Glamorgan.

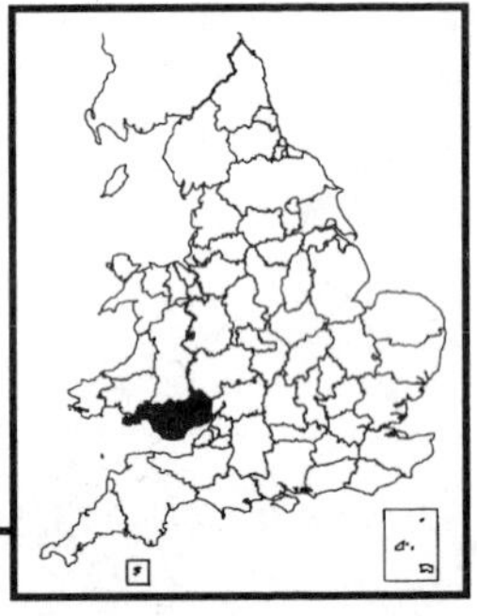

MAES-Y-GWERNEN HOTEL,
School Road, Abercraf, Swansea Valley,
South Wales SA9 1XD

Tel: 01639 730218
Fax: 01639 730765

Residential and supper licence; 8 bedrooms, all with private bathrooms; Children and pets welcome; Leisure facilities; Neath 15 miles, Pontardawe 9; £.

This well-furnished hotel is set in private grounds on the southern edge of the Brecon Beacons National Park. All rooms are en suite, and luxury garden chalets are available. Amenities include a health spa, sauna and solarium, as well as a bar, lounges and gardens exclusive to residents. The hotel is winner of several national quality awards. Major credit cards are accepted. ♛♛♛♛ *Highly Commended, AA Best Newcomer 1994. Les Routiers Guest House of the Year 1995.* **See also Colour Advertisement on page 15.**

MAES MANOR HOTEL,
Blackwood,
South Wales NP2 OAG

Tel: 01495 220011
Fax: 01495 228217

Fully licensed; 27 bedrooms, all with private bathrooms; Children and pets welcome; Conference facilities; Caerphilly 7 miles; £/££.

In the heart of the Welsh valleys in 9 acres of wooded grounds, this imposing late-Victorian stone house caters for leisure and business visitors with equal facility and panache. A cocktail bar with superb views of the surrounding countryside is a popular meeting place and the Seasons Restaurant is well-known for its mouth-watering luncheons and dinners. No less worthy is the accommodation, rooms being delightfully furnished and blessed with fine en suite facilities, six-channel television, direct-dial telephone and tea and coffee-makers. Throughout the year a comprehensive in-house programme of live entertainment is organised, including candlelight dinner-dances, 'sixties' style evenings with disco and live bands. *AA/RAC* ***.

EGERTON GREY COUNTRY HOUSE HOTEL,
Porthkerry, Vale of Glamorgan, Near Cardiff, South Wales CF62 3BZ

Tel: 01446 711666
Fax: 01446 711690

Restaurant licence; 10 bedrooms, all with private bathrooms; Historic interest; Leisure and conference facilities; Cardiff 10 miles; ££.

A recommended centre from which to explore the lovely and uncrowded Gower Peninsula and the Brecon Beacons, this stylish and distinguished country house was opened as a small and luxurious hotel as recently as 1988. Only 10 miles from Cardiff, it is set in a secluded, wooded valley in seven acres of gardens, with views down to Porthkerry Park and the sea. The excellent facilities accorded guests include exquisitely furnished bedrooms (all with private bathrooms), two dining rooms, library and magnificent Edwardian drawing room. Within the grounds is an all-weather tennis court and also a croquet lawn. Only a short stroll away is a well-maintained country park with an 18-hole pitch and putt course. The cuisine is outstanding and dining here by candlelight is a memorable experience. Recommended by all hotel and restaurant guides. *WTB ♛♛♛♛ Highly Commended, "Taste of Wales" Cuisine Award.*

FAIRYHILL HOTEL,
Reynoldston, Gower, Swansea, South Wales SA3 IBS

Tel: 01792 390139
Fax: 01792 391358

Hotel and restaurant licence; 8 bedrooms, all with private bathrooms; Historic interest; Children over 8 years welcome, pets by arrangement; Swansea 11 miles; £££.

Only a five-minute drive from the superb sandy and secluded beaches and coastal scenery of 'glorious Gower', this 18th century mansion has been beautifully refurbished to offer the highest standards of accommodation and service with the cuisine exceptional for quality as well as value under the supervision of Paul Davies who is already widely acknowledged for his culinary expertise. The house stands in 24 acres of parkland and woods which teem with wildlife and there is a trout stream and a lake. Croquet may be played on the lawns. Decorated and furnished in individual style, each of the bedrooms has a bathroom en suite, remote-control colour television, telephone and compact disc stereo system. ♛♛♛♛ *Highly Commended, AA Two Rosettes and Courtesy & Care Award 1996, Egon Ronay Wine Cellar of the Year*

PLEASE MENTION THIS GUIDE WHEN YOU WRITE OR PHONE TO ENQUIRE ABOUT ACCOMMODATION. IF YOU ARE WRITING, A STAMPED, ADDRESSED ENVELOPE IS ALWAYS APPRECIATED.

IRELAND

Kildare

THE KILDARE HOTEL & COUNTRY CLUB,

Straffan, Tel: (01) 627 3333
Co. Kildare Fax: (01) 627 3312

Fully licensed; 45 bedrooms, all with private bathrooms; Historic interest; Children and pets welcome; Leisure and conference facilities; Dublin 17 miles; ££££.

The 330-acre grounds of the Kildare Hotel and Country Club are nestled amidst lush green woodlands, just 17 miles from Dublin, Ireland's capital city. Already acclaimed as one of the finest in the world, this magnificent Five Star hotel offers you the highest standards of comfort and service, combined with the elegance and charm of an Irish country house. You can relax and be lavishly pampered or indulge in any of the quality leisure activities available, including the prestigious Par 72 championship golf course designed by Arnold Palmer. 45 bedrooms, all individually appointed to the highest standard. Be it for business or pleasure, The Kildare Hotel and Country Club is the most rewarding place to stay. *AA Five Red Stars, RAC, Relais & Chateaux Purple Award.* **See also Colour Advertisement on page 13.**

The **£** symbol when appearing at the end of the italic section of an entry shows the anticipated price, during 1997, for single full Bed and Breakfast.

Under £40	**£**	**Over £55 but under £70**	**£££**
Over £40 but under £55	**££**	**Over £70**	**££££**

This is meant as an indication only and does not show prices for Special Breaks, Weekends, etc. Guests are therefore advised to verify all prices on enquiring or booking.

SCOTLAND

Aberdeenshire

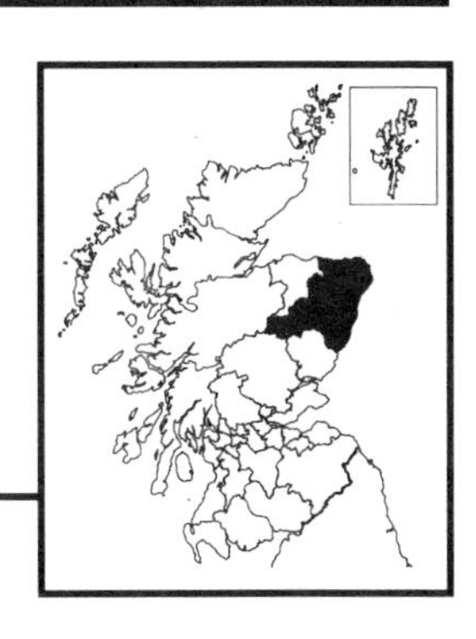

including the City of Aberdeen, Banff and Buchan.

TULLICH LODGE,
By Ballater,
Aberdeenshire AB35 5SB

Tel: 013397 55406*
Fax: 013397 55397

Fully licensed; 10 bedrooms, all with private bathrooms; Children and pets welcome; Aberdeen 17 miles, Braemar 14; ££££.

Small and friendly, this Victorian baronial mansion has a warm, informal atmosphere and its location on a wooded knoll overlooking the River Dee underlines its attraction as a tranquil base from which to explore Royal Deeside. Upholding the finest traditions of Scottish hospitality, the house, built of local pink granite, enjoys fine views on all sides and the pleasant town of Ballater is within strolling distance. This is a convivial place in which to stay with an intimate and well-stocked bar with an open fire, where guests foregather prior to a memorable dining experience in the spruce, panelled dining room. Guest rooms are delightfully furnished and are equipped with private bathroom or shower, radio and direct-dial telephone.

BALGONIE COUNTRY HOUSE,
Braemar Place, Ballater,
Aberdeenshire AB35 5RQ

Tel and Fax: 01339 755482*

Full hotel licence; 9 bedrooms, all with private bathrooms; Children welcome; Aberdeen 17 miles, Braemar 14; £££.

Royal Deeside is one of the most beautiful and unspoilt parts of Scotland and this Edwardian-style house takes full advantage of its glorious position on the outskirts of Ballater. Balgonie House, enjoying magnificent views, has all the requisites as a perfect base from which to explore the bounties of the area. Scenery apart, golf, hill walking, touring the Whisky and Castle Trails may all be enjoyed, with the assurance of superlative Scottish food upon one's return, including local game, beef and seafood, complemented by a notable wine list and attentive service, so well organised by proprietors, John and Priscilla Finnie. Individually decorated and furnished, bedrooms each have a private bathroom, colour television and direct dial telephone. ♛♛♛♛ *De Luxe, AA Two Red Stars and Two Rosettes.*

BANCHORY LODGE HOTEL,
Banchory,
Aberdeenshire AB31 5HS

Tel: 01330 822625
Fax: 01330 825019

Fully licensed; 22 bedrooms, all with private bathrooms; Historic interest; Children and pets welcome; Conference facilities; Stonehaven 11 miles; £££.

Built as a coaching inn in the 16th century and graduating into an elegant Georgian manor house, Banchory Lodge stands in lovely wooded surroundings beside the River Dee, world-famous for its salmon. It is natural therefore that angling enthusiasts are attracted by its hospitable atmosphere, to say nothing of its high standards of service, cuisine and accommodation. Log fires, fresh flowers, traditional furnishings and original paintings add to the air of tranquillity. There is also ample scope for golf, tennis, putting and bowls nearby as well as numerous forest walks and nature trails. The best of fresh local produce features on the imaginative menus presented in the spacious dining room. ♛♛♛♛ *Highly Commended, AA Three Red Stars, RAC Blue Ribbon.*

Argyll

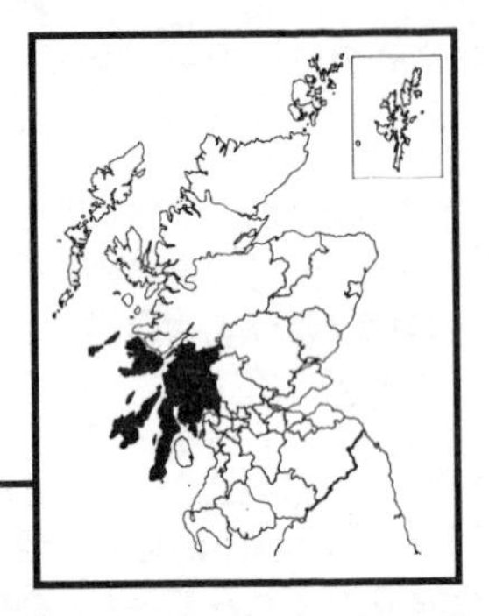

INVERCRERAN COUNTRY HOUSE HOTEL,
Glen Creran, Appin, By Oban,
Argyll PA38 4BJ

Tel: 01631 730414*
Fax: 01631 730532

Residential licence; 9 bedrooms, all with private bathrooms; Children over 5 years welcome; Ballachulish 16 miles; £££.

An outstanding small and intimate country house hotel situated in picturesque and secluded Glen Creran, Invercreran is a haven of tranquillity where the Kersley family have built up a wonderful reputation for the facilities they provide and the kind attention they extend to guests. Nestling against a hillside within 25 acres of verdant gardens, the house is delightfully furnished and has a congenial and relaxing ambience. Bedrooms have full en suite facilities, colour television, direct-dial telephone, radio alarm and hair dryer; one is located on the ground floor. Overlooking the terrace and with scenic mountain views, the semi-circular restaurant is the setting for the superb Scottish cuisine. Take note of the inventive sweets and extensive wine list. ♛♛♛♛ *De Luxe.*

PUBLISHER'S NOTE

While every effort is made to ensure accuracy, we regret that FHG Publications cannot accept responsibility for errors, omissions or misrepresentations in our entries or any consequences thereof. Prices in particular should be checked because we go to press early. We will follow up complaints but cannot act as arbiters or agents for either party.

Ayrshire

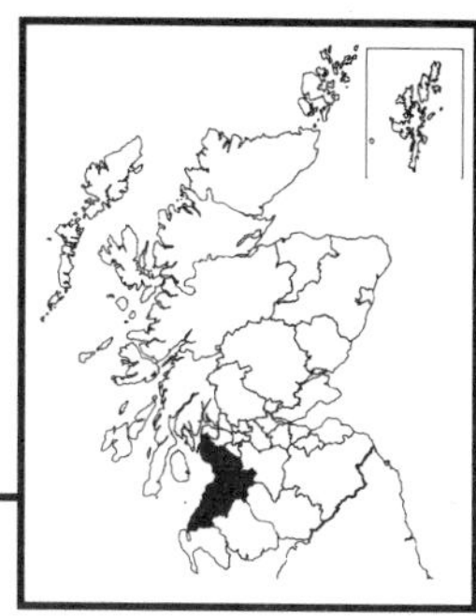

MONTGREENAN MANSION HOUSE HOTEL,
Montgreenan Estate, Near Kilwinning,
Ayrshire KA13 7QZ

Tel: 01294 557733
Fax: 01294 850397

Full hotel licence; 21 bedrooms, all with private bathrooms; Historic interest; Children welcome; Leisure and conference facilities; Kilwinning 2 miles; £££.

Guests return again and again to be spoiled in the peaceful setting of this grand Georgian mansion, to stroll through the acres of woods and gardens with distant views of Ailsa Craig and the Arran Hills. Delightfully furnished in keeping with its opulent origins, with modern conveniences skilfully introduced, the time-honoured appeal of this elegant country house remains undiminished. Bedrooms are appointed to de luxe standard, and the tempting menus on offer in the restaurant are complemented by an outstanding wine list. As a centre for Burns Country, with perhaps a few rounds on the superb golf courses for which Ayrshire is noted, there can be no finer place. ♛♛♛♛ *Highly Commended, AA*** and One Rosette, RAC *** HCR.*

Available from most bookshops, the 1997 edition of THE GOLF GUIDE covers details of every UK golf course – well over 2000 entries – for holiday or business golf. Hundreds of hotel entries offer convenient accommodation, accompanying details of the courses – the 'pro', par score, length etc.

Endorsed by The Professional Golfers' Association (PGA) and including Holiday Golf in Ireland, France, Portugal, Spain and the USA.

£8.99 from bookshops or £9.80 including postage (UK only) from FHG Publications, Abbey Mill Business Centre, Paisley PAI lJT

Dumfriesshire

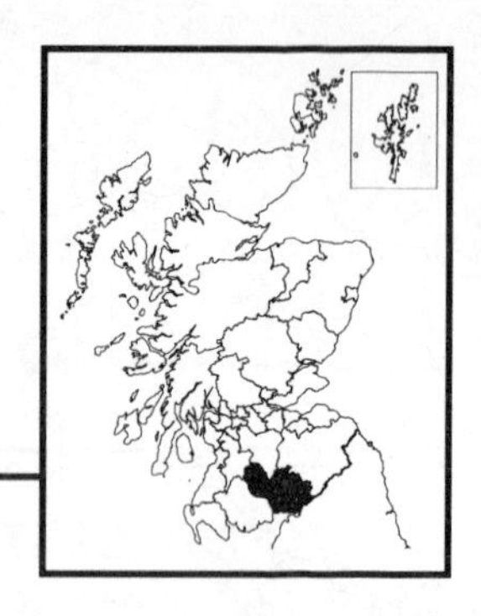

THE DRYFESDALE HOTEL,
Lockerbie,
Dumfriesshire DG11 2SF

Tel: 01576 202427
Fax: 01576 204187

Fully licensed; 15 bedrooms, all with private bathrooms; Historic interest; Children and pets welcome; Conference facilities; Dumfries 11 miles; ££.

The wide facade of this attractive hotel exudes a warm welcome, its modern aspect conveyed by various extensions made since the 18th century when the original building was a manse. Gracing five acres of magnificent grounds, the hotel enjoys magnificent views over the peaceful rolling countryside of Dumfries and Galloway. Despite its tranquil situation, the hotel is within easy reach of the A74 (M74) main Scottish/English link road and major cities. A fine reputation has been acquired for the excellent cuisine, splendid à la carte and table d'hôte meals being served in the spacious dining room, whilst less formal fare is dispensed in the lounge bar which offers a selection of some 100 malt whiskies. Guest rooms are beautifully appointed, each having en suite facilities, colour television, direct-dial telephone and tea and coffee makers. Six ground floor rooms serve the needs of disabled guests, one specifically designed for wheelchair use. The hotel is only half a mile from the pleasant town of Lockerbie and guests have free access to the local squash club; permits may also be obtained for fishing in some of the country's finest rivers. Facilities for golf, tennis and sailing also exist locally. Easy road and rail communication renders this fine hotel a popular rendezvous for meetings and conferences, three separate rooms accommodating up to 40 delegates. ♛♛♛♛ *Highly Commended.*

KIRKLAND COUNTRY HOUSE HOTEL,
Ruthwell,
Dumfriesshire DG1 4NP

Tel: 01387 870284

Licensed; 7 bedrooms, all with private bathrooms; Historic interest; Children welcome; Dumfries 9 miles, Annan 6; £.

This family-run country house hotel is peacefully situated outside the village of Ruthwell, famous as the site of an 18ft high cross carved with runic characters which dates back to the 8th century.The house itself is a former manse, and offers a warm welcome to visitors to this unspoiled and scenic area. Comfortable accommodation is available in double/twin or family rooms, with a honeymoon suite with four-poster for that special occasion. A wide range of country pursuits can be enjoyed in the surrounding area, and the village is on the Solway Heritage Trail. ♛♛♛ *Commended.*

The **£** symbol when appearing at the end of the italic section of an entry shows the anticipated price, during 1997, for single full Bed and Breakfast.

Under £40	**£**	**Over £55 but under £70**	**£££**
Over £40 but under £55	**££**	**Over £70**	**££££**

This is meant as an indication only and does not show prices for Special Breaks, Weekends, etc. Guests are therefore advised to verify all prices on enquiring or booking.

Edinburgh & Lothians

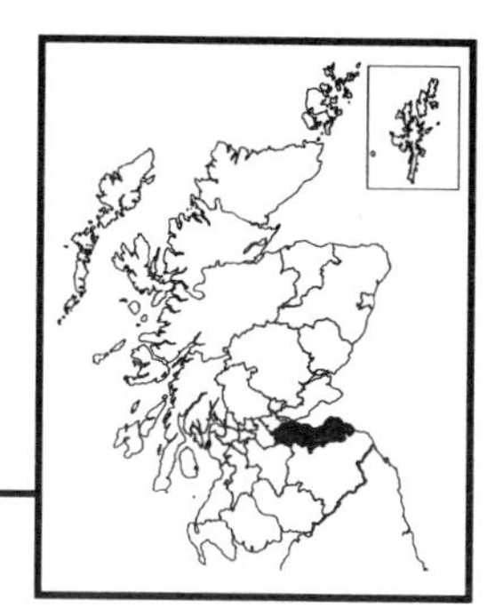

DALHOUSIE CASTLE,
Bonnyrigg, Near Edinburgh, Midlothian EH19 3JB

Tel: 01875 820153
Fax: 01875 821936

Fully licensed; 28 bedrooms, all with private bathrooms; Historic interest; Children and pets welcome; Conference facilities; Edinburgh 9 miles, Dalkeith 2; ££££.

For a warm, wholehearted Scottish welcome amidst the splendour of an imposing 13th century castle, a visit to this fascinating place is an experience that will linger long in the memory. A log fire crackles a welcome in the lovely, oak-panelled library with its 'secret bar' and views of the River South Esk; the ancient dungeons have been transformed into a restaurant which provides a most unusual setting for the enjoyment of first class Scottish and French cooking featuring salmon, venison and game complemented by an interesting selection of wines. The superb suites and bedrooms, several historically themed, all have private bath and shower, colour television, radio, direct-dial telephone, and tea and coffee-makers. Within easy reach of the more populous areas of Scotland, the castle has a long tradition of hospitality and is a popular venue for functions of all sizes and types. Weddings may be solemnised in a private chapel. ♛♛♛♛ *Highly Commended, Johansens, Egon Ronay, Taste of Scotland.*

Fife

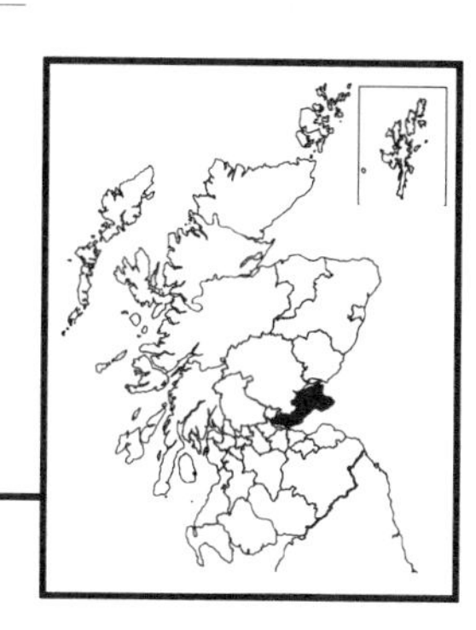

BALBIRNIE HOUSE HOTEL,
Balbirnie Park, Markinch, Fife KY7 6NE

Tel: 01592 610066
Fax: 01592 610529

Fully licensed; 30 bedrooms, all with private bathrooms; Historic interest; Children welcome, pets in bedrooms only; Leisure and conference facilities; Kirkcaldy 8 miles; ££££.

Balbirnie is a delightful Grade 'A' Listed mansion house, the centrepiece of a 400-acre estate, which includes an 18-hole golf course. Located in the heart of Fife, only half an hour between both Edinburgh and St Andrews, the hotel comprises memorable and delightful public rooms, 30 individually designed bedrooms and suites, and private dining rooms, together with a range of traditional or hi-tech special event, banqueting and conference areas. Balbirnie is many things to many people and several things to individuals — feature breaks, corporate gatherings, tailor-made special events, just call for details. Alan C. Russell is Managing Director and Co-Proprietor. ♛♛♛♛♛ *De Luxe, AA Four Red Stars, 1995 Regional Hotel of the Year.* **See also Colour Advertisement on page 14.**

THE SANDFORD COUNTRY HOUSE HOTEL,
Newton Hill, Wormit, Near Dundee,
Fife DD6 8RG

Tel: 01382 541802
Fax: 01382 542136

Licensed; 16 bedrooms, all with private bathrooms; Historic interest; Leisure and conference facilities; Dundee 3 miles; £££.

Set in seven acres of private grounds, this Listed country house was built for the Valentine family of Dundee at the turn of the century and offers guests a comfortable atmosphere in the most tranquil of surroundings. Traditional Scottish and European cuisine is served in the Cocktail Bar and in the Garden Room Restaurant, the high standard menus complemented by a sophisticated and sensibly priced wine list. The classical Minstrel's Gallery is a luxurious room in which to relax in front of an open fire, accompanied perhaps by a dram from a selection of over 30 fine malt whiskies. Neighbouring Newton Hill Country Sports estate offers a variety of leisure activities. ♛♛♛♛ *Highly Commended, Ashley Courtenay, Taste of Scotland.*

Inverness-shire

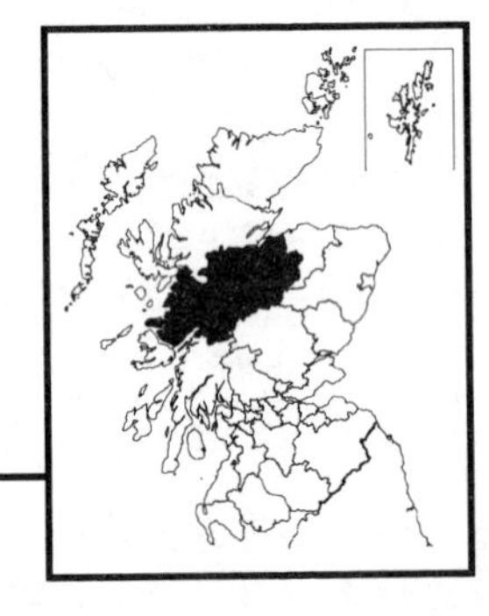

ARISAIG HOUSE,
Beasdale, By Arisaig,
Inverness-shire PH39 4NR

Tel: 01687 450622*
Fax: 01687 450626

Residential licence; 14 bedrooms, all with private bathrooms; Historic interest; Children over 10 years welcome; Conference facilities; Arisaig 3 miles; ££££.

Beautifully situated among rhododendrons and mature oak and beech woods, Arisaig House gazes out towards mountains and a distant island-studded loch. Here one finds true tranquillity, where comfort reigns supreme and every effort is made to ensure that each guest enjoys a truly unforgettable holiday. Only the freshest of produce, including local game in season and seafood, is cooked to order and served in the elegant dining room, accompanied by a wine list carefully chosen to ensure value and quality. Bedrooms are tastefully decorated in relaxing shades and are appointed with a full range of facilities, including of course a luxurious bathroom. Leisurely pursuits such as billiards and croquet may be enjoyed in and around the hotel, while those wishing to explore farther afield may take the legendary "Road to the Isles" and visit Skye and the Outer Hebrides; nearer at hand the islands of Eigg, Muck, Rhum and Canna can be visited by boat trips from Arisaig. Whatever the season, whether escaping for a short break or longer stay, the warm welcome at Arisaig House will make the journey, long or short, more than worthwhile. ♛♛♛♛ *De Luxe, AA Three Red Stars, Egon Ronay, Good Food Guide, Good Hotel Guide.*

POLMAILY HOUSE HOTEL,
Drumnadrochit,
Inverness-shire IV3 6XT

Tel: 01456 450343
Fax: 01456 450813

Restricted hotel licence; 11 bedrooms, all with private bathrooms; Children and pets welcome; Leisure facilities; Inverness 15 miles; £.

Set in 18 acres on the southern slopes of Glen Urquhart, close to Loch Ness, Polmaily House is a hotel of great character, comfort and atmosphere and sets itself apart from others in both attitude and facilities. All rooms are en suite, and amenities include an indoor heated swimming pool, croquet and tennis court. The setting for families is relaxed and cheerful, where parents and children alike can feel at ease. All areas of the Highlands can be visited in a day from Polmaily, making it an ideal setting located at the gateway to magnificent Glen Affric.

THE OSPREY HOTEL,
Kingussie,
Inverness-shire PH21 1EN

Tel and Fax: 01540 661510

Restricted hotel licence; 8 bedrooms, all with private bathrooms; Children over 10 years and pets welcome; Inverness 42 miles; £.

Overlooking the Memorial Gardens, the Osprey is an excellent base from which to explore the Highlands. It is situated close to RSPB reserves, and many outdoor sports are available locally. Guests are assured of a warm, friendly atmosphere, superb food and accommodation, and an extensive list of well-chosen wines and malt whiskies. For brochures, reservations or general enquiries please telephone Robert or Aileen, who will be pleased to help. 👑👑👑 *Commended, AA Rosette for Cuisine, Taste of Scotland.*

Isle of Arran

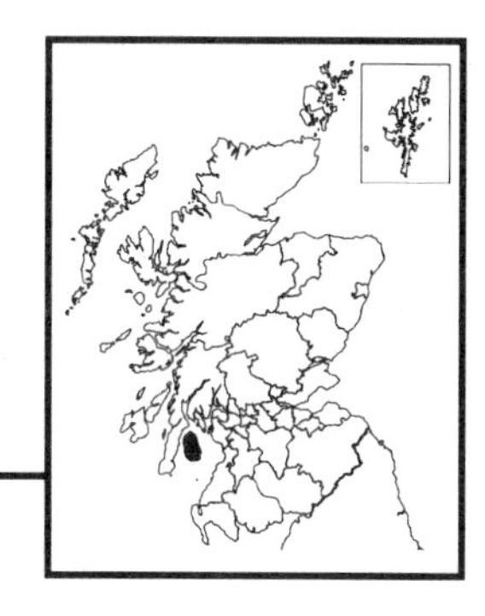

CATACOL BAY HOTEL,
Catacol,
Isle of Arran

Tel: 01770 830231
Fax: 01770 830350

Licensed; Children and pets welcome; Lochranza 2 miles.

Escape from the pressures of mainland life and stay awhile by clear shining seas, a rocky coastline and breathtaking hills and mountains. Enjoy the comfortable, friendly atmosphere of our small country house hotel where good cooking is our speciality. There is an extensive bar menu and meals are served from 12 noon until 10pm. The hotel is centrally heated and open all year; reduced rates for children. Entertainment is arranged during the summer months. Details of Special Breaks and brochure on request. *Les Routiers.*

BURLINGTON HOTEL, Shore Road, Whiting Bay, Isle of Arran KA27 8PZ

Tel: 01770 700255*
Fax: 0374 595327

Hotel licence; 9 bedrooms, all with private facilities; Children and pets welcome; £.

Experience traditional Scottish hospitality in this sea-front Edwardian hotel which is situated immediately opposite steps to a sandy beach. Recently refurbished, all the attractively decorated bedrooms have private facilities, hospitality trays, hairdryers and colour television. Using the best local produce and drawing on his extensive repertoire, Chef Robin Gray creates menus to suit all tastes, with a range of carefully selected wines to complement his cooking. Open to non-residents, the Burlington Restaurant offers varied table d'hôte and à la carte menus in a stylish, relaxed atmosphere. For relaxing, there is a comfortable residents' lounge with outstanding views of the Bay, Holy Isle and across to the Ayrshire coast. Arrangements can be made for ponytrekking, sailing, golf, paragliding, boat trips and guided tours of the island.

Isle of Harris

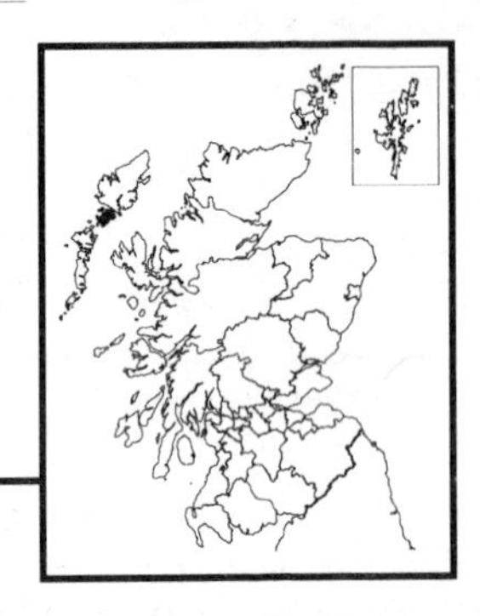

ARDVOURLIE CASTLE, Isle of Harris HS3 3AB

Tel: 01859 502307*
Fax.: 01859 502348

Residential licence; 4 bedrooms, all with private bathrooms; Historic interest; Children welcome, pets by arrangement; ££.

Built in late Victorian times and refurbished in the best traditions of the period, this haven 'far from the madding crowd' offers peace, plenty, comfort and communion with nature. There is a reassuring sense of unhurried times past induced by the numerous Victorian pieces and antiques and some of the rooms have gas lighting and fires. The spacious and well-appointed bedrooms have immense character with four-poster, half-tester and Edwardian beds and lovely views. The cuisine is generous and of high standard. Terraced lawns dotted with ornamental shrubs lead down to the shores of Loch Seaforth. Inclement weather may be temporarily forgotten by browsing in a library stocked with over a thousand titles.

Isle of Mull

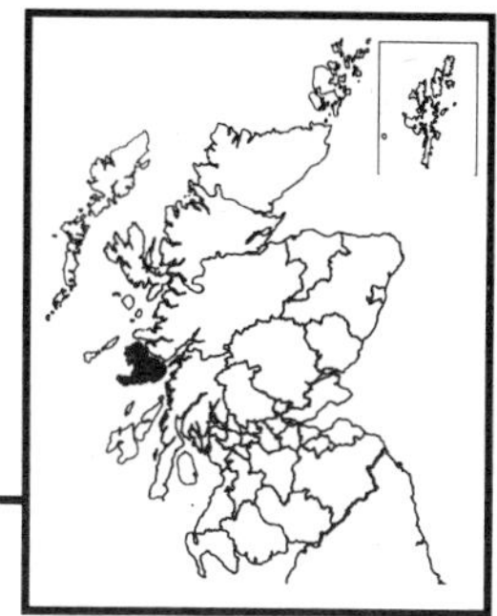

ARDFENAIG HOUSE,
By Bunessan,
Isle of Mull PA67 6DX

Tel: 01681 700210*
Fax: 01681 700210

Restricted hotel licence; 5 bedrooms, all with private bathrooms; Leisure facilities; Salen 40 miles; £££.

Romantic and remote, Ardfenaig House stands in 15 acres of grounds in the south-west corner of the island surrounded by woodland, moorland and sea. The front garden leads down to an old stone jetty where the Fiona Jean tugs gently at her mooring. With the pressures of city life an eon away, this is the perfect place for bird watchers, artists and those who just wish to take in the magnificent loch views and listen to the silence. Malcolm and Jane Davidson welcome up to 10 guests in warm and comfortable surroundings. A log fire burns in the hearth most days and visitors will enjoy good food and wines. Sailing, rowing and mountain biking are active diversions available; fishing and croquet for the passively inclined. ♛♛♛ *Highly Commended.*

DRUIMARD COUNTRY HOUSE,
Dervaig,
Isle of Mull PA75 6QW

Tel: 01688 400345/400291*
Fax: 01688 400345

Restaurant licence; 6 bedrooms, all with private bathrooms; Children and pets welcome; Tobermory 5 miles; ££.

In the peaceful setting of the beautiful Isle of Mull, this cosy and handsomely restored Victorian house, standing on a hillside with panoramic loch, river and sea views, is acclaimed for its wonderfully varied and generous cuisine. Vegetarians and vegans are well catered for and children have their own menu. Haydn and Wendy Hubbard, the owners, have created a caring ambience at this recommended retreat and the accommodation is extremely well appointed and comfortable, all the centrally heated bedrooms (including a lovely suite) having remote-control colour television, direct-dial telephone and tea and coffee-making facilities. Britain's smallest professional theatre stands within the grounds, entertaining audiences between April and October. ♛♛♛♛ *Highly Commended, Egon Ronay, Taste of Scotland.*

Kirkcudbrightshire

BALCARY BAY HOTEL,
Auchencairn, Near Castle Douglas,
Kirkcudbrightshire DG7 1QZ

Tel: 01556 640217*
Fax: 01556 640272

Fully licensed; 17 bedrooms, all with private bathrooms; Children and pets welcome; Dumfries 21 miles, Castle Douglas 7; ££.

Whether it be relaxing in the cocktail bar overlooking the bay or reclining on a four-poster bed, visitors will reflect that their choice of Balcary Bay Hotel was a wise one. The personal supervision of the resident owners ensures that efficiency is matched by friendliness and that a family atmosphere prevails. Imaginative cuisine is based on local delicacies including seafood and is complemented by an impressive wine list. Centrally heated throughout, the hotel offers well appointed bedrooms, all with en suite facilities. This is an ideal location for exploring the gardens and National Trust properties of South-West Scotland and enjoying the popular outdoor pursuits of walking, birdwatching and golf. 👑👑👑👑 *Highly Commended, AA***, RAC *** and Merit Award, Egon Ronay, Good Hotel Guide.*

Please mention
Recommended COUNTRY HOTELS
when seeking refreshment or
accommodation at a Hotel
mentioned in these pages.

Lanarkshire

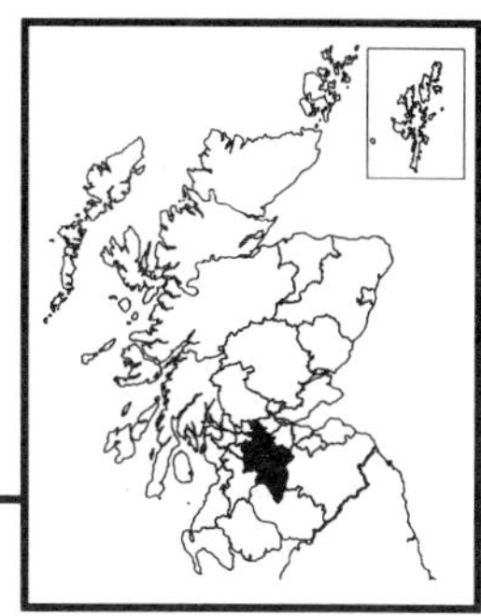

SHIELDHILL HOTEL,
Shieldhill Road, Biggar,
Lanarkshire ML12 6NA

Tel: 01899 220035
Fax: 01899 221092

Full hotel licence; 11 bedrooms, all with private bathrooms; Historic interest; Children over 10 years welcome; Conference facilities; Biggar 4 miles; £££.

Extensively refurbished in recent years with the painstaking attention to detail that is the mark of a truly first-class establishment, Shieldhill has gained a reputation for excellence. A range of bedrooms and suites is available to suit all requirements, all individually decorated in beautiful wallpapers and fabrics and equipped to the highest standards. For that very special occasion, the magnificent Chancellor Suite offers a king-size bed and a double jacuzzi — truly the ultimate in romantic luxury! The generous menu features imaginative combinations of fresh ingredients and is accompanied by an out-of-the-ordinary wine list. All in all, this fine hotel is well worth tracking down. ♛♛♛♛ *Highly Commended, AA *** and Two Rosettes, RAC *** and Comfort Award.*

NOTE

All the information in this book is given in good faith in the belief that it is correct. However, the publishers cannot guarantee the facts given in these pages, neither are they responsible for changes in policy, ownership or terms that may take place after the date of going to press. Readers should always satisfy themselves that the facilities they require are available and that the terms, if quoted, still apply.

Moray

including Morayshire and part of Banffshire, and Cullen, Dufftown and Banff.

KNOCKOMIE HOTEL, Grantown Road, Forres, Morayshire IV36 0SG

Tel: 01309 673146
Fax: 01309 673290

Fully licensed; 14 bedrooms, all with private bathrooms; Historic interest; Children and pets welcome by prior arrangement; Conference facilities; Elgin 12 miles; ££££.

An attractive country hotel of good solid worth, Knockomie will appeal to anglers, golfers, walkers, tourists, businessmen — in fact all who appreciate the combination of a superb setting, excellent food and first class facilities (not forgetting the collection of fine malt whiskies!). The Resident Director, Gavin Ellis, backed by a courteous and efficient staff, goes out of his way to ensure the well-being of guests to this most rewarding corner of Scotland. Activity holidays may be arranged, tailored to guests' requirements, which may cover golf, fishing, walking and pony trekking. The guest rooms are particularly well appointed, each having a private bathroom, colour television with satellite, tea and coffee facilities and a hairdryer. For that special occasion (or special person), a romantic "champagne break" may make dreams come true. ♛♛♛♛ *Highly Commended, AA *** and Rosette.*

ROTHES GLEN HOTEL, Rothes, Morayshire AB38 7AQ

Tel: 01340 831254
Fax: 01340 831566

Hotel licence; 16 bedrooms, all with private bathrooms; Conference facilities; Elgin 9 miles; £££.

Impressive in 10 acres of grounds, Rothes Glen bears more than a passing resemblance to Balmoral Castle, which is not surprising as they shared the same architect. This haven of tranquillity, comfort and good company enjoys lovely views of the Spey Valley, famed for its multitude of malt whisky distilleries. Loch and mountain scenery charms the eye, and the ancient city of Elgin and the quiet beaches of the Moray Firth are close by. Relaxation may also be sought in the pleasant lawned grounds in which one may play croquet or putting. After a day's activities, guests may dine well on the freshest of fine Scottish produce; later, restful repose is guaranteed in delightfully appointed rooms.

Orkney Isles

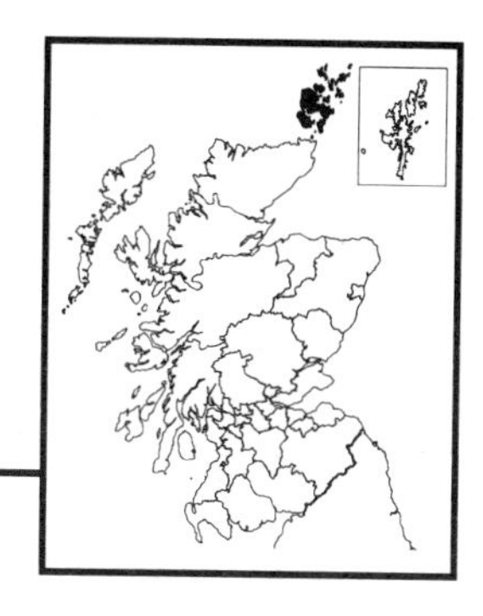

MERKISTER HOTEL,
Loch Harray, Dounby,
Orkney Islands KW17 2LF

Tel: 0185 677 1366*
Fax: 0185 677 1515

Fully licensed; 14 bedrooms, all with private bathrooms; Historic interest; Children and pets welcome; Finstown 6 miles; £.

Away from it all in the truest sense, this fine hotel provides a wonderful opportunity to commune with nature in peaceful surroundings and enjoy some of the best loch fishing in Britain and, what is more, the cuisine is really out of this world. Guest rooms are delightfully furnished; all have en suite facilities, colour television, direct-dial telephone, tea-makers and appointments that would shame many a 5-star establishment. Standing on the shores of Harray Loch, the emphasis here, naturally enough, is on fishing and many major events are held. Novices are welcomed and boats, outboards and ghillies may be arranged. The views from the hotel are breathtaking and other activities available include golf, squash and rock climbing. ♛♛♛♛ *Commended, Egon Ronay, Good Food Guide, Vegetarian Food Guide.*

Perth & Kinross

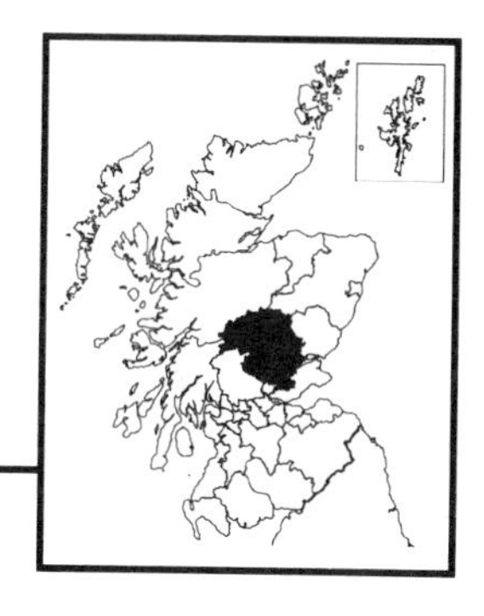

GUINACH HOUSE,
Ular Road, Aberfeldy,
Perth & Kinross PH15 2ET

Tel: 01887 820251
Fax: 01887 829607

Restricted hotel licence; 7 bedrooms, all with private bathrooms; Children welcome; Pitlochry 8 miles; £/££.

Warm, cosy and beautifully furnished, this little country house hotel is acquiring a growing reputation for its magnificent cuisine, thanks to the culinary expertise of international master-chef, Bert MacKay. Imagination combines with abundance to provide a mouthwatering selection of dishes, many in the French tradition and home produce is much in evidence. A homely and happy base from which to explore the sights and sporting attractions of Central Scotland, the house stands in 3 acres of mature and verdant grounds within strolling distance of Aberfeldy's town centre and 18-hole golf course. Guest rooms are tastefully decorated and are blessed with en suite facilities, colour television, central heating and tea and coffee-makers. ♛♛♛ *Highly Commended, AA Two Rosettes.*

FARLEYER HOUSE HOTEL,

Aberfeldy,
Perth & Kinross PH15 2JE

Tel: 01887 820332
Fax: 01887 829430

Fully licensed; 15 bedrooms, all with private bathrooms; Historic interest; Children welcome; Leisure and conference facilities; A9 12 miles, Aberfeldy 3; ££££.

Situated in almost exactly the geographical centre of Scotland, Farleyer House is the perfect base from which to explore this beautiful and historic part of Scotland. Sympathetically and lovingly refurbished, it provides the ideal backdrop for the unique culinary skills of Richard Lyth, who makes imaginative use of the plentiful local game, fish and fresh vegetables. Leisure facilities include a 9-hole golf course in the grounds and use of the heated swimming pool at the nearby Kenmore Country Club. ♛♛♛♛ *De Luxe, Good Food Guide, "Tayside Restaurant of the Year" 1996.*

DUNEARN HOUSE HOTEL & RESTAURANT,

High Street, Auchterarder,
Perth & Kinross PH3 1DB

Tel and Fax: 01764 664774

Full hotel licence; 4 bedrooms, 2 with private bathrooms; Children welcome; Crieff 8 miles; £.

Ceud mile failte o Auchterarder (a hundred thousand welcomes from Auchterarder). Whatever your language, the warmest of welcomes awaits you in Auchterarder, in the heart of picturesque Perthshire. Built in 1861, this recently converted Victorian country house is reminiscent of a bygone era, with its crackling log fires, Victorian cornicing, stained glass windows and period decor — but with twentieth century comforts. Dine in style in our elegant dining room, where you will find it difficult to choose from our imaginative à la carte menu which changes frequently and offers mouth-watering cuisine at affordable prices. Alternatively, our library and adjacent cosy bar create just the right setting in which to have a quiet drink or tasty bar meal. Our aim is to make our guests feel at home in our home, and this often results in visitors arriving as guests and leaving as friends. Further details from Fiona Corlett. ♛♛♛ *Commended.*

DALMUNZIE HOUSE,

Spittal Of Glenshee, Blairgowrie,
Perth & Kinross PH10 7QG

Tel: 01250 885224*
Fax: 01250 885225

Full hotel licence; 17 bedrooms, 16 with private bathrooms; Historic interest; Children and pets welcome; Leisure and conference facilities; Braemar 13 miles; ££.

Dalmunzie enjoys a glorious position in the mountains of the Scottish Highlands, 18 miles north of Blairgowrie and 15 miles south of Braemar on the A93. All bedrooms but one have en suite facilities, and are of individual character and centrally heated. In the lovely dining room guests can enjoy traditional Scottish fare made with locally produced ingredients wherever possible, complemented with wine from the well-stocked cellar.The hotel stands in a superb sporting estate of over 6500 acres where many activities can be pursued, such as tennis, fishing, hillwalking, ski-ing and golf over Britain's highest golf course (9 holes) which is on the doorstep. ♛♛♛ *Commended, Taste of Scotland.*

KINLOCH HOUSE HOTEL,
By Blairgowrie,
Perth & Kinross PH10 6SG

Tel: 01250 884237*
Fax: 01250 884333

Fully licensed; 21 bedrooms, all with private bathrooms; Children and pets welcome; Conference facilities; Blairgowrie 2 miles; DB&B ££££.

Victorian in origin but extended in 1911, this is a fine example of a Scottish country house, which stands in 25 acres of woods and parkland grazed by Highland cattle. With far-reaching views and superbly placed in the Perthshire Highlands, the hotel is ideally situated for country pursuits, yet the main urban centres, and even the coast, are within easy reach. Nearby there is great trout and salmon fishing and golf, as well as superb walking terrain and many historic houses and whisky distilleries to visit.The hotel has its own Sportsman's Room , complete with drying facilities, deep-freeze etc. On a more relaxed note, guest rooms are decorated and furnished to the very highest standards; all have private amenities and some have four-poster or half-tester beds. The cuisine at this warm and restful retreat will cap a pleasure-spent day, with the menu offering an extensive selection of classic and traditional Scottish dishes for which many accolades have been received. Golden moments of delightful anticipation, studying the possibilities of the menu in the cocktail bar, will presage a memorable meal. David and Sarah Shentall are to be complimented on the organisation and standards of service at this happy and distinguished hotel which must rank high on the list of recommendations for a true Scottish holiday. ♛♛♛♛ *De Luxe, AA Three Red Stars and Three Rosettes, Johansens Country Hotel of the Year 1994.*

KILLIECRANKIE HOTEL,
Killiecrankie, By Pitlochry,
Perth & Kinross PH16 5LG

Tel: 01796 473220*
Fax: 01796 472451

Fully licensed; 10 bedrooms, all with private bathrooms; Children and pets welcome; Blair Atholl 3 miles; ££.

At the northern entrance to the forested Pass of Killiecrankie, scene of the rout between William of Orange's Scottish army and the Jacobites in 1689, this charmingly appointed former manse is run in friendly and informal style by Colin and Carole Anderson. Spectacular scenery unfolds on all sides of the hotel's four acres of wooded grounds and gardens, attracting many species of wildlife. Guest rooms are very comfortable and prettily decorated with pine furniture; all have private bathroom, colour television, radio, telephone, and tea and coffee tray.The table d'hôte dinners use only the best Scottish produce available.There are many activities to fill your holiday, including golf, walking, fishing and sightseeing around the many places of historic interest in the area. ♛♛♛♛ *Highly Commended, Two AA Rosettes.*

THE GREEN HOTEL,
2 The Muirs, Kinross,
Perth & Kinross KY13 7AS

Tel: 01577 863467
Fax: 01577 863180

Fully licensed; 47 bedrooms, all with private bathrooms; Children and pets welcome; Leisure and conference facilities; Dunfermline 9 miles; ££.

Once a coaching inn, The Green Hotel is now better known as an hotel with an impressive range of leisure activities and a wealth of modern facilities. Families are welcome, suites with baby listening devices being available. Bedrooms all have a bath or shower en suite,as well as satellite television, radio and telephone. Energy may be expended in a variety of ways, such as swimming in the indoor pool, squash, table tennis or, more sedately, putting, croquet and pool. After such diversions the Defiance Bar proves a popular meeting place and offers a wide range of meals, including a special children's menu. The Restaurant is the venue for superb à la carte and table d'hôte dinners with Continental dishes vying for attention with traditional fare. ♛♛♛♛♛ *Highly Commended.* **See also Colour Advertisement on page 14.**

BALLATHIE HOUSE HOTEL,
Kinclaven, By Stanley,
Perth & Kinross PH1 4QN

Tel: 01250 883268
Fax: 01250 883396

Hotel licence; 28 bedrooms, all with private bathrooms; Historic interest; Children and pets welcome; Leisure and conference facilities; Perth 2 miles; £££/££££.

Standing in its own 1500 acre estate overlooking the River Tay, this impressive baronial mansion has been carefully and sympathetically restored and refurbished, and stands today as a country hotel of unique charm and character. Elegant antique and period furnishings blend perfectly with the restful decor to create an ambience which is both tranquil and relaxing, and positively conducive to a feeling of well being. Fresh local salmon and other fine Scottish produce feature on the daily changing menus; special diets can be catered for by arrangement. A range of bedrooms is available, all equipped to the highest standards with private bathrooms, colour television, telephone and refreshment facilities. Leisure activities include Tay salmon fishing, tennis, croquet, putting and walking in the extensive grounds, and the hotel is centrally placed for visiting the many attractions of the area. ♛♛♛♛ *De Luxe, AA Two Rosettes, Winner Taste of Scotland Hotel of the Year.*

DUPPLIN CASTLE,
Dupplin Estate, By Perth,
Perth & Kinross PH2 0PY

Tel: 01738 623224
Fax: 01738 444140

6 bedrooms, all with private bathrooms; Children over 12 years welcome, pets by arrangement; Conference facilities; Perth 5 miles; ££.

Sweeping lawns and mature woodland, part of 30 acres of private parkland, surround this fine Scottish mansion. Rising phoenix-fashion from the ashes of a consuming fire in 1969 and designed by one of Scotland's leading architects, the castle is luxuriously furnished and its elegant rooms retain the ambience of more sedate years with antiques and paintings contributing to the mood. Derek and Angela Straker are justly proud of their lovely home and supervise the outstanding country house cooking with guests dining in house party style. (Please book in advance of arrival). Guest rooms are blessed with the finest up-to-date appointments and there are impressive views over the Earn Valley. Sporting opportunities within easy reach include excellent golf, fishing, shooting and horse racing.

---

* The appearance of an asterisk after the telephone number indicates that the hotel in question is closed for a period during the winter months. Exact dates should be ascertained from the hotel itself.

DALSHIAN HOUSE,
Old Perth Road, Pitlochry,
Perth & Kinross PH16 5JS

Tel and Fax: 01796 472173

Unlicensed; 7 bedrooms, all with private bathrooms; Children and pets welcome; Pitlochry 1½ miles; £.

Quiet, secluded and set in its own parklands one and a half miles south of Pitlochry, Dalshian House is an early 19th century farmhouse built in 1812. The original public rooms are elegantly furnished and the spacious bedrooms retain their original character. There are four double, one twin and two family bedrooms, all en suite with colour television and welcome tea/coffee tray. The resident owners, Malcolm and Althea Carr, have created an atmosphere of comfort and quality, with a reputation for good food. Please send for brochure giving full details. ♛♛♛ *Commended.*

Ross-shire

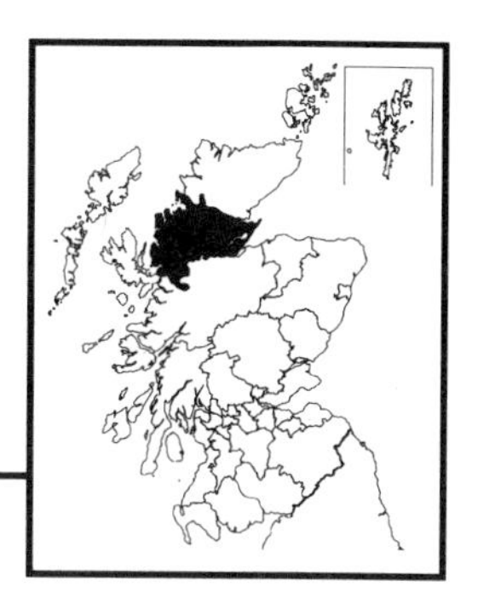

CONCHRA HOUSE HOTEL,
Ardelve, Kyle of Lochalsh,
Ross-shire IV40 8DZ

Tel: 01599 555233
Fax: 01599 555433

Table licence; 6 bedrooms, 3 with private bathrooms; Historic interest; Children welcome, pets by arrangement; Conference facilities; Kyle of Lochalsh 8 miles; £.

Dating back to the 1760's, this attractive mansion has performed several functions over the years. Now, carefully refurbished and updated by the present proprietors, Colin and Mary Deans, both of whom are members of the Evangelical Alliance for Scotland, it serves visitors to the rugged and romantic magnificence of the Wester Ross Highlands with distinction. Just off the A87 road to Kyle of Lochalsh, Conchra (an old Gaelic word now meaning 'fold' or 'haven') stands in extensive grounds which form part of a 2500-acre estate. Ideal for those seeking to get away from it all, guests will find excellent accommodation in the main house and splendidly modernised adjacent self-catering farm cottages. The wholesome, typically Scottish cuisine represents fine value. ♛♛♛ *Highly Commended, Taste of Scotland, Johansens.*

PUBLISHER'S NOTE

While every effort is made to ensure accuracy, we regret that FHG Publications cannot accept responsibility for errors, omissions or misrepresentations in our entries or any consequences thereof. Prices in particular should be checked because we go to press early. We will follow up complaints but cannot act as arbiters or agents for either party.

KINKELL HOUSE HOTEL, Easter Kinkell, Conon Bridge, Ross-shire IV7 8HY

Tel: 01349 861270
Fax: 01349 865902

Restricted hotel licence; 7 bedrooms, all with private bathrooms; Children and pets welcome; Muir of Ord 4 miles; ££.

Recently extended to cater for the ever-growing numbers of escapees from urban stress, this splendid little house provides all the essentials for a relaxing and rewarding break. The captivating scenery of the Black Isle, dominated by lofty Ben Wyvis (3429ft) is happily augmented by the comforts of this handsomely restored Victorian farmhouse. Rich furnishings and antiques abound and the accommodation features spacious, centrally heated rooms with en suite facilities and tea and coffee-makers. Steve and Marsha Fraser, the Proprietors, are benign supervisors of the well-being of their guests with great attention given to the planning of the excellent cuisine. There are numerous sights and sporting diversions in this lovely area, especially hill walking and climbing, fishing and golf. ♛♛♛ *Highly Commended, AA** and Rosette.*

COUL HOUSE HOTEL, Contin, By Strathpeffer, Ross-shire IV14 9EY

Tel: 01997 421487
Fax: 01997 421945

Full hotel licence; 20 bedrooms, all with private bathrooms; Historic interest; Children and pets welcome; Leisure and conference facilities; Strathpeffer 2 miles; £££.

Ancient home of the Mackenzies of Coul, this lovely home stands today as eloquent testimony to the flair and imagination of the proprietors, Ann and Martyn Hill. The comfortable bedrooms, all superbly appointed with colour teletext television, direct-dial telephone, private bathrooms and several thoughtful extras, enjoy wonderful views over forest and mountain. The elegant dining room features a "Taste of Scotland" à la carte menu. A wide range of special interest breaks are available, ranging from pony trekking and golf to "Highland Heritage" and "Highland Passport" weeks which enable one to explore fully the unique heritage of this beautiful part of Scotland. ♛♛♛♛ *Highly Commended, AA*** and Rosette, Taste of Scotland, Decanter Wine List of the Year, Ashley Courtenay, Ackerman.*

KINCRAIG HOUSE HOTEL,
Invergordon,
Ross-shire IV18 0LF

Tel: 01349 852587
Fax: 01349 852193

Fully licensed; 19 bedrooms, all with private bathrooms; Historic interest; Children and pets welcome; Dingwall 11 miles; ££.

Less than half an hour's drive from Inverness, Kincraig House stands amidst some of Scotland's most magnificent scenery, gazing over the Cromarty Firth. The resident proprietors, Harry and Sandra Dixon, have created here a splendid country house hotel, where the emphasis is very firmly on comfort and relaxation. The building is largely unchanged since Victorian times; inside, oak panelled walls and superb furnishings blend harmoniously with modern appointments such as colour television, telephones, tea and coffee makers, and private facilities. The extensive à la carte menu has justly gained many compliments; a daily bar menu is also available. Excellent road communications make this an ideal base for the business person or holidaymaker.

MANSFIELD HOUSE HOTEL,
Scotsburn Road, Tain,
Ross-shire IV19 1PR

Tel: 01862 892052
Fax: 01862 892260

Fully licensed; 18 bedrooms, all with private bathrooms; Historic interest; Children and pets welcome; Conference facilities; Invergordon 10 miles; ££.

The Mansfield House Hotel is an elegant Victorian country house under the personal management of the Lauritsen family. It is situated in the heart of the Highland golfing area, only 10 minutes from the Royal Dornoch Golf Club and within easy reach of at least a dozen others. The hotel can arrange discounted green fees at Tain Golf Club. With de luxe rooms, good conference facilities, and first class dining facilities, the hotel makes an excellent venue for business or social golf. We also take special care of non-golfing guests. Please call or fax for brochure and tariff. ♛♛♛♛ *Highly Commended, AA and RAC ***, Taste of Scotland, Scotland's Commended, Les Routiers.* **See also Colour Advertisement on page 14.**

MORANGIE HOUSE HOTEL,
Tain,
Ross-shire IV19 1PY

Tel: 01862 892281
Fax: 01862 892872

Fully licensed; 26 bedrooms, all with private bathrooms; Historic interest; Children welcome, pets by arrangement; Invergordon 10 miles; ££.

A beautifully modernised and sumptuously decorated Victorian mansion close to the shores of the Dornoch Firth and just 10 minutes from Dornoch, this is an ideal base from which to explore the Northern Highlands, with peerless opportunities for fishing, hill walking and golf (discounted green fees can be arranged). Diversions close at hand include a bowling green, tennis courts and a fine beach. Guest rooms have en suite bathrooms, television, direct-dial telephone and coffee-makers, and the master bedroom has a large four-poster and a bathroom with a whirlpool corner bath. The best of Highland cuisine served in our award-winning restaurant features salmon, venison and game in season, and there is a comprehensive selection of malt whiskies. Quality Weekend Breaks available — details on request. ♛♛♛♛ *Highly Commended, AA and RAC***, Ashley Courtenay, Les Routiers.*

PLEASE MENTION THIS GUIDE WHEN YOU WRITE OR PHONE TO ENQUIRE ABOUT ACCOMMODATION.
IF YOU ARE WRITING, A STAMPED, ADDRESSED ENVELOPE IS ALWAYS APPRECIATED.

Stirling

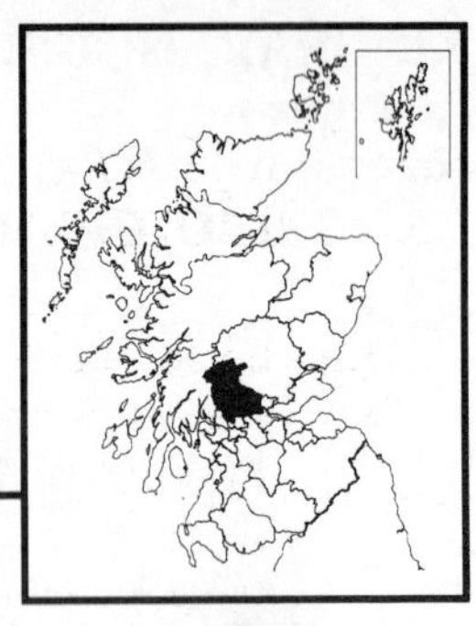

CULCREUCH CASTLE & COUNTRY PARK,

Fintry,
Stirlingshire G63 OLW

Tel: 01360 860228/860555
Fax: 01360 860556

Fully licensed; 8 bedrooms, all with private bathrooms; Historic interest; Children welcome, pets by arrangement; Conference facilities; Balfron 5 miles; ££.

Standing four-square amidst beautiful scenery, Culcreuch Castle is a great survivor: built in 1296 it remains in remarkable condition. Part of a 1000-acre estate, it provides elegant accommodation for visitors to picturesque central Scotland and Loch Lomond, Stirling and the Trossachs in particular, whilst Glasgow may be reached in under half an hour. The views from this fascinating place are breathtaking and within its stout walls are handsome furnished suites and bedrooms, some with four-posters. Some 200 yards from the castle is a new development of eight Scandinavian style holiday lodges. Guests may dine well in either the ornate, panelled Castle Restaurant or in the 700-year old Dungeon Diner in a far happier state of mind than previous occupants! *Commended.*

Hotels with Conference Facilities

These hotels cater for meetings, conferences and seminars of varying sizes. Brief details are listed below — please see the main entry under the appropriate county heading for a fuller description.

ENGLAND

BUCKINGHAMSHIRE

The Grovefield Hotel, Taplow Common Road, Burnham SL1 8LP (01628 603131; Fax: 01628 668078). 8 meeting rooms suitable for up to 300 delegates (80 residential).

CAMBRIDGESHIRE

The Nyton, 7 Barton Road, Ely CB7 4HZ (01353 662459; Fax: 01353 666619). 2 meeting rooms suitable for up to 30 delegates.

Melbourn Bury, Melbourn, Royston SG8 6DE (01763 261151; Fax: 01763 262375). Facilities for up to 24 boardroom-style, up to 50 theatre-style.

CHESHIRE

Alderley Edge Hotel, Macclesfield Road, Alderley Edge SK9 7BJ (01625 583033; Fax: 01625 586343). Three conference rooms for between 30 and 120 persons; secretarial services.

Broxton Hall Hotel, Whitchurch Road, Broxton, Chester CH3 9JS (01829 782321; Fax: 01829 782330). Boardroom for meetings, maximum 30.

Rookery Hall, Worleston, Near Nantwich CW5 6DQ (01270 610016; Fax: 01270 611211). 3 large conference rooms, bar area, 2 syndicate rooms; smaller meeting rooms also available.

Willington Hall Hotel, Willington, Tarporley CW6 0NB (01829 752321; Fax: 01829 752596). Small conferences and meetings up to 16.

CORNWALL

Tredethy Country Hotel, Helland Bridge, Bodmin PL30 4QS (01208 841262; Fax: 01208 841707). 3 meeting rooms, (up to 40); OHP, video.

Meudon Hotel, Mawnan Smith, Falmouth TR11 5HT (01326 250541; Fax: 01326 250543). 3 rooms for between 12 and 60 persons

Old Rectory Country House Hotel, St Keyne, Liskeard PL14 4RL (01579 342617). Suitable for small meetings up to 30.

Penventon Hotel, West End, Redruth TR15 1TE (01209 214141; Fax: 01209 219164). Meeting rooms, OHP, fax, video, TV. Up to 200 delegates .

Alverton Manor, Tregolls Road, Truro TR1 1XQ (01872 76633; Fax: 01872 222989). Conference facilities available.

CUMBRIA

Talkin Tarn House Hotel, Brampton, Carlisle CA8 1LS (016977 2340; Fax: 016977 2089). Suitable for small meetings up to20.

Nanny Brow Country House Hotel, Clappersgate, Ambleside LA22 9NF (015394 32036; Fax: 015394 32450). Facilities available.

Rothay Manor Hotel, Rothay Bridge, Ambleside LA22 0EH (015394 33605; Fax: 015394 33607). Meeting room suitable for 20.

Brantwood Country Hotel, Stainton, Penrith CA11 0EP (01768 862748; Fax: 01768 890164). 2 meeting rooms suitable for up to 50. OHP, video, flipcharts.

DERBYSHIRE

Riverside Country House Hotel, Ashford-in-the-Water, Bakewell DE45 1QF (01629 814275; Fax: 01629 812873). Suitable for small meetings for between 12 and 15 persons.

Cavendish Hotel, Baslow DE45 1SP (01246 582311; Fax: 01246 582312). Facilities for up to 20 persons.

Fischer's Baslow Hall, Calver Road, Baslow DE45 1RR (01246 583259; Fax: 01246 583818). Daily and 24hr delegate rates; private meeting rooms available.

DEVON

Tytherleigh Cot Hotel, Chardstock, Axminster EX13 7BN (01460 221170; Fax: 01460 221291). Can cater for 25 theatre-style; separate syndicate room for up to 10.

The Edgemoor, Bovey Tracey TQ13 9LE (01626 832466; Fax: 01626 834760). 2 meeting rooms, suitable for 50; OHP, TV, video, flipcharts.

Ilsington Country Hotel, Ilsington, Near Bovey Tracey TQ13 9RR (01364 661452; Fax: 01364 661307). 4 rooms, OHP, flipcharts, TV, video etc.

Royal Beacon Hotel, Exmouth EX8 2AF (01395 264886; Fax: 01395 268890). Facilities available.

Buckland-Tout-Saints, Goveton, Kingsbridge TQ7 2DS (01548 853055; Fax: 01548 856261). 2 meeting rooms (maximum 30) for directors and senior managers.

Lydford House Hotel, Lydford, Okehampton EX20 4AU (01822 820347; Fax: 01822 820442). Suitable for small meetings up to 20; OHP, photocopier etc.

Whitechapel Manor, South Molton EX36 3EG (01769 573377; Fax: 01769 573797. 2 meeting rooms suitable for up to 30.

Cherrybrook Hotel, Two Bridges, Yelverton PL20 6SP (Tel/Fax: 01822 880260). 2 meeting rooms suitable for 25.

DORSET

Chedington Court Hotel, Chedington, Beaminster DT8 3HY (01935 891265; Fax: 01935 891442). Small meetings only catered for.

Anvil Hotel, Pimperne, Blandford DT11 8UQ (01258 453431). Meeting room suitable for up to 25.

Eype's Mouth Country Hotel, Eype, Bridport DY6 6AL (01308 423300; Fax: 01308 420033). 3 meeting rooms, suitable for up to 130; OHP, TV, video, microphone, flipchart.

Plumber Manor, Sturminster Newton DT10 2AF (01258 472507; Fax: 01258 473370). Up to 25 delegates (16 residential); OHP, screen, flipcharts.

Kemps Country House Hotel, East Stoke, Wareham BH20 6AL (01929 462563; Fax: 01929 405287). Facilities available.

Cromwell House Hotel, Lulworth Cove, Wareham BH20 5RJ (01929 400253; Fax: 01929 400566). Small conferences and meetings.

Moonfleet Manor, Near Weymouth DT3 4ED (01305 786948; Fax: 01305 774395). Various syndicate rooms plus meeting room suitable for up to 50.

CO. DURHAM

Headlam Hall, Near Gainford, Darlington DL2 3HA (01325 730238/730691; Fax: 01325 730790). 3 conference rooms; TV, video, over-head projectors etc.

Raven Country Hotel, Broomhill, Ebchester DH8 6RY (01207 560367; Fax: 01207 560262). 3 meeting rooms, suitable for up to 120 delegates; OHP etc available.

ESSEX

Pontlands Park Country Hotel, Great Baddo, Near Chelmsford CM2 8HR (01245 476444; Fax: 01245 478393). Suitable for small residential conferences; 2 meeting rooms.

Bell Inn & Hill House, Horndon-on-the-Hill SS17 8LD (01375 673154; Fax: 01375 361611). Facilities available.

GLOUCESTERSHIRE

Lower Slaughter Manor, Lower Slaughter GL54 2HP (01451 820456; Fax: 01451 822150). Board room and syndicate room with all facilities (suitable for up to 18).

Burleigh Court, Burleigh, Minchinhampton GL5 2PF (01453 883804; Fax: 01453 886870). Meeting room, wide range of equipment available.

Wyck Hill House Hotel, Burford Road, Stow-on-the -Wold GL54 1HY (01451 831936; Fax: 01451 832243). 3 rooms available.

Tewkesbury Park Hotel Country Club Resort, Lincoln Green Lane,Tewkesbury, GL20 7DN (01684 295405; Fax: 01684 292386). Several fully equipped meeting rooms available.

Hatton Court Hotel, Upton Hill, Upton St Leonards GL4 8DE (01452 617412; Fax: 01452 612945). 3 conference rooms and 3 syndicate rooms; maximum 60 delegates.

HAMPSHIRE

Esseborne Manor Hotel, Hurstbourne Tarrant, Andover SP11 0ER (01264 736444; Fax: 01264 736725). Facilities for maximum of 25 delegates.

New Park Manor, Lyndhurst Road, Brockenhurst SO42 7QH (01590 623467; Fax: 01590 622268). Social functions and conferences catered for.

Ashburn Hotel, Fordingbridge SP6 1JP (01425 652060; Fax: 01425 652150). 2 conference rooms (suitable 30/120).

Passford House, Mount Pleasant Lane, Near Lymington SO41 8LS (01590 682398; Fax: 01590 683494). Suitable for up to 30.

Bramble Hill Hotel, Bramshaw, Near Lyndhurst SO43 7JG (01703 813165). Small meeting room suitable for 20 people.

Fifehead Manor, Middle Wallop, Stockbridge SO20 8EG (01264 781565; Fax: 01264 781400). Facilities available.

Busketts Lawn Hotel, Woodlands, Near Southampton SO40 7GL (01703 292272; Fax: 01703 292487). 2 meeting rooms suitable for up to 100; OHP and screen, TV, video.

Botley Park Hotel, Botley, Southampton SO32 2UA (01489 780888; Fax: 01489 789242). 9 conference/banqueting rooms catering for 2-200.

Woodlands Lodge Hotel, Bartley Road, Ashurst, Woodlands SO4 2GN (01703 292257; Fax: 01703 293090). 3 meeting rooms; up to 16 residential.

HEREFORD & WORCESTER

Dumbleton Hall, Dumbleton, Near Evesham (01386 881240; Fax: 01386 882142). Conference suite.

New Priory Hotel, Stretton Sugwas, Hereford HR4 7AR (01432 760264; Fax: 01432 761809). 2 meeting rooms, up to 80 seated.

Penrhos Court Hotel, Penrhos Court, Kington (01544 230720; Fax: 01544 230754). Suitable for exhibitions, presentations and meetings.

Pengethley Manor Hotel, Pengethley Park, Near Ross-on-Wye HR9 6LL (01989 730211; Fax: 01989 730238). Conference centre with exclusive private facilities.

HERTFORDSHIRE

West Lodge Park Hotel, Cockfosters Road, Hadley Wood EN4 0PY (0181-440 8311; Fax: 0181-449 3698). 2 main conference rooms and 3 syndicate rooms; inclusive delegate rates available.

Briggens House Hotel, Briggens Park, Stanstead Abbotts, Near Ware SG12 8LD (01279 829955; Fax: 01279 793685). 9 conference rooms suitable for meetings from 2 to 120 persons.

ISLES OF SCILLY

St Martin's on the Isle Hotel, St Martin's TR25 0QW (01720 422092; Fax: 01720 422298). 2 meeting rooms, up to 48 residential.

KENT

Eastwell Manor Hotel, Eastwell Park, Boughton Lees, Ashford TN25 4HR (01233 219555; Fax: 01233 635530). Facilities for boardroom and other corporate meetings for up to 50 delegates.

Garden Hotel, 167 The Street, Boughton, Faversham ME13 9BH (01227 751411; Fax: 01227 751801). Private room available for meetings; audio-visual equipment, fax, photocopying.

Brandshatch Place Hotel, Fawkham Valley Road, Fawkham DA3 8NQ (01474 872239; Fax: 01474 879652). 7 conference and syndicate rooms catering for up to 150.

LANCASHIRE

Northcote Manor, Langho Road, Blackburn BB6 8BE (01254 240555; Fax: 01254 246568). Facilities for up to 20 board-room style.

Woolton Redbourne Hotel, Acrefield Road, Woolton, Liverpool L25 5JN (0151-428 2152/421 1500; Fax: 0151-421 1501). Available for small conferences up to 16 persons.

Mains Hall, Mains Lane, Singleton FY6 7LE (01253 885130; Fax: 01253 894132). Comprehensive facilities including fax and photocopying for up to 60 delegates.

Holland Hall Hotel, Lafford Lane, Upholland WN8 0QZ (01695 624426: Fax: 01695 622433). Banqueting and conference facilities for up to 200.

LEICESTERSHIRE

The Priest House, Kings Mills, Castle Donington DE74 2RR (01332 810649; Fax: 01332 811141). Facilities for up to 130; 8 rooms including boardroom.

Barnsdale Lodge Hotel, The Avenue, Rutland Water North Shore, Exton LE15 8AB (01572 724678; Fax: 01572 724961). 3 conference rooms suitable for 2 to 200 delegates.

Normanton Park Hotel, Rutland Water South Shore, Oakham LE15 7HG (01780 720315; Fax: 01780 721086). Business meetings and seminars, suitable for up to 70 delegates.

LINCOLNSHIRE

Washingborough Hall Country House Hotel, Church Hill, Washingborough LN4 1BE (01522 790340; Fax: 01522 792936). Full conference facilities available.

Petwood House Hotel, Woodhall Spa LN10 6QF (01526 352411; Fax: 01526 353473). 4 suites accommodating up to 150 theatre-style.

Eagle Lodge Hotel, The Broadway, Woodhall Spa LN10 6ST (01526 353231; Fax: 01526 352797). Falcon Room suitable for 5-50 delegates.

NORFOLK

The Old Rectory, Great Snoring, Fakenham NR21 0HP (01328 820597; Fax: 01328 820048). Facilities for seminars for 10 to 12 delegates.

Park Farm Country Hotel, Hethersett, Norwich NR9 3DL (01603 810264; Fax: 01603 812104). 6 conference rooms with all standard equipment, suitable for 15-120 delegates. Competitive daily and 24hr rates.

Park House, Sandringham, King's Lynn PE35 6EH (01485 543000; Fax: 01485 540663). Meeting room suitable for 40.

Norfolk Mead Hotel, Coltishall, Norwich NR12 7DN (01603 737531; Fax: 01603 737521). 2 meeting rooms suitable for 20.

Kingfisher Hotel, Stalham NR12 9AN (01692 581974; Fax: 01692 582544). Function room (can be divided), up to 100 theatre-style.

NORTHUMBERLAND

Riverdale Hall Hotel, Bellingham NE48 2JT (01434 220254; Fax: 01434 220457). 2 meeting rooms suitable for up to 30; OHP, flip chart etc.

Linden Hall Hotel & Health Spa, Longhorsley, Morpeth NE65 8XF (01670 516611; Fax: 01670 788544). 5 superbly equipped conference suites, the largest catering for up to 300.

OXFORDSHIRE

Studley Priory Hotel, Horton-cum-Studley, Oxford OX33 1AZ (01865 351203/351254; Fax: 01865 351613). Facilities for up to 20 classroom-style, 30 boardroom-style, 50 theatre-style.

Westwood Country Hotel, Hinksey Hill Top, Oxford OX1 5BG (01865 735408; Fax: 01865 736536). 2 meeting rooms, suitable for up to 50.

The Springs Hotel, Wallingford Road, North Stoke, Wallingford OX10 6BE (01491 836687; Fax: 01491 836877). 3 conference rooms with facilities for up to 50 delegates.

SHROPSHIRE

Longmynd Hotel, Church Stretton SY6 6AG (01694 722244; Fax: 01694 722216). Facilities available.

Redfern Hotel, Cleobury Mortimer DY14 8AA (01299 270395; Fax: 01299 271011). 2 meeting rooms suitable for up to 20 delegates.

The Moor Hall, Stoke St Milborough, Near Ludlow SY8 3EG (01584 823209; Fax: 01584 823387). Facilities for small meetings (up to 30).

Dinham Hall Hotel, By the Castle, Dinham, Ludlow SY8 1EJ (01584 876464; Fax: 01584 876019). The Merchant Suite, a 14th century timbered room, seats up to 24.

Bourton Manor, Bourton, Much Wenlock TF13 6QE (01746 36531; Fax: 01746 36683). Meeting room suitable for up to 40.

Rowton Castle Hotel, Halfway House, Shrewsbury SY5 9EP (01743 884044; Fax: 01743 884949). The fully equipped Cardeston Suite can seat up to 150 theatre-style; the Oak Room can accommodate up to 20 for private meetings.

SOMERSET

Combe Grove Manor, Brassknocker Hill, Monkton Combe, Bath BA2 7HS (01225 834644; Fax: 01225 834561). Three meeting rooms suitable for up to 80 delegates.

Ston Easton Park, Ston Easton, Near Bath BA3 4DF (01761 241631; Fax: 01761 241377). Facilities for up to 24 boardroom-style or up to 50 theatre-style.

Daneswood House Hotel, Cuck Hill, Shipham BS25 1RD (01934 843145; Fax: 01934 843824). Facilities available.

Holbrook House Hotel, Holbrook, Near Wincanton BA9 8BS (01963 32377; Fax: 01963 32681). 2 rooms suitable for 30/40 delegates.

STAFFORDSHIRE

Jarvis Newton Park Hotel, Newton Solney, Near Burton-upon-Trent DE15 0SS (01283 703568; Fax: 01283 703214). 5 meeting rooms suitable for up to 100 (60 residential).

Stone House Hotel, Stone ST15 0BQ (01785 815531; Fax: 01785 814764). 3 function rooms accommodating 8-190 delegates.

SUFFOLK

Wood Hall Hotel & Country Club, Shottisham, Woodbridge IP12 3EG (01394 411283; Fax: 01394 410007). Facilities for conferences and exhibitions (up to 150).

EAST SUSSEX

Powdermills Hotel, Powdermill Lane, Battle TN33 0SP (01424 775511; Fax: 01424 774540). Large pavilion to seat up to 300 delegates.

Netherfield Place Hotel, Battle TN33 9PP (01424 774455; Fax: 01424 774024). The Bayeux Room and Abbey Room are 2 private conference rooms. Daily/overnight delegate rates on request.

WEST SUSSEX

Burpham Country Hotel, Old Down, Burpham BN18 9RJ (01903 882160; Fax: 01903 884627). Facilities for small meetings and seminars.

Ghyll Manor, Rusper, Near Horsham RH12 4PX (01293 871571; Fax: 01293 871419). Facilities available.

WARWICKSHIRE

Chapel House Hotel and Restaurant, Friars Gate, Atherstone CV9 1EY (01827 718949; Fax: 01827 717702). Maximum of 20 delegates boardroom-style; audio-visual aids on request.

Nailcote Hall, Berkswell CV7 7DE (01203 466174; Fax: 01203 470270). Conference rooms, syndicate rooms and private dining facilities.

Aylesbury House Hotel, Packwood, Near Hockley Heath B94 6PL (01564 779207; Fax: 01564 770917). Facilities for up to 80.

Welcombe Hotel & Golf Course, Warwick Road, Stratford-upon-Avon CV37 0NR (01789 295252; Fax: 01789 414666). 6 private rooms accommodating up to 140 delegates.

Ettington Park, Alderminster, Stratford-upon-Avon CV37 8BU (01789 450123; Fax: 01789 450472). Conference rooms and business centre; maximum 70 delegates.

WEST MIDLANDS.

Coombe Abbey, Brinklow Road, Binley, Coventry CV3 2AB (01203 450450; Fax: 01203 635101). 10 syndicate rooms suitable for 10 to 200 delegates.

WILTSHIRE.

The Manor House Hotel, Castle Combe, Chippenham SN14 7HR (01249 782206; Fax: 01249 782159). Dunstanville Suite (50 theatre-style) and several boardrooms seating from 10 to 20 delegates.

Crudwell Court, Crudwell, Malmesbury SN16 9EP (01666 577194; Fax: 01666 577853). Conservatory to seat up to 30.

Whatley Manor, Near Easton Grey, Malmesbury SN16 0RB (01666 822888; Fax: 01666 826120). Fully equipped Terrace Room Suite is suitable for up to 25 delegates.

Bishopstrow House, Warminster BA12 9HH (01985 212312; Fax: 01985 216769). Conference and banqueting facilities; up to 60 theatre-style.

EAST YORKSHIRE

The Manor House, Northlands, Walkington, Near Beverley HU17 8RT (01482 881645; Fax: 01482 866501). Small meetings/conferences up to 20 persons catered for.

NORTH YORKSHIRE

Elmfield Country House, Arrathorne, Bedale DL8 1NE (01677 450558; Fax: 01677 450557). Small meetings/conferences catered for.

Boar's Head Country Hotel, Ripley Castle Estate, Near Harrogate HG3 3AY (01423 771888; Fax: 01423 771509). 9 conference and banqueting suites.

Red Hall, Great Broughton, Stokesley TS9 7ET (Tel & Fax: 01642 712300). 2 rooms suitable for small meetings.

Stakesby Manor Hotel, High Stakesby, Whitby YO21 1HL (01947 602773; Fax: 01947 602140). Facilities available.

Parsonage Country House Hotel, Main Street, Escrick, York YO4 6LE (01904 728111; Fax: 01904 728151). Several well appointed rooms and suites suitable for up to 160 persons.

WEST YORKSHIRE

Holme Castle Country Hotel, Holme, Holmfirth HD7 1QG (01484 686764; Fax: 01484 687775). Suitable for small meetings; flipchart, TV, VCR.

Bagden Hall Hotel, Scissett, Near Huddersfield HD8 9LE (01484 865330; Fax: 01484 861001). Facilities available.

Linton Springs Hotel, Sicklinghall Road, Wetherby LS22 4AF (01937 585353; Fax: 01937 587579). The Linton Suite, The Terrace Room and a boardroom available for meetings from 5 to 50 persons.

WALES

NORTH WALES. **Mynydd Ednyfed Country House,** Criccieth LL52 0PH (01766 523269). Conference room (up to 60).

NORTH WALES. **Penmaenuchaf Hall Hotel,** Penmaenpool, Dolgellau LL40 1YB (01341 422129; Fax: 01341 422129). Fully equipped facilities for up to 19 delegates residential and up to 50 non-residential.

NORTH WALES. **Bodysgallen Hall,** Llandudno LL30 1RS (01492 584466; Fax: 01492 582519). 3 rooms with facilities for 4-50 delegates; boardroom seating 26.

DYFED. **Hotel Penrallt,** Aberporth, Cardigan SA43 2BS (01239 810227; Fax: 01239 811375). Small conference room and secretarial services.

DYFED. **Waterwynch Bay Hotel**, Tenby SA70 8TJ (01834 842464; Fax: 01834 845076). Small meetings/conferences catered for (maximum 30).

POWYS. **Llangoed Hall**, Llyswen, Brecon LD3 0YP (01874 754525; Fax: 01874 754545). Facilities for up to 50 theatre-style and boardroom for up to 28.

POWYS. **Maesmawr Hall Hotel,** Caersws SY17 5SF (01686 688255; Fax: 01686 688410). One large and 2 smaller conference rooms suitable for up to 120 delegates.

POWYS. **Gliffaes Country House Hotel,** Crickhowell NP8 1RH (01874 730371; Fax: 01874 730463). Small meetings up to 16 catered for.

POWYS. **Elan Valley Hotel,** Rhayader LD6 5HN (01597 810448). 3 rooms suitable for 10-80 delegates, with TV, video, flipcharts.

SOUTH WALES. **Maes Manor Hotel,** Blackwood NP2 0AG (01495 220011; Fax: 01495 228217). Large function room suitable for up to 250. Corporate discount rates.

SOUTH WALES. **Egerton Grey Country House Hotel,** Porthkerry (01446 711666; Fax: 01446 711690). Facilities available.

SCOTLAND

ABERDEENSHIRE. **Banchory Lodge Hotel,** Banchory AB31 5HS (01330 822625; Fax: 01330 825019). Facilities for up to 25 delegates.

AYRSHIRE. **Montgreenan Mansion,** Montgreenan Estate, Near Kilwinning KA13 7QZ (01294 557733; Fax: 01294 850397). Small conferences for up to 30 delegates.

DUMFRIESSHIRE. **The Dryfesdale Hotel,** Lockerbie DG11 2SF (01576 202427; Fax: 01576 204187). 2 conference rooms, one 40 maximum, one 10 maximum.

EDINBURGH & LOTHIANS. **Dalhousie Castle Hotel,** Bonnyrigg, Near Edinburgh EH19 3JB (01875 820153; Fax: 01875 821936). 5 well-equipped conference rooms make an unusual venue for all kinds of business meetings.

FIFE. **Balbirnie House Hotel,** Markinch KY7 6NE (01592 610066; Fax: 01592 610529). 5 meeting rooms, suitable for up to 150 (60 residential).

FIFE. **Sandford Country House Hotel**, Newton Hill, Wormit, Near Dundee DD6 8RG (01382 541802; Fax: 01382 542136). Suite and conference rooms suitable for up to 45 delegates; corporate activity days organised.

INVERNESS-SHIRE. **Arisaig House**, Beasdale, By Arisaig PH39 (01687 450622; Fax: 01687 450626). Room seating up to 10 persons, suitable for board meetings etc.

LANARKSHIRE. **Shieldhill Hotel**, Shieldhill Road, Biggar ML12 6NA (01899 220035; Fax: 01899 221092). Boardroom and theatre-style facilities, ideal for small conferences. Daily and 24hr rates, also exclusive use.

MORAYSHIRE. **Knockomie Hotel,** Grantown Road, Forres IV36 0SG (01309 673146; Fax: 01309 673290). Strathcoma Room up to 25, Cockburn Room up to 12; gardens available for courses.

MORAYSHIRE. **Rothes Glen Hotel,** Rothes AB38 7AQ (01340 831254; Fax: 01340 831566). Conference room with facilities for up to 24 persons.

PERTH & KINROSS. **Farleyer House Hotel**, Aberfeldy PH15 2JE (01887 820332; Fax: 01887 829430).2 meeting rooms suitable for up to 25.

PERTH & KINROSS. **Kinloch House Hotel,** By Blairgowrie PH10 6SG (01250 884237; Fax: 01250 884333). Meeting room suitable for up to 20 boardroom-style.

PERTH & KINROSS. **Dalmunzie House,** Spittal of Glenshee, Blairgowrie PH10 7QG (01250 885224; Fax: 01250 885225). Meeting/conference facilities available for up to 25 persons.

PERTH & KINROSS. **The Green Hotel**, 2 The Muirs, Kinross KY13 7AS (01577 863467; Fax: 01577 863180). 4 meeting rooms suitable for up to 120 (47 residential).

PERTH & KINROSS. **Dupplin Castle,** Dupplin Estate, By Perth PH2 0PY (01738 623224; Fax: 01738 444140). Suitable for small meetings/conferences up to 12 persons.

PERTH & KINROSS. **Ballathie House Hotel,** Kinclaven, By Stanley PH1 4QN (01250 883268; Fax: 01250 883396. Suitable for small meetings/conferences up to 12 persons; inclusive rates and exclusive lets available.

ROSS-SHIRE. **Conchra House Hotel,** Ardelve, Kyle of Lochalsh IV40 8DZ (01599 555233; Fax: 01599 555433). Conference and recreation centre accommodating up to 50 theatre-style, 30 boardroom-style.

ROSS-SHIRE. **Coul House Hotel,** Contin, By Strathpeffer IV14 9EY (01997 421487; Fax: 01997 421945). Conference facilities for up to 20 residential, 40 non-residential.

ROSS-SHIRE. **Mansfield House Hotel,** Scotsburn Road, Tain IV19 1PR (01862 892062; Fax: 01862 892260). 2 meeting rooms, suitable for up to 40; OHP, slide projector etc.

STIRLINGSHIRE. **Culcreuch Castle,** Fintry G63 0LW (01360 860228; Fax: 01360 860556). Full conference facilities for up to 110 (60 residential).

IRELAND

KILDARE.**The Kildare Hotel & Country Club,** Straffan (353 1 627 3333; Fax: 353 1 627 3312). 4 meeting rooms suitable for up to 160 (90 residential).

Hotels with Leisure Facilities

These hotels have indoor/outdoor leisure facilities. Brief details are listed below — please see the main entry under the appropriate county heading for a fuller description.

ENGLAND

CHESHIRE

Rookery Hall, Worleston, Near Nantwich CW5 6DQ (01270 610016; Fax: 01270 611211). Tennis, croquet, fishing; golf nearby by arrangement.

Willington Hall Hotel, Willington, Tarporley CW6 0NB (01829 752321; Fax: 01829 752596). Hard tennis court.

CORNWALL

Tredethy Country Hotel, Helland Bridge, Bodmin PL30 4QS (01208 841262; Fax: 01208 841707). Heated outdoor pool.

Trelawne Hotel, Mawnan Smith, Falmouth TR11 5HS (01326 250226; Fax: 01326 250909). Indoor pool, games room.

Steep House, Portmellon Cove, Mevagissey PL26 2PH (01726 843732). Swimming pool (summer).

Kilbol Country House Hotel, Polmassick, Mevagissey PL26 6HA (01726 842481). Swimming pool, clock golf, croquet.

Penventon Hotel, West End, Redruth TR15 1TE (01209 214141; Fax: 01209 219164). Indoor pool, sauna, jacuzzi, gym.

Rose-in-Vale Country House Hotel, Mithian, St Agnes TR5 0QD (01872 552202; Fax: 01872 552700). Heated outdoor pool, solarium.

Bossiney House Hotel, Tintagel PL34 0AX (01840 770240; Fax: 01840 770501). Indoor heated pool, sauna, solarium; putting green.

CUMBRIA

Lovelady Shield Country House Hotel, Nenthead Road, Near Alston CA9 3LF (01434 381203; Fax: 01434 381515). Hard tennis court, croquet.

Nanny Brow Country House Hotel, Clappersgate, Ambleside LA22 9NF (015394 32036; Fax: 015394 32450). Spa bath and solarium.

Appleby Manor Country House Hotel, Roman Road, Appleby-in-Westmorland CA16 6JB (017683 51571). Indoor swimming pool, sauna, jacuzzi, steam room, solarium; table tennis.

DEVON

Tytherleigh Cot Hotel, Chardstock, Axminster EX13 7BN (01460 221170; Fax: 01460 221291). Outdoor heated swimming pool, sauna, solarium.

Ilsington Country Hotel, Ilsington, Near Bovey Tracey TQ13 9RR (01364 661452; Fax: 01364 661307). Indoor heated pool, sauna, steam room, spa, gym, sunbed.

Preston House Hotel, Saunton, Braunton EX33 1LG (01271 890472; Fax: 01271 890555). Swimming pool, sauna, solarium.

Lydford House Hotel, Lydford, Okehampton EX20 4AU (01822 820347; Fax: 01822 820442). Riding stables in grounds.

DORSET

The Lodge Country House Hotel, Beaminster DT8 3BL (01308 863468). Outdoor swimming pool, 2 tennis courts.

Chedington Court Hotel, Chedington, Beaminster DT8 3HY (01935 891265; Fax: 01935 891442). 18-hole golf course, putting, croquet; billiards, snooker.

Anvil Hotel, Pimperne, Blandford DT11 8UQ (01258 453431). Clay pigeon shooting/tuition.

Dower House Hotel, Rousdon, Near Lyme Regis DT7 3RB (01297 21047; Fax: 01297 24748). Indoor heated pool and sauna.

Knoll House Hotel, Studland, Near Swanage BH19 3AZ (01929 450450). Indoor and outdoor swimming pools; sauna, jacuzzi, gym; adventure playground and games room.

Plumber Manor, Sturminster Newton DT10 2AF (01258 472507; Fax: 01258 473370). Tennis court and croquet.

Cromwell House Hotel, Lulworth Cove, Wareham BH20 5RJ (01929 400253; Fax: 01929 400566). Heated swimming pool (May to October).

Shirley Hotel, West Lulworth BH20 5RL (Tel & Fax: 01929 400358). Heated indoor pool, spa; giant chess.

Moonfleet Manor, Near Weymouth DT3 4ED (01305 786948; Fax: 01305 774395). Leisure Centre with 3 pools, gym, sauna, sunbed; tennis, bowls, squash etc; children's indoor and outdoor play areas.

CO. DURHAM

Stanhope Old Hall, Stanhope, Weardale, Bishop Auckland DL13 2PF (01388 528451; Fax: 01388 527795). Quad biking, four-wheel drive safaris.

Headlam Hall, Near Gainford, Darlington DL2 3HA (01325 730238/730691; Fax: 01325 730790). Indoor pool, sauna; snooker; tennis, croquet; cycling, fishing.

ESSEX

Pontlands Park Country Hotel, Great Baddo, Near Chelmsford CM2 8HR (01245 476444; Fax: 01245 478393). Indoor and outdoor pools, sauna and jacuzzi.

GLOUCESTERSHIRE

Halewell Close, Withington, Near Cheltenham GL54 4BN (01242 890238; Fax: 01242 890332). Outdoor swimming pool, trout lake.

Lower Slaughter Manor, Lower Slaughter GL54 2HP (01451 820456; Fax: 01451 822150). Indoor pool, sauna; all-weather tennis court, croquet.

Burleigh Court, Burleigh, Minchinhampton GL5 2PF (01453 883804; Fax: 01453 886870). Outdoor pool, croquet.

Tewkesbury Park Hotel Country Club Resort, Lincoln Green Lane, Tewkesbury, GL20 7DN (01684 295405; Fax: 01684 292386). Indoor heated pool, sauna, solarium, steam room; fitness studio, squash, tennis, golf.

Hatton Court Hotel, Upton Hill, Upton St Leonards GL4 8DE (01452 617412; Fax: 01452 612945). Outdoor heated swimming pool; sauna, solarium, jacuzzi, exercise equipment; croquet.

HAMPSHIRE

Esseborne Manor Hotel, Hurstbourne Tarrant, Andover SP11 0ER (01264 736444; Fax: 01264 736725). All-weather tennis court, croquet.

New Park Manor, Lyndhurst Road, Brockenhurst SO42 7QH (01590 623467; Fax: 01590 622268). Outdoor heated swimming pool, tennis court, biking; equestrian centre with BHS riding school.

Whitley Ridge Country House Hotel, Beaulieu Road, Brockenhurst SO42 7QL (01590 622354; Fax: 01590 622856). New tennis court.

Ashburn Hotel, Fordingbridge SP6 1JP (01425 652060; Fax: 01425 652150). Heated outdoor pool (summer).

String of Horses, Sway, Near Lymington SO41 6EH (Tel and Fax: 01590 682631). Heated outdoor swimming pool.

Passford House, Mount Pleasant Lane, Near Lymington SO41 8LS (01590 682398; Fax: 01590 683494). Indoor and outdoor pools, sauna, gym; tennis, croquet, petanque.

Busketts Lawn Hotel, Woodlands, Near Southampton SO40 7GL (01703 292272; Fax: 01703 292487). Outdoor pool, putting, croquet, mini football pitch.

Botley Park Hotel, Botley, Southampton SO32 2UA (01489 780888; Fax: 01489 789242). Swimming pool, sauna/steam room, gym, sunbeds; snooker; 3 outdoor tennis courts, squash, golf.

HEREFORD & WORCESTER

Collin House Hotel, Collin Lane, Broadway WR12 7PB (01386 858354). Open-air pool.

The Mill at Harvington, Anchor Lane, Harvington, Evesham WR11 5NR (Tel and Fax: 01386 870688). Heated outdoor swimming pool, tennis court, croquet, fishing.

The Bowens Country House, Fownhope HR1 4PS (Tel and Fax: 01432 860430). Grass tennis court and putting green.

Pengethley Manor Hotel, Pengethley Park, Near Ross-on-Wye HR9 6LL (01989 730211; Fax: 01989 730238). Outdoor heated pool; 9-hole golf improvement course, croquet; snooker.

HERTFORDSHIRE

West Lodge Park Hotel, Cockfosters Road, Hadley Wood EN4 0PY (0181-440 8311; Fax: 0181-449 3698). Putting, croquet, golf practice net.

Briggens House Hotel, Briggens Park, Stanstead Abbotts, Near Ware SG12 8LD (01279 829955; Fax: 01279 793685). Outdoor heated swimming pool, 9-hole golf course, tennis, croquet, boules.

Windcliffe Manor Hotel, Sandrock Road, Niton PO38 2NG (Tel/Fax: 01983 730215). Heated outdoor pool.

ISLES OF SCILLY

St Martin's on the Isle Hotel, St Martin's TR25 0QW (01720 422092; Fax: 01720 422298). Indoor pool, tennis, yacht.

KENT

Eastwell Manor Hotel, Eastwell Park, Boughton Lees, Ashford TN25 4HR (01233 219555; Fax: 01233 635530). Tennis, croquet, pitch and putt.

Wallett's Court, Westcliffe, Dover CT15 6EW (01304 852424; Fax: 01304 853430). Tennis.

Brandshatch Place Hotel, Fawkham Valley Road, Fawkham DA3 8NQ (01474 872239; Fax: 01474 879652). Indoor swimming pool, sauna, steam room, spa; gymnasium and aerobics; tennis.

LANCASHIRE

Shaw Hill Hotel, Golf & Country Club, Whittle-le-Woods, Near Chorley PR6 7PP (01257 269221; Fax: 01257 261223). Golf course.

LEICESTERSHIRE

The Priest House, Kings Mills, Castle Donington DE74 2RR (01332 810649; Fax: 01332 811141). Fishing, clay shooting, canoeing.

Hambleton Hall, Oakham LE15 8TH (01572 756991; Fax: 01572 724721). Outdoor heated pool.

LINCOLNSHIRE

Washingborough Hall Country House Hotel, Church Hill, Washingborough LN4 1BE (01522 790340; Fax: 01522 792936). Outdoor heated swimming pool.

Petwood House Hotel, Woodhall Spa LN10 6QF (01526 352411; Fax: 01526 353473). Croquet, putting, snooker.

NORFOLK

Park House, Sandringham, King's Lynn PE35 6EH (01485 543000; Fax: 01485 540663). Leisure facilities for disabled guests and carers/families.

Park Farm Country Hotel, Hethersett, Norwich NR9 3DL (01603 810264; Fax: 01603 812104). Indoor swimming pool, sauna, solarium, steam room, gymnasium; tennis.

Norfolk Mead Hotel, Coltishall, Norwich NR12 7DN (01603 737531; Fax: 01603 737521). Outdoor pool; fishing, boating, croquet.

NORTHUMBERLAND

Riverdale Hall Hotel, Bellingham, NE48 2JT (01434 220254; Fax: 01434 220457). Indoor swimming pool and sauna.

Linden Hall Hotel & Health Spa, Longhorsley, Morpeth NE65 8XF (01670 516611; Fax: 01670 788544). 12-metre swimming pool, spa bath, steam room, solarium, fitness gym; croquet, putting, clay pigeon shooting.

OXFORDSHIRE

Studley Priory Hotel, Horton-cum-Studley, Oxford OX33 1AZ (01865 351203/351254; Fax: 01865 351613). Clay pigeon shooting, grass tennis, croquet, golf.

Westwood Country Hotel, Hinksey Hill Top, Oxford OX1 5BG (01865 735408; Fax: 01865 736536). Sauna, jacuzzi and gym.

The Springs Hotel, Wallingford Road, North Stoke, Wallingford OX10 6BE (01491 836687; Fax: 01491 836877). Outdoor heated swimming pool, sauna; tennis, croquet.

SHROPSHIRE

Longmynd Hotel, Church Stretton SY6 6AG (01694 722244; Fax: 01694 722216). Outdoor heated pool, sauna, solarium, trim gym; pitch and putt.

The Moor Hall, Stoke St Milborough, Near Ludlow SY8 3EG (01584 823209; Fax: 01584 823387). Croquet, archery, clay pigeon shooting, fishing.

Dinham Hall Hotel, By the Castle, Dinham, Ludlow SY8 1EJ (01584 876464; Fax: 01584 876019). Sauna, mini-gymnasium.

Rowton Castle Hotel, Halfway House, Shrewsbury SY5 9EP (01743 884044; Fax: 01743 884949). Privately owned leisure complex with full facilities available for guests.

SOMERSET

Ston Easton Park, Ston Easton, Near Bath BA3 4DF (01761 241631; Fax: 01761 241377). Tennis, fishing, ballooning, riding, croquet; billiards.

Combe Grove Manor, Brassknocker Hill, Monkton Combe, Bath BA2 7HS (01225 834644; Fax: 01225 834561). Indoor and outdoor pools, sauna, hydro spa beds, solarium; gym, aerobics studio; croquet, golf driving range.

Combe House Hotel, Holford, Bridgwater TA5 1RZ (Tel & Fax: 01278 741382). Indoor swimming pool, hard tennis court.

The Beacon Country House Hotel, Beacon Road, Minehead TA24 5SD (01643 703476; Fax: 01643 702668). Outdoor swimming pool.

Holbrook House Hotel, Holbrook, Near Wincanton BA9 8BS (01963 32377; Fax: 01963 32681). Outdoor heated pool, tennis, squash.

STAFFORDSHIRE

Stone House Hotel, Stone ST15 0BQ (01785 815531; Fax: 01785 814764). Indoor pool, sauna, sunbed, gym; tennis.

SUFFOLK

Wood Hall Hotel & Country Club, Shottisham, Woodbridge IP12 3EG (01394 411283; Fax: 01394 410007). Heated outdoor pool, sauna, solarium, squash, tennis.

EAST SUSSEX

Netherfield Place Hotel, Battle TN33 9PP (01424 774455; Fax: 01424 774024). All-weather tennis courts, croquet.

Powdermills Hotel, Powdermill Lane, Battle TN33 0SP (01424 775511; Fax: 01424 774540).Outdoor swimming pool; fishing.

Beauport Park Hotel, Battle Road, Hastings TN38 8EA (01424 851222; Fax: 01424 852465). Outdoor heated pool; tennis, croquet, badminton, outdoor chess, boules, putting.

Fairseat House, Newick, Near Lewes BN8 4PJ (01825 722263). Heated covered swimming pool.

WEST SUSSEX

Ghyll Manor, Rusper, Near Horsham RH12 4PX (01293 871571; Fax: 01293 871419). Tennis and croquet.

WARWICKSHIRE

Nailcote Hall, Berkswell CV7 7DE (01203 466174; Fax: 01203 470270). Swimming pool, steam room, children's pool, solarium; gym.

Aylesbury House Hotel, Packwood, Near Hockley Heath B94 6PL (01564 779207; Fax: 01564 770917). Croquet, putting, assault course.

Welcombe Hotel & Golf Course, Warwick Road, Stratford-upon-Avon CV37 0NR (01789 295252; Fax: 01789 414666). 18-hole golf course, 2 all-weather tennis courts.

Ettington Park, Alderminster, Stratford-upon-Avon CV37 8BU (01789 450123; Fax: 01789 450472). Swimming pool, sauna, spa bath; tennis, riding.

WILTSHIRE

The Manor House Hotel, Castle Combe, Chippenham SN14 7HR (01249 782206; Fax: 01249 782159). Outdoor swimming pool, tennis, croquet, trout fishing, 18-hole golf course.

Crudwell Court, Crudwell, Malmesbury SN16 9EP (01666 577194; Fax: 01666 577853). Outdoor heated swimming pool, croquet lawn.

Whatley Manor, Near Easton Grey, Malmesbury SN16 0RB (01666 822888; Fax: 01666 826120). Outdoor swimming pool, tennis, croquet; sauna, solarium, jacuzzi; snooker, table tennis.

Bishopstrow House, Warminster BA12 9HH (01985 212312; Fax: 01985 216769). Indoor and outdoor pools, gym, sauna, solarium; health & beauty treatments; indoor and outdoor tennis.

NORTH YORKSHIRE

Elmfield Country House, Arrathorne, Bedale DL8 1NE (01677 450558; Fax: 01677 450557). Solarium, games room.

Boar's Head Country Hotel, Ripley Castle Estate, Near Harrogate HG3 3AY (01423 771888; Fax: 01423 771509). Tennis, access to Castle grounds.

Beansheaf Hotel, Malton Road, Kirby Misperton, Malton (01653 668614; Fax: 01653 668370). Sauna.

WEST YORKSHIRE

Bagden Hall Hotel, Scissett, Near Huddersfield HD8 9LE (01484 865330; Fax: 01484 861001). 9-hole golf course.

Linton Springs Hotel, Sicklinghall Road, Wetherby LS22 4AF (01937 585353; Fax: 01937 587579). Tennis court, golf driving range.

WALES

NORTH WALES. **Mynydd Ednyfed Country House**, Criccieth LL52 0PH (01766 523269). All-weather tennis, gym, solarium.

NORTH WALES. **Bodysgallen Hall,** Llandudno LL30 1RS (01492 584466; Fax: 01492 582519). Indoor swimming pool, sauna, steam room, spa bath, three treatment rooms; clubroom.

DYFED. **Hotel Penrallt**, Aberporth, Cardigan SA43 2BS (01239 810227; Fax: 01239 811375). Outdoor heated pool, sauna, solarium, gym; tennis.

DYFED. **Waterwynch Bay Hotel**, Tenby SA70 8TJ (01834 842464; Fax: 01834 845076). Bowling green, croquet, putting; snooker, bridge.

POWYS. **Gliffaes Country House Hotel,** Crickhowell NP8 1RH (01874 730371; Fax: 01874 730463). Hard tennis court, croquet, putting; trout and salmon fishing; snooker.

SOUTH WALES. **Maes-y-Gwernen Hotel,** Abercraf, Swansea Valley SA9 1XD (01639 730218; Fax: 01639 730765). Sauna, jacuzzi, solarium, gym.

SOUTH WALES. **Egerton Grey Country House Hotel,** Porthkerry (01446 711666; Fax: 01446 711690). All-weather tennis court, pitch and putt, croquet.

SCOTLAND

AYRSHIRE. **Montgreenan Mansion,** Montgreenan Estate, Near Kilwinning KA13 7QZ (01294 557733; Fax: 01294 850397). Practice golf course, tennis, croquet; billiard room.

FIFE. **Balbirnie House Hotel,** Markinch KY7 6NE (01592 610066; Fax: 01592 610529). Golf course, snooker.

FIFE. **Sandford Country House Hotel**, Newton Hill, Wormit, Near Dundee DD6 8RG (01382 541802; Fax: 01382 542136). Clay pigeon shooting, off-road driving, fly fishing.

INVERNESS-SHIRE. **Polmaily House Hotel,** Drumnadrochit IV3 6XT (01456 450343; Fax: 01456 450813). Indoor heated pool, croquet, tennis.

ISLE OF MULL. **Ardfenaig House,** By Bunessan PA67 6DX (01681 700210; Fax: 01681 700210). Sailing, rowing, mountain biking; croquet.

PERTH & KINROSS. **Farleyer House Hotel,** Aberfeldy PH15 2JE (01887 820332; Fax: 01887 829430). 9-hole golf course.

PERTH & KINROSS. **Dalmunzie House,** Spittal of Glenshee, Blairgowrie PH10 7QG (01250 885224; Fax: 01250 885225). Golf, tennis, fishing, clay pigeon shooting.

PERTH & KINROSS. **Ballathie House Hotel,** Kinclaven, By Stanley PH1 4QN (01250 883268; Fax: 01250 883396. Tennis, croquet, putting; fishing.

PERTH & KINROSS. **The Green Hotel**, 2 The Muirs, Kinross KY13 7AS (01577 863467; Fax: 01577 863180). Indoor swimming pool, sauna, gym, golf, tennis; curling and trout fishing in season.

ROSS-SHIRE. **Coul House Hotel,** Contin, By Strathpeffer IV14 9EY (01997 421487; Fax: 01997 421945). 9-hole pitch and putt course.

IRELAND

KILDARE.The Kildare Hotel & Country Club, Straffan (353 1 627 3333; Fax: 353 1 627 3312). Indoor pool, sauna, jacuzzi, gym; golf, tennis.

ONE FOR YOUR FRIEND 1997

FHG Publications have a large range of attractive holiday accommodation guides for all kinds of holiday opportunities throughout Britain. They also make useful gifts at any time of year. Our guides are available in most bookshops and larger newsagents but we will be happy to post you a copy direct if you have any difficulty. We will also post abroad but have to charge separately for post or freight. The inclusive cost of posting and packing the guides to you or your friends in the UK is as follows:

Farm Holiday Guide ENGLAND, WALES and IRELAND
Board, Self-catering, Caravans/Camping, Activity Holidays. **£5.50**

Farm Holiday Guide SCOTLAND
All kinds of holiday accommodation. **£4.00**

SELF-CATERING HOLIDAYS IN BRITAIN
Over 1000 addresses throughout for Self-catering and caravans in Britain. **£5.00**

BRITAIN'S BEST HOLIDAYS
A quick-reference general guide for all kinds of holidays. **£4.00**

The FHG Guide to CARAVAN & CAMPING HOLIDAYS
Caravans for hire, sites and holiday parks and centres. **£4.00**

BED AND BREAKFAST STOPS
Over 1000 friendly and comfortable overnight stops. Non-smoking, The Disabled and Special Diets Supplements. **£5.50**

CHILDREN WELCOME! FAMILY HOLIDAY & ATTRACTIONS GUIDE
Family holidays with details of amenities for children and babies. **£5.00**

SCOTTISH WELCOME
Introduced by Katie Woods. A new guide to holiday accommodation and attractions in Scotland. **£4.80**

Recommended SHORT BREAKS HOLIDAYS IN BRITAIN
'Approved' accommodation for quality bargain breaks. Introduced by John Carter. **£4.80**

Recommended COUNTRY HOTELS OF BRITAIN
Including Country Houses, for the discriminating. **£4.80**

Recommended WAYSIDE AND COUNTRY INNS OF BRITAIN
Pubs, Inns and small hotels. **£4.80**

PGA GOLF GUIDE Where to play. Where to stay
Over 2000 golf courses in Britain with convenient accommodation. Endorsed by the PGA. Holiday Golf in France, Portugal, Spain and USA. **£9.80**

PETS WELCOME!
The unique guide for holidays for pet owners and their pets. **£5.50**

BED AND BREAKFAST IN BRITAIN
Over 1000 choices for touring and holidays throughout Britain. Airports and Ferries Supplement. **£4.00**

THE FRENCH FARM AND VILLAGE HOLIDAY GUIDE
The official guide to self-catering holidays in the 'Gîtes de France'. **£9.80**

Tick your choice and send your order and payment to FHG PUBLICATIONS, ABBEY MILL BUSINESS CENTRE, SEEDHILL, PAISLEY PA1 1TJ (TEL: 0141-887 0428. FAX: 0141-889 7204). **Deduct** 10% for 2/3 titles or copies; 20% for 4 or more.

Send to: NAME ....

ADDRESS ....

....

....POST CODE ....

I enclose Cheque/Postal Order for £..

SIGNATURE..DATE ....

Please complete the following to help us improve the service we provide. How did you find out about our guides:

❑ Press ❑ Magazines ❑ TVRadio ❑ Family/Friend ❑ Other.

MAP SECTION

The following seven pages of maps indicate the main cities, towns and holiday centres of Britain. Space obviously does not permit every location featured in this book to be included but the approximate position may be ascertained by using the distance indications quoted and the scale bars on the maps.

Map 1

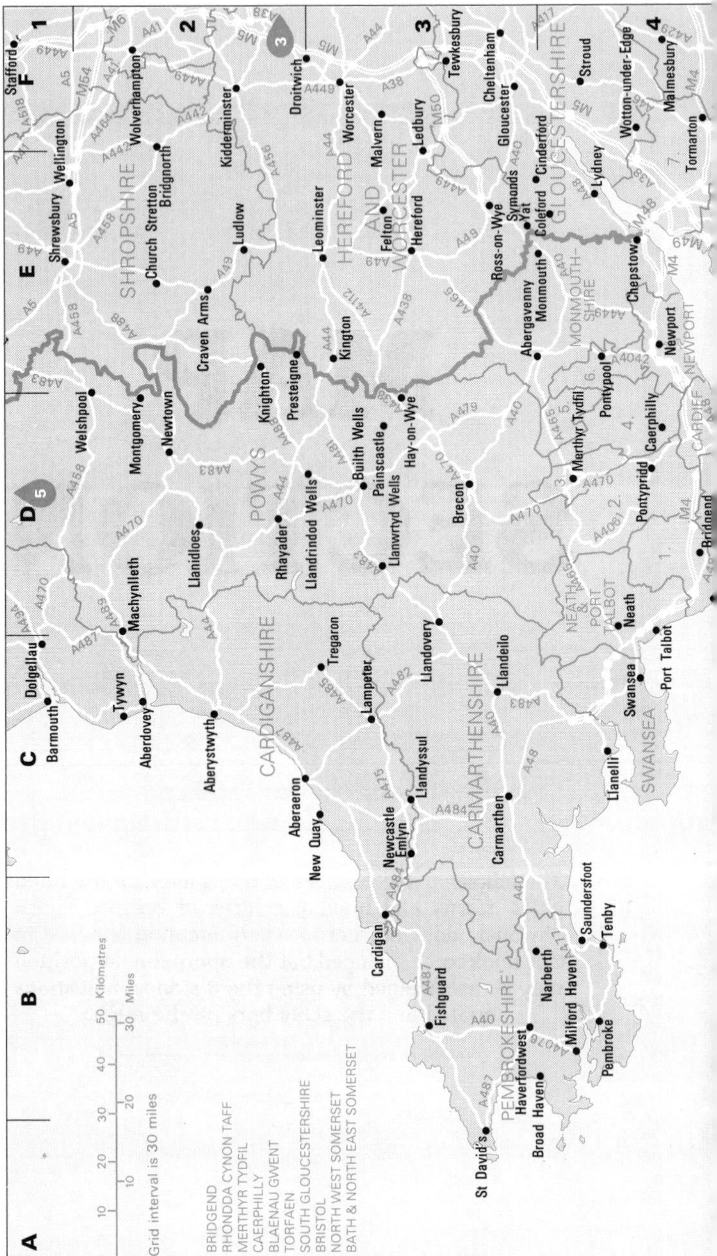

A
B
C
D
E
F
1
2
3
4
Grid interval is 30 miles
0 10 20 30 40 50 Kilometres
0 10 20 30 Miles
1. BRIDGEND
2. RHONDDA CYNON TAFF
3. MERTHYR TYDFIL
4. CAERPHILLY
5. BLAENAU GWENT
6. TORFAEN
7. SOUTH GLOUCESTERSHIRE
8. BRISTOL
9. NORTH WEST SOMERSET
10. BATH & NORTH EAST SOMERSET
SHROPSHIRE
POWYS
CARDIGANSHIRE
CARMARTHENSHIRE
PEMBROKESHIRE
SWANSEA
NEATH & PORT TALBOT
CARDIFF
NEWPORT
MONMOUTH-SHIRE
HEREFORD AND WORCESTER
GLOUCESTERSHIRE
Stafford
Wolverhampton
Wellington
Shrewsbury
Bridgnorth
Church Stretton
Kidderminster
Ludlow
Craven Arms
Droitwich
Worcester
Leominster
Malvern
Felton
Hereford
Ledbury
Tewkesbury
Cheltenham
Gloucester
Ross-on-Wye
Symonds Yat
Coleford
Cinderford
Stroud
Lydney
Wotton-under-Edge
Malmesbury
Tormarton
Chepstow
Monmouth
Abergavenny
Newport
Pontypool
Caerphilly
Pontypridd
Merthyr Tydfil
Bridgend
Neath
Port Talbot
Swansea
Llanelli
Welshpool
Montgomery
Newtown
Knighton
Presteigne
Kington
Builth Wells
Painscastle
Hay-on-Wye
Llandrindod Wells
Llanwrtyd Wells
Brecon
Rhayader
Llanidloes
Machynlleth
Dolgellau
Barmouth
Tywyn
Aberdovey
Aberystwyth
Tregaron
Lampeter
Llandovery
Llandeilo
Aberaeron
New Quay
Llandyssul
Newcastle Emlyn
Carmarthen
Cardigan
Fishguard
Narberth
Saundersfoot
Tenby
Haverfordwest
Milford Haven
Pembroke
Broad Haven
St David's
M6
M5
M50
M4
M48
M49
M54
A5
A41
A38
A44
A49
A40
A48
A449
A458
A470
A483
A487
A484
A485
A482
A475
A479
A438
A4112
A465
A4042
A4061
A456
A442
A464
A518
A494
A489
A481
A46
A429
A417
A477
A4076

Map 2

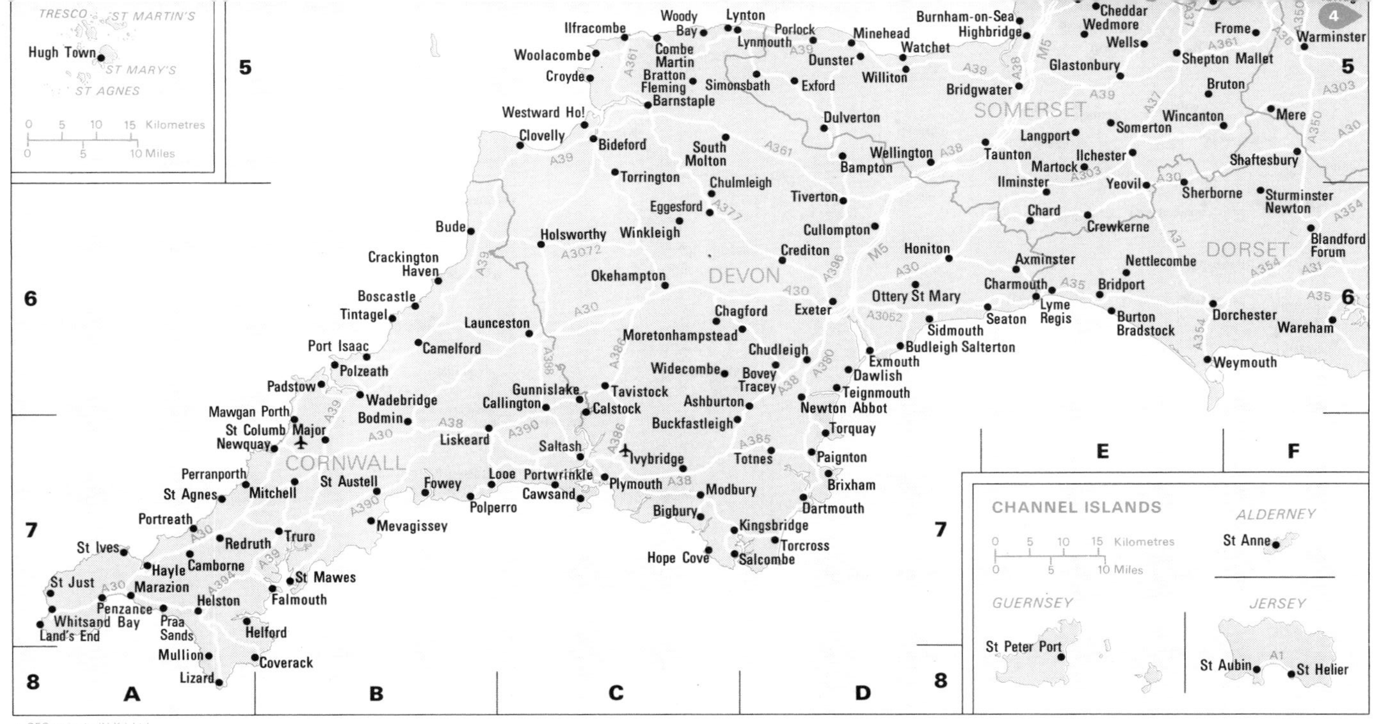

SOMERSET
DEVON
CORNWALL
DORSET
Ilfracombe
Woolacombe
Croyde
Woody Bay
Lynton
Lynmouth
Porlock
Combe Martin
Bratton Fleming
Barnstaple
Simonsbath
Exford
Dunster
Minehead
Watchet
Williton
Burnham-on-Sea
Highbridge
Bridgwater
Cheddar
Wedmore
Wells
Glastonbury
Frome
Shepton Mallet
Warminster
Bruton
Mere
Wincanton
Somerton
Langport
Taunton
Ilchester
Martock
Yeovil
Sherborne
Shaftesbury
Sturminster Newton
Blandford Forum
Ilminster
Chard
Crewkerne
Westward Ho!
Clovelly
Bideford
Torrington
South Molton
Dulverton
Wellington
Bampton
Chulmleigh
Tiverton
Eggesford
Cullompton
Bude
Holsworthy
Winkleigh
Crediton
Honiton
Axminster
Nettlecombe
Crackington Haven
Okehampton
Charmouth
Bridport
Lyme Regis
Ottery St Mary
Boscastle
Tintagel
Launceston
Chagford
Exeter
Sidmouth
Seaton
Burton Bradstock
Dorchester
Wareham
Port Isaac
Camelford
Moretonhampstead
Chudleigh
Budleigh Salterton
Exmouth
Weymouth
Polzeath
Widecombe
Bovey Tracey
Dawlish
Padstow
Wadebridge
Gunnislake
Tavistock
Teignmouth
Mawgan Porth
Callington
Calstock
Ashburton
Newton Abbot
St Columb Major
Bodmin
Liskeard
Buckfastleigh
Torquay
Newquay
Saltash
Ivybridge
Totnes
Paignton
Perranporth
St Austell
Fowey
Looe
Portwrinkle
Plymouth
Brixham
St Agnes
Mitchell
Polperro
Cawsand
Modbury
Bigbury
Dartmouth
Portreath
Mevagissey
Kingsbridge
Truro
Redruth
Torcross
St Ives
Hope Cove
Salcombe
Hayle
Camborne
St Mawes
St Just
Marazion
Falmouth
Penzance
Helston
Whitsand Bay
Praa Sands
Land's End
Helford
Mullion
Coverack
Lizard
TRESCO
ST MARTIN'S
Hugh Town
ST MARY'S
ST AGNES
0 5 10 15 Kilometres
0 5 10 Miles
CHANNEL ISLANDS
0 5 10 15 Kilometres
0 5 10 Miles
ALDERNEY
St Anne
GUERNSEY
St Peter Port
JERSEY
St Aubin
St Helier
A B C D E F
5 6 7 8
4

Map 3

A
B
C
D
E
F
1
2
3
4
LINCOLNSHIRE
NOTTINGHAMSHIRE
DERBYSHIRE
STAFFS
LEICESTERSHIRE
NORTHAMPTONSHIRE
WARWICKSHIRE
WEST MIDLANDS
CAMBRIDGESHIRE
BEDFORDSHIRE
NORFOLK
SUFFOLK
Bakewell
Leek
Matlock
Mansfield
Newark
Ashbourne
Nottingham
Derby
Stafford
Burton-upon-Trent
East Midlands
Loughborough
Melton Mowbray
Lichfield
Oakham
Stamford
Leicester
Uppingham
Wolverhampton
Birmingham
National Exhibition Centre
Market Harborough
Coventry
Rugby
Kettering
Leamington Spa
Warwick
Daventry
Northampton
Stratford-upon-Avon
Towcester
Evesham
Broadway
Banbury
Brackley
Buckingham
Milton Keynes
Moreton-in-Marsh
Stow-on-the-Wold
Chipping Norton
Cheltenham
Kingham
Bicester
Skegness
Sleaford
Boston
Grantham
Spalding
Peterborough
Huntingdon
Bedford
Baldock
Hitchin
Luton
Cambridge
Ely
Newmarket
Haverhill
Stansted
Braintree
Hunstanton
King's Lynn
Downham Market
Wells-next-the-Sea
Blakeney
Sheringham
Cromer
Holt
Overstrand
Mundesley-on-Sea
North Walsham
Stalham
Fakenham
East Dereham
Swaffham
Watton
Wroxham
Horning
Hemsby
Norwich
Acle
Caister
Great Yarmouth
Lowestoft
Bungay
Beccles
Kessingland
Thetford
Diss
Harleston
Halesworth
Southwold
Bury St Edmunds
Framlingham
Saxmundham
Stowmarket
Aldeburgh
Lavenham
Woodbridge
Sudbury
Hadleigh
Ipswich
Dedham
Harwich
Colchester
M1
M6
M40
M42
M45
M69
M11
A1
A5
A6
A14
A15
A16
A17
A47
A45
A52
A11
A12
A10
A140
A134
A143
A149
A148
A1065

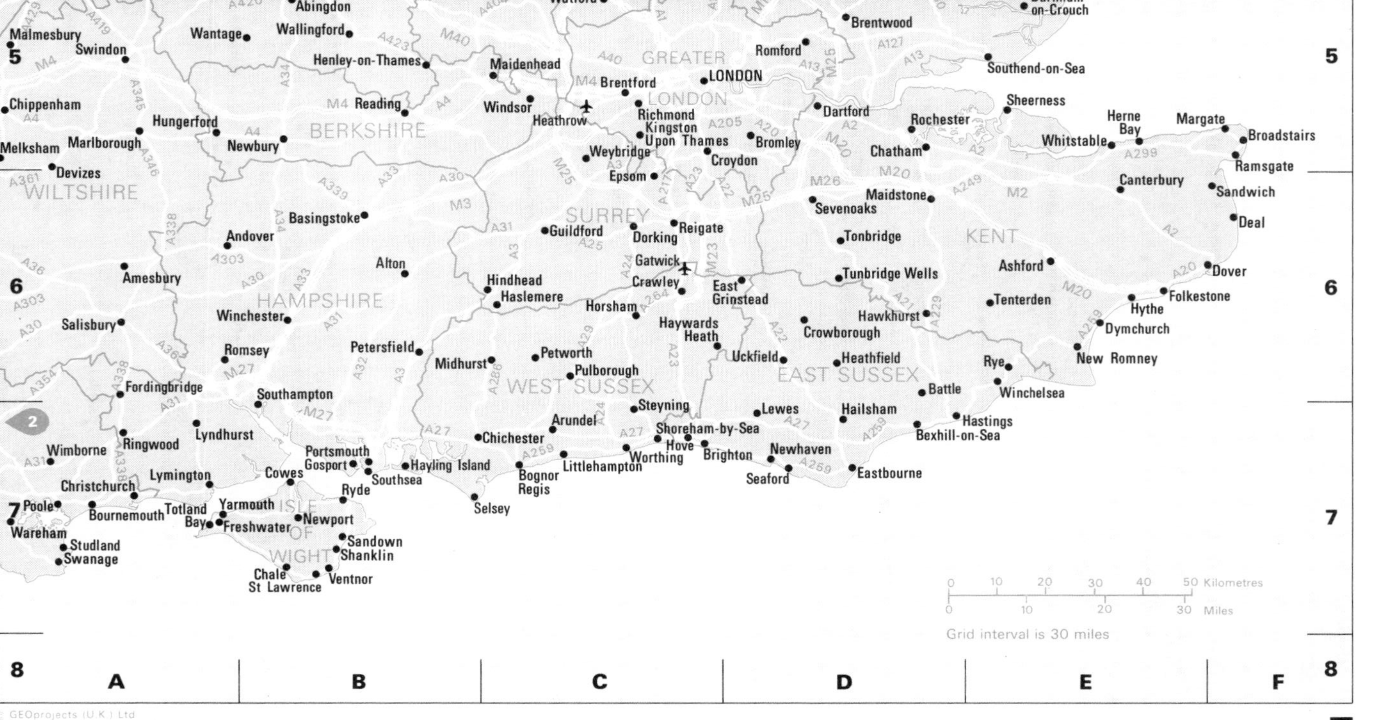

Malmesbury
Swindon
Chippenham
Melksham
Devizes
Marlborough
Hungerford
Newbury
Wantage
Abingdon
Wallingford
Henley-on-Thames
Reading
Maidenhead
Windsor
Heathrow
Brentford
Richmond
Kingston Upon Thames
Weybridge
Epsom
Croydon
Bromley
LONDON
GREATER LONDON
Romford
Brentwood
Dartford
Southend-on-Sea
Burnham-on-Crouch
Sheerness
Rochester
Chatham
Maidstone
Sevenoaks
Tonbridge
Tunbridge Wells
Whitstable
Herne Bay
Margate
Broadstairs
Ramsgate
Sandwich
Deal
Canterbury
Dover
Folkestone
Hythe
Dymchurch
New Romney
Ashford
Tenterden
KENT
Rye
Winchelsea
Hastings
Bexhill-on-Sea
Battle
Hawkhurst
Crowborough
Heathfield
Hailsham
Eastbourne
EAST SUSSEX
Uckfield
Lewes
Newhaven
Seaford
Brighton
Hove
Shoreham-by-Sea
Worthing
East Grinstead
Haywards Heath
Crawley
Gatwick
Reigate
Dorking
Guildford
SURREY
Horsham
Steyning
Pulborough
Petworth
Littlehampton
Arundel
WEST SUSSEX
Bognor Regis
Chichester
Selsey
Midhurst
Haslemere
Hindhead
Hayling Island
Petersfield
Alton
Basingstoke
BERKSHIRE
Andover
Winchester
HAMPSHIRE
Romsey
Southampton
Portsmouth
Gosport
Southsea
Ryde
Cowes
Newport
Sandown
Shanklin
Ventnor
St Lawrence
Chale
ISLE OF WIGHT
Yarmouth
Freshwater
Totland Bay
Lymington
Lyndhurst
Ringwood
Fordingbridge
Salisbury
Amesbury
WILTSHIRE
Wimborne
Christchurch
Bournemouth
Poole
Wareham
Studland
Swanage
Watford
M4
M25
M20
M2
M3
M40
M23
M26
M27
A1
A3
A2
A20
A21
A22
A23
A24
A27
A30
A31
A34
A303
A338
A259
0 10 20 30 40 50 Kilometres
0 10 20 30 Miles
Grid interval is 30 miles
A B C D E F
5 6 7 8

Map 4

Map 5

DUMFRIES AND GALLOWAY
Girvan
New Galloway
Dumfries
Langholm
Newton Stewart
Annan
Gretna
Longtown
Brampton
Castle Douglas
Gatehouse of Fleet
Wigtown
Kirkcudbright
Silloth
Carlisle
Wigton
Port William
Maryport
Cockermouth
Bassenthwaite
Workington
Penrith
Keswick
Whitehaven
Ennerdale Bridge
Ullswater
Appleby
CUMBRIA
Shap
Gosforth
Little Langdale
Ambleside
Hawkshead
Seascale
Coniston
Windermere
Kendal
Ramsey
Broughton-in-Furness
Newby Bridge
Peel
ISLE OF MAN
Millom
Ulverston
Grange-over-Sands
Kirkby Lo
Port Erin
Douglas
Castletown
Barrow-in-Furness
Port St Mary
Morecambe
Lancaster
Fleetwood
Blackpool
LANCASHI
Lytham St Annes
Preston
Southport
Chorley
Formby
Wigan
Amlwch
MERSEYSIDE
Liverpool
ANGLESEY
Hoylake
Birkenhead
Holyhead
Llanerchymedd
Llandudno
Colwyn Bay
Rhyl
Prestatyn
Menai Bridge
Beaumaris
Llangefni
Conwy
Abergele
FLINT-SHIRE
Northwich
Bangor
ABERCONWY & COLWYN
Chester
CHESHI
Caernarvon
Denbigh
Llanrwst
Llanberis
Ruthin
Betws-y-Coed
DENBIGH-SHIRE
Nantwich
Wrexham
GWYNEDD
Corwen
WREXHAM
Portmadoc
Ffestiniog
Bala
Llangollen
Nefyn
Criccieth
Penrhyndeudraeth
Pwllheli
Llanbedrog
Harlech
Oswestry
Wem
Abersoch
Aberdaron
SHROPSHIRE
Dolgellau
Barmouth
Welshpool
Shrewsbury
POWYS
Tywyn
Machynlleth
A B C D
1 2 3 4 5 6 7

Map 6

0 10 20 30 40 50 Kilometres
0 10 20 30 Miles
Grid interval is 30 miles

1. STOCKTON-ON-TEES
2. MIDDLESBROUGH
3. KINGSTON UPON HULL
4. NORTH EAST LINCOLNSHIRE

E F G H
1 2 3 4 5 6 7

Morpeth
Whitley Bay
Tynemouth
South Shields
Corbridge
Newcastle-upon-Tyne
Sunderland
TYNE AND WEAR
Durham
DURHAM
HARTLEPOOL
Bishop Auckland
Redcar
Middleton-in-Teesdale
Middlesbrough
Saltburn-by-the-Sea
REDCAR & CLEVELAND
Barnard Castle
Darlington
Guisborough
Whitby
Stokesley
Richmond
Northallerton
Leyburn
Middleham
Thirsk
Helmsley
Pickering
Scarborough
Cayton Bay
Filey
NORTH YORKSHIRE
Ripon
Castle Howard
Malton
Flamborough
Bridlington
Sledmere
Grassington
Huby
Driffield
Skipton
Harrogate
York
YORK
EAST RIDING OF YORKSHIRE
Hornsea
Ilkley
Bingley
Beverley
Bradford
Leeds
Selby
Heptonstall
WEST YORKSHIRE
Hull
Withernsea
Halifax
Goole
NORTH LINCOLNSHIRE
Huddersfield
Scunthorpe
Grimsby
Cleethorpes
Barnsley
Doncaster
SOUTH YORKSHIRE
Glossop
Gainsborough
Louth
Sheffield
Mablethorpe
Worksop
Alford
Buxton
Chesterfield
Lincoln
Horncastle
Bakewell
Mansfield
Skegness
Matlock
Leek
DERBYSHIRE
NOTTINGHAMSHIRE
LINCOLNSHIRE
Newark
Ashbourne
Sleaford
Boston
Nottingham
Grantham
Derby
East Midlands
Spalding
Burton-upon-Trent
Loughborough
Melton Mowbray
LEICESTERSHIRE
Lichfield
Stamford
Oakham
Leicester
Uppingham
Peterborough

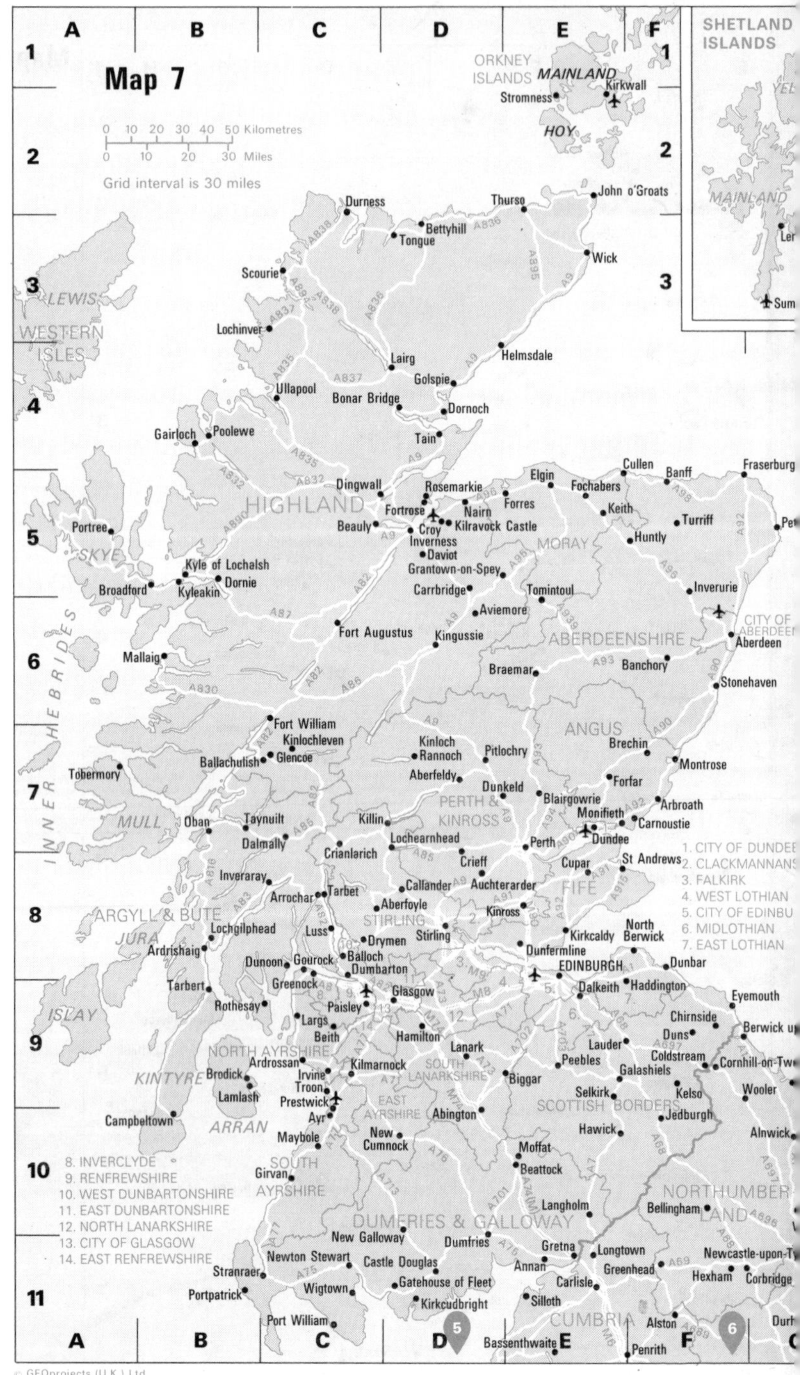
Map 7
0 10 20 30 40 50 Kilometres
0 10 20 30 Miles
Grid interval is 30 miles
A
B
C
D
E
F
1
2
3
4
5
6
7
8
9
10
11
SHETLAND ISLANDS
MAINLAND
ORKNEY ISLANDS
MAINLAND
Kirkwall
Stromness
HOY
John o'Groats
Thurso
Durness
Bettyhill
Tongue
Wick
Scourie
LEWIS
WESTERN ISLES
Lochinver
Lairg
Helmsdale
Golspie
Ullapool
Bonar Bridge
Dornoch
Gairloch
Poolewe
Tain
Cullen
Banff
Fraserburg
Elgin
Fochabers
Dingwall
Rosemarkie
HIGHLAND
Fortrose
Nairn
Forres
Keith
Turriff
Beauly
Croy
Kilravock Castle
Portree
Inverness
Huntly
MORAY
Daviot
SKYE
Kyle of Lochalsh
Grantown-on-Spey
Broadford
Kyleakin
Dornie
Carrbridge
Tomintoul
Inverurie
Aviemore
CITY OF ABERDEEN
Fort Augustus
Kingussie
ABERDEENSHIRE
Aberdeen
Mallaig
Braemar
Banchory
Stonehaven
INNER HEBRIDES
Fort William
ANGUS
Kinlochleven
Kinloch Rannoch
Pitlochry
Brechin
Ballachulish
Glencoe
Montrose
Tobermory
Aberfeldy
Forfar
Dunkeld
PERTH & KINROSS
Blairgowrie
Arbroath
MULL
Oban
Taynuilt
Killin
Monifieth
Carnoustie
Dundee
Lochearnhead
Dalmally
Crianlarich
Perth
1. CITY OF DUNDEE
2. CLACKMANNANS
3. FALKIRK
4. WEST LOTHIAN
5. CITY OF EDINBU
6. MIDLOTHIAN
7. EAST LOTHIAN
Crieff
St Andrews
Inveraray
Cupar
Callander
Auchterarder
FIFE
Arrochar
Tarbet
Aberfoyle
ARGYLL & BUTE
Kinross
STIRLING
North Berwick
JURA
Lochgilphead
Luss
Drymen
Stirling
Kirkcaldy
Ardrishaig
Dunfermline
Dunoon
Gourock
Balloch
EDINBURGH
Dunbar
Dumbarton
Greenock
Tarbert
Glasgow
Dalkeith
Haddington
Eyemouth
Rothesay
Paisley
ISLAY
Largs
Chirnside
Beith
Hamilton
Duns
Berwick u
NORTH AYRSHIRE
Lanark
Lauder
Coldstream
Ardrossan
Kilmarnock
SOUTH LANARKSHIRE
Peebles
Cornhill-on-Tw
KINTYRE
Brodick
Irvine
Galashiels
Troon
Biggar
Lamlash
Prestwick
EAST AYRSHIRE
Selkirk
Kelso
Wooler
SCOTTISH BORDERS
Campbeltown
Ayr
Abington
Jedburgh
ARRAN
Maybole
New Cumnock
Hawick
Alnwick
8. INVERCLYDE
9. RENFREWSHIRE
10. WEST DUNBARTONSHIRE
11. EAST DUNBARTONSHIRE
12. NORTH LANARKSHIRE
13. CITY OF GLASGOW
14. EAST RENFREWSHIRE
SOUTH AYRSHIRE
Moffat
Girvan
Beattock
NORTHUMBERLAND
Langholm
Bellingham
DUMFRIES & GALLOWAY
New Galloway
Dumfries
Gretna
Longtown
Newcastle-upon-T
Newton Stewart
Castle Douglas
Annan
Stranraer
Greenhead
Hexham
Corbridge
Carlisle
Gatehouse of Fleet
Portpatrick
Wigtown
Silloth
Kirkcudbright
Port William
CUMBRIA
Alston
Durh
Bassenthwaite
Penrith
5
6